FOURIER TRANSFORM INFRARED
A Constantly Evolving Technology

ELLIS HORWOOD SERIES IN ANALYTICAL CHEMISTRY
Series Editors: Dr MARY MASSON, University of Aberdeen,
and Dr JULIAN F. TYSON, Amherst, USA
Consultant Editors: Prof. J. N. MILLER, Loughborough University of Technology, and
Dr R. A. CHALMERS, University of Aberdeen

FOURIER TRANSFORM INFRARED

A Constantly Evolving Technology

SEAN JOHNSTON   M.Sc., B.Sc.
Instrument Manager
Laser Monitoring Systems Ltd, Humberside, UK

ELLIS HORWOOD
NEW YORK   LONDON   TORONTO   SYDNEY   TOKYO   SINGAPORE

PHYSICS

First published in 1991 by
ELLIS HORWOOD LIMITED
Market Cross House, Cooper Street,
Chichester, West Sussex, PO19 1EB, England

A division of
Simon & Schuster International Group
A Paramount Communications Company

Typeset by Ellis Horwood Limited
Printed and bound in Great Britain
by Bookcraft Limited, Midsomer Norton, Avon

British Library Cataloguing in Publication Data

Johnston, Sean F.
Fourier transform infrared: A constantly evolving technology. —
(Ellis Horwood series in analytical chemistry)
I. Title   II. Series
543
ISBN 0–13–327479–9

Library of Congress Cataloging-in-Publication Data

Johnston, Sean, 1956–
Fourier transform infrared: a constantly evolving technology / Sean Johnston
p. cm. — (Ellis Horwood series in analytical chemistry)
Includes bibliographical references and index.
ISBN 0–13–327479–9
1. Fourier transform infrared spectroscopy. I. Title. II. Series.
QC454.F7J65   1991
543'.08583–dc20   91–22683
                                                                          CIP

Table of Contents

To my wife, Libby,
who brings life into the world

Preface

Most users of Fourier tranform infrared (FTIR) spectrometers today know them as benchtop instruments of great value in analytical chemistry. Yet Fourier spectrometers have been found on telescopes at remote mountain observatories, on U-2 aircraft, in huts at the south pole, and in space probes to the outer planets. They have filled entire laboratories, been interpreted by vacuum-tube computers, and even operated by hand crank and the naked eye.

This book includes some history of this important technology for those who use it or plan to use it. It also marks the centenary of the first use of the method. Fourier transform infrared spectrometry had its origins in the nineteenth century, a time of enormous advances in optics, mathematics, and engineering. Despite crucial contributions by some of the best remembered scientists of that time (including some of the first Nobel Prize winners), the potential of FTIR remained tantalizingly out of reach, and the method was nearly forgotten. Researchers devoted the following decades to developing other spectroscopic techniques, and to gradually improving the methods of detecting, analysing and recording their weak signals.

In the mid twentieth century, a number of unrelated lines of research came fortuitously together.

Post-war developments in analogue and digital computers made large-scale calculations practical. Information theory provided a solid foundation for the mathematics of digital spectroscopy. And, discovery of fundamental advantages of the technique gave impetus to experimental tests.

Over the next twenty years, ideas were translated into practice by a few dozen people, culminating in gradual acceptance of Fourier spectroscopy by spectroscopists, and eventually commercial exploitation by over two dozen companies.

Today, users of FTIR instruments have expanded from the initially small group of far-infrared physicists to analytical chemists, and to literally thousands of applications in quality control, process monitoring, and routine analysis. Recent FTIR spectrometers can be found in factories, nuclear fusion research laboratories, and at the end of fibre-optic probes.

Fourier spectrometry is a good example of a technical revolution overthrowing the old order. Revolution may actually be a poor analogy, because its impact was anything but sudden. Instead, FTIR gradually overtook optical spectroscopy like the waging of a drawn-out guerilla war: there were the first rebels, initial isolated skirmishes, staged battles, morale-boosting successes, public defections to the rebel camp, and a final direct assault on the last hold-outs. The war itself has been followed by a period in which the last stalwart defenders give up by retirement, and younger conscripts enter the field knowing only the new order. The story of FTIR shows that, like social change, scientific progress is characterized by long periods of stability, punctuated by dramatic realignment to new theories, technologies or situations.

This book tells the chronological story of the important discoveries in FTIR, gives a grounding in the underlying theory, and outlines the prospects for the future. The physical principles rather than the mathematics of the technique have been emphasized. While this may give a less precise and succinct description of the foundations of the method, it should make them accessible to a wider range of readers. Unlike two decades ago, most users of FTIR instrumentation today are no longer physicists. And unlike today, most users ten years hence may not be analytical chemists.

Readers may use the book either for its historical or technological content, or, preferably, both. This approach is possible only because of the unusually long evolution of the technology; an idea ahead of its time, FTIR took decades to reach a practical form. The fundamental building blocks of the theory of Fourier transform technology were assembled gradually, with no overlying cohesion.

The references in the text are mainly to key original papers. Accessibility in most western libraries has also been a factor in their selection. Regrettably, proceedings of some of the early conferences are not available to most readers. Nor are the proceedings of the proliferating annual or semi-annual conferences today, at which the technical details of new equipment and new applications often receive their only airing. No attempt has been made to cite all references in a particular field; since the late 1970s, the rate of publications in FTIR has exploded, as chemists embraced the technique.

This book concentrates on the principles of FTIR, the design of FTIR spectrometers, and important accessories rather than on applications (except where they have influenced design). The level is appropriate to persons having or studying for a first degree. Readers need not be chemists, engineers, physicists, laboratory technicians or amateurs of science history — but I hope that each will find some useful information here.

The evolution of FTIR technology involved the best of science and engineering over the past century, and will continue to do so in the coming decades. I hope that it imbues some added respect for the FTIR spectrometer you may use, or more trust in the spectra you interpret.

ACKNOWLEDGEMENTS

I would like to thank those individuals who have not only contributed to Fourier ("FTIR") spectrometry but also helped with this book. In particular, Dr R. Beer, Professor P. B. Fellgett, Dr M. A. Ford, Professor H. A. Gebbie, Mr H. Lossau, Dr L. Mertz, Dr R. C. Milward, Dr C. M. Randall, and Professor H. Sakai provided much useful information.

I would also like to thank my colleagues, past and present, with whom I learned the theory and practice of FTIR technology.

Dr D. A. Robinson and staff at the Science Museum, London, made available their instrument collection and files. A number of spectrometer manufacturers augmented published accounts with information from their early days in the business.

The following institutions and companies have given their permission to reproduce quotations and illustrations for this book:

Academic Press Inc., Beckman-RIIC Ltd, Bomem Inc, Chelsea Instruments Ltd, Elsevier Scientific Publishing Ltd, Mattson Instruments Ltd, NEI Parsons Ltd, Optical Society of America, Pergamon Press PLC, Polytec GmbH, and Taylor & Francis Ltd.

Hedon, East Yorkshire, England
March, 1991

Sean Johnston

1

Introduction

In 1800, science was just beginning to coalesce into distinct disciplines. There was not yet a well-defined description for what the sciences comprised and excluded. The Victorian era, with its enthusiasm for categorizing the world, had not yet begun.

The lack of definition was apparent in how scientists referred to themselves. The gentlemen dabbling in physics and chemistry were still known as Natural Philosophers. The terms 'scientist' and 'physicist' were coined by William Whewell in 1840, and came into common use only much later. Few of the practitioners of science cared for the new labels. Michael Faraday, the pioneer of research in electricity and magnetism, wrote:

> I perceive also another new and good word, the *scientist*. Now can you give us one for the French *physicien*? Physicist is both to my mouth and ears so awkward that I think I shall never be able to use it. The equivalent of three separate sounds of *i* in one word is too much. (Ross, 1962)

Faraday referred to himself as an experimental philosopher throughout his career. Even Lord Kelvin, fifty years later, preferred the word *naturalist*. A magazine of the period said of the word *physicist* "four sibilant consonants fizz like a squib".

The contents of the scientific larder were also meagre. At the turn of the nineteenth century, the very nature of light was unknown. The effects of electromagnetism were confined principally to parlour demonstrations of static charge. Most English-speaking scientists were only just beginning to use the mathematical tools of calculus invented by Isaac Newton 150 years earlier.

Scientific instruments were generally marvels of brass and glass made for measuring time, or angles, or pressure. Engineering science was a relatively new discipline. For the first time, bridges, boilers, and barometers were being designed according to systematic rules rather than rule of thumb.

In this context, the first seeds of Fourier transform infrared (FTIR) spectrometry were sown.

The slow confirmation that light behaves like a wave led by the late nineteenth century to masterpieces of instrumental precision: the interferometers of Albert A.

Michelson. Michelson spent his career using these devices to investigate phenomena as diverse and fundamental as the constancy of the speed of light, the existence of an aether, the diameter of stars, and the nature of spectral emissions. In common with his contemporaries, Michelson believed that all major physical phenomena had been discovered. It remained to improve the accuracy of measurements, so that subtle secondary effects could be found.

His measurements were painstaking and laborious. They required extensive computations, far beyond the capabilities of manual calculation — so he invented a mechanical computer. Michelson's efforts were mainly solitary; the theoretical physicist Lord Rayleigh, working out some of the mathematics behind the techniques, did not fully understand the nature of the problem. Few experimenters were as adept as Michelson, and settled for easier methods.

As the study of light led beyond the visible to the infrared and toward ever longer wavelengths, experimenters found ever decreasing amounts of energy at their disposal. In the early decades of the twentieth century, scientists began to analyse more closely the nature of their equipment to wring every available bit of sensitivity from them. The instrument came to be seen not merely as a means to an experimental end, but worthy of study in its own right — particularly if that study led to better instruments. Where optics had been a driving technology in the advance of scientific instruments in the nineteenth century, electronics was the key technology for the twentieth.

Around 1950, a number of unrelated lines of research converged.

Pierre Jacquinot, working on under-funded physics research at a French university, realised that interferometers could capture much more light than spectrometers based on the prism instrumentation that had been developed over the preceding half-century. This throughput advantage of interferometers would be important for far infrared studies, especially for researchers without the means to purchase expensive and elaborate spectrometers. Peter Fellgett, studying light detectors and their fundamental limitations for his doctoral thesis at the University of Cambridge, discovered that by illuminating the detector with many wavelengths continuously rather than consecutively as in existing spectrometers, measurement noise could be significantly reduced. This multiplex advantage could be applied to interferometers.

The Second World War had seen the development of analogue and digital computers, initially for calculating projectile trajectories and mathematical tables. The nature of the interferometric method required intensive calculation, for which such computing machines were indispensable.

In the same few years, Claude Shannon while at Bell Laboratories in the USA worked out the principles of information theory. With the development of digital computers, mathematical ideas of discrete sampling and filtering — crucial to Fourier spectroscopy — received a firm foundation.

Over the next two decades, the theory was translated into practice by a handful of people, culminating in superb measurements of the infrared spectra of planets by Janine and Pierre Connes in France. Despite the enthusiastic research of far infrared specialists, other spectroscopists mistrusted the results of such an unintuitive technology.

Commercial exploitation began in the early 1960s owing to the missionary zeal of a few enthusiasts. A full decade was to elapse before the commercial instruments became popular with a large number of scientists. By the late 1970s, chemists had begun to adopt FTIR, and today represent its largest market. Through the 1980s the FTIR technique has percolated downward from research chemistry laboratories to the routine analytical chemistry workbench, and towards the quality control department. The need for increasingly robust and reliable instruments has driven a continual development towards simplicity, ease of operation and higher performance.

Applications of FTIR technology have expanded from the original studies in far infrared physics to routine analytical chemistry, and now extend to the factory floor for quality control and industrial process monitoring. The number of FTIR spectrometers in use has risen exponentially since the 1950s; the instruments are now among the most popular used in chemistry laboratories.

The development of FTIR instrumentation has attracted investigators from an unusually broad range of fields for over one hundred years; the technology makes use of disparate fields of knowledge like no other before it. The engineering employed in FTIR spectrometers has borrowed from the best of its day, continuing right up to the present.

Today, exactly a century after Michelson's first investigations and nearly two hundred years after the fundamental discoveries of optical interference, Fourier transform spectroscopy is firmly established as a primary technique in analytical chemistry. The development of FTIR has been unusually long; while an elegant concept, Fourier spectroscopy has continually challenged the contemporary technology. The advance of FTIR reflects the progress in several technologies over the last century: optics, electronics, mathematics and computing. The following chapters attempt to describe the principles of this interdisciplinary technology in their historical context.

Fortuitous, ingenious, elegant, non-intuitive — all describe FTIR spectroscopy and its development.

REFERENCE

Ross, S. (1962), Scientist: The Story of a Word, *Annals of Science*, **18**, 65.

Part I
Classical times

2

Origins

At the turn of the nineteenth century, a revolution in science was about to occur. At the time, science was still carried out as a pastime by enthusiastic gentlemen. The fields of physics, chemistry and instrument design were indistinct. Engineering was dominated by a "cut and try" approach. Analytical chemistry, statistics, and mathematical physics existed only in rudimentary form.

It was a period of rapid advance in science, however. Increasing industrialization of society caused new discoveries to be rapidly turned into practical applications. One of the fastest-growing fields was to be optical science and spectroscopy: the science of light was about to be transformed.

2.1 THE STATUS IN 1800

Until the nineteenth century, it was generally accepted that light could be described in terms of particles. The influence of Isaac Newton's theory of optics had held sway for over a century. Before Newton, there had been no general theory of what light was. The properties of simple lenses and mirrors were well understood, but there were several mysteries. Why, for example, did a prism produce colours from a beam of white light? Why did a beam of light bend in glass, and why did different glasses affect the beam to different degrees? Why were the edges of shadows filligreed by delicate patterns of light and dark?

Newton, starting at the age of 24, performed a series of cogent experiments followed by careful analysis. Although he published some of his findings a decade later, most did not appear until 1704, when he was 62 years old. He delayed their publication out of a desire "to avoid being engaged in Disputes" about his theories: during the same period, Christian Huygens, a Dutch mathematician, and others were expounding their own contradictory theories of light. Where Huygens believed light to be analogous to waves in water, Newton reasoned that all observations were explainable by "corpuscles". He was convinced that all the evidence showed that light consisted not of waves, but of particles:

> For, to me, the fundamental supposition itself seems impossible, viz., that waves or vibrations of any fluid can, like the rays of light, be propagated in

straight lines without continued and very extravagant spreading and bending into the quiescent medium, where they are terminated by it. (Newton 1666)

2.1.1   Light waves *vs.* particles

Isaac Newton's *Opticks* laid out his theory of the nature of light. According to the experiments he performed and knew of, light could be entirely interpreted as made up of particles or "corpuscles". This corpuscular or "ballistic" theory explained the reflection of light, the fact that it travelled in straight lines, and its refraction through transparent materials. Even the production of a rainbow or spectrum could be accounted for: different colours consisted of corpuscles of different kinetic energies. Travelling through transparent materials caused slowing of the particles and separation into the colours of the spectrum.

The observation of several other effects cannot be explained by the corpuscular theory. Interference and polarization of light (described below) are more straightforward to understand by considering light to consist of waves.

The theory of light was to turn upside-down in the nineteenth century, and again in the twentieth. By late Victorian times, Newton's corpuscular theory was discredited and of interest only to historians of science. This view was short-lived, though. With the growth of quantum mechanics in the twentieth century, it has since become accepted that all "particles" (such as electrons, protons, etc.) share characteristics of waves. This wave/particle duality of physical quantities is a more realistic model of reality. For some experimental observations, a wave picture is easier to understand; for others, a kinetic or particle interpretation is more natural. These must be recognized as aspects of the same reality, but are models that work well in practice. In this book, we will treat Fourier transform spectroscopy in its natural context: in terms of the wave picture.

2.2   THE DISCOVERY OF INTERFERENCE

In 1802, Thomas Young, a 29 year old English physician and natural philosopher, discovered a new optical effect that raised the first doubts about the corpuscular theory. Allowing a beam of light to pass through a pair of closely spaced slits, he observed the appearance on the wall beyond. Light from the two slits had overlapped on the wall to yield not a brighter patch of light, but a pattern of dark and bright bands. Light added to light could, it seemed, yield darkness. Young explained his observation in terms of the interference of light waves:

> The law is that when two portions of the same light arrive at the eye by two different paths, either exactly in the same direction or in two very close directions, the light is of maximum intensity when the difference of the paths travelled is a multiple of a certain length, and of minimum intensity for the intermediate state of interfering portions; this length takes different values for light of different colours. (Young 1802)

He concluded that "there must be a close resemblance between the nature of sound and that of light." Young's explanation of the dark and light bands seemed to him straightforward. He extended his theory to other unexplained optical phenomena; unfortunately, some of these interpretations were clearly wrong in the eyes of other investigators. To make matters worse, Young was "neither systematic, ordered, nor precise, which attracted critics from his contemporaries" (Ronchi 1956). In 1805, he was humiliated by published professional and personal criticisms in the *Edinburgh Review,* which effectively destroyed his reputation. Young retired from the scientific arena and devoted his considerable talents to other pursuits.

2.3 GROWTH OF THE UNDULATORY THEORY

Despite Young's simple explanation of his "interference bands", resistance in the scientific community was strong. Light waves could account for interference phenomena, but did not seem to explain the everyday characteristics of light such as reflection, refraction and dispersion. Newton's analysis was accepted in full, despite having lain almost unextended for over a century. Nevertheless, others began to investigate interference effects. The wave or "undulatory" theory of light, originally proposed by Huygens in 1678, gradually attracted an enthusiastic camp of supporters. The first of these was Augustin Fresnel, a French engineer who had been employed for twelve years in the design of roads and bridges.

In his free time, Fresnel studied scientific problems. In 1815, he suddenly gained more free time: having declared his opposition to Napoleon, he lost his post and was confined to a small village. Fresnel began to correspond with François-Jean Arago, astronomer at the Observatoire de Paris, about the theory of light. With the encouragement of Arago, Fresnel was able to pursue his ideas freely, in contrast to Young who had been defeated by unwarranted criticism.

Arago pointed Fresnel to the recent studies on light, but Fresnel, reading neither English nor Latin, was forced to perform his own experiments and rediscover the undulatory theory. Fresnel and Arago developed a complete, mathematical theory of light in terms of wave motion. In 1819, the Academy of Sciences in Paris awarded a prize to Fresnel for the work.

Writing an elementary treatise on the theory in 1822, Fresnel pointed out that other elementary effects such as the absorption of light by materials remained to be explained. His eventual interpretation of polarization phenomena was further strong evidence for the undulatory theory.

While Young's experiment had been interesting, Fresnel's explanations were convincing. By the middle of the 19th century, scientific opinion had swung to accept the wave nature of light; the corpuscular theory was abandoned en masse.

2.3.1 The interference of light

When light from a single source is divided into two parts and recombined, it is possible to see the effects of interference: dark and bright areas in the combined beam. The two portions of the light beam must travel a different path length, and the effect is usually easier to see with monochromatic (single colour) light. Interferometry in the 19th century consisted in the invention of many geometrical arrangements to observe and use the effects of interference. The dark and bright interference bands or "fringes" are caused by the constructive and destructive interference of light waves. When the path difference between two waves brings them into step at the overlap point, they add constructively and produce a bright fringe; when the path difference is a half-wavelength longer, a dark fringe results.

When more than one wavelength is present in the light source, each individual wavelength interferes with itself, producing an interference pattern. These individual patterns overlap to yield a composite pattern which is usually a white smear but in certain geometries resembles a spectrum.

2.3.2　Polarization

Polarization is another effect that can only be understood by considering light to consist of waves. The effect was first noted with certain rock crystals: the amount of light transmitted through two crystals in series depended on their relative orientation. Rotating one by 90° was sufficient to extinguish the light.

If light waves are considered analogous to the waves travelling along a cord, it will be seen that the wave vibrates in a direction perpendicular to its direction of motion: it is said to be a "transverse" vibration. Looking in the direction of the wave motion, it is apparent that it can vibrate in any perpendicular direction, e.g. vertically, horizontally or diagonally. The vibrations may even rotate as the wave progresses, moving in curved paths such as circles or ellipses.

In ordinary light, the vibrations are randomly mixed, making it impossible to separate any one direction of vibration from the rest. Special devices known as polarizers can perform this separation, though. A polarizer acts to absorb or reflect certain polarizations better than others, leading to a net polarization of the light transmitted through it. The first polarizers were crystals such as calcite and tourmaline, which can be cut and polished to transmit mainly light of a single vibrational direction.

Not only special crystals can polarize light, though. Light reflected from any material is partially polarized, because the vibrations in one direction interact more with the molecules of the substance. The phenomenon of polarization by reflection was discovered in 1808 when E. L. Malus happened to look through a crystal of polished calcite at the windows of Luxembourg palace. He saw that the amount of light reflected from the windows varied as he rotated the crystal, but that light reflected from other objects had an almost constant intensity. Besides glass, another common example of a reflective polarizer is a water surface. Light reflected from a polished glass surface or the surface of water is partially polarized. At a particular angle characteristic of the material (known as Brewster's angle, after its discoverer) one polarization is completely blocked. When a sheet of glass or a water surface is viewed through a polarizer, the intensity can be varied: the polarized light reflected from the surface will be blocked by the polarizer unless the two vibrational directions coincide.

2.3.3 Research into interference phenomena

After Young's first discovery of interference and Fresnel's detailed theory, several decades passed until the subject moved in a direction useful to spectroscopy. The French researchers Hippolyte Fizeau and Leon Foucault, working initially together and later in opposition, were prominent in experimental optics from the 1840s.

They began to measure interference patterns using increasingly large optical path differences. Instead of a few wavelengths of difference in path between the two interfering beams (as measured by previous investigators) they studied light with increasingly large displacements. The difference in path, determined by counting interference fringes, went beyond 50 000 wavelengths.

These large path differences proved essential in comparing very similar colours having slight differences in wavelength. By 1862, now working alone, Fizeau had used his interference device to count the fringes from various light sources. He observed that different sources produced variations in fringe contrast, noting the case of yellow sodium light as an example. In sodium light, as the path difference was gradually increased, the fringes become initially less intense (almost dying out) and then more intense again. This cycle seemed to repeat, no matter how long the path difference became.

Fizeau explained this effect as the interference of two close wavelengths: the sodium light must consist of two very similar colours, having slightly different wavelengths. The principle is shown in Fig. 2.1. As the path difference between two beams of this light was increased, the waves were first in step — producing bright fringes — and then at a larger path difference were out of step, causing a minimum of intensity. By measuring the path difference needed to go from bright to dark fringes, Fizeau could determine the ratio of wavelengths of the two colours.

Pierre Connes (1984) writes that the contributions of Fizeau were central to the subject: '...he was building the first variable-path interferometer for wavelength measurement by fringe counting, surely the ancestor of all present so-called "Fourier interferometers"...'

2.4 HARMONIC ANALYSIS

While optics was being revised, other fields were also advancing. Mathematics was being extended to give more practical tools for computations.

Joseph Fourier has been called the first theoretical physicist. He was pioneer in applying rigorous mathematics to practical problems. His example of the mathematical treatment of applied physics was followed through the nineteenth century by such well-known scientists as Ampère, Laplace, Lord Rayleigh, Lord Kelvin, Maxwell, Kirchhoff, Helmholtz and Gibbs — those responsible for most formulae found in undergraduate physics texts today.

Studying the propagation of heat from about 1805, he invented the idea of harmonic series, which could be applied to solve previously intractable mathematical problems. Fourier proved that any mathematical function could be "decomposed" into a sum of sine waves, or "harmonics". This meant that even very complicated mathematical relationships could be considered as the sum of a large (in some cases

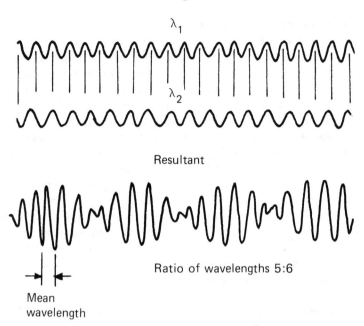

Fig. 2.1 — Principle of wavelength comparison used by Fizeau. Curves show interferograms of two individual wavelengths (top and middle), and their combination (bottom). If thousands of fringes are counted, very small ratios can be determined.

infinite) number of simple expressions. A schematic illustration of this is shown in Fig. 2.2. Because sinusoidal functions are relatively easy to deal with mathematically, solutions to unmanageable equations could be found by solving each term of the Fourier series and adding the results. Fourier used this method specifically for solving problems in the conduction of heat through materials of various shapes. "Fourier series" proved fundamental to interferential spectroscopy some decades later.

Investigators in France, Germany, England and the United States were thus active in studying phenomena such as interference, polarization, and relationships between light, electricity and magnetism. The nineteenth century saw the nature of light and electromagnetism unveiled, culminating in the theory of James Clerk-Maxwell that the two phenomena were in fact aspects of the same thing. Researchers justifiably felt that this unified theory of electromagnetism, which had been a vaguely described collection of mysteries a century earlier, tied up most of the loose ends of physics. With theoretical physics within sight of completion, attention began to turn to applications.

2.5   THE BEGINNINGS OF OPTICAL SPECTROSCOPY

In the early 1800s, several investigators sought a source of monochromatic light for their researches. Light of a single, pure colour was required to make microscope observations free of chromatic aberrations, for example, and to make accurate observations of the optical properties of glasses and crystals.

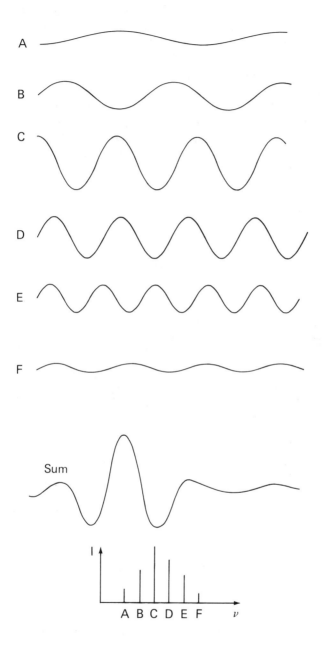

Fig. 2.2 — Decomposition of a mathematical function into its component harmonics.

As early as 1752, Thomas Melvill reported that common salt burning in a flame produced bright, homogeneous yellow light. He examined its nature by using a prism as Newton had done: light from the flame was passed through a small hole to a glass prism, where it was dispersed into its component colours. Melvill discovered that, instead of a continuous spectrum of colours from red to violet, the salt flame spectrum was discontinuous — patches of light with dark spaces between.

2.5.1 Invention of the spectroscope

Melvill was unable to see more than vague patches in his spectrum, because of the way his "spectroscope" was constructed (Fig. 2.3). It was another fifty years before Wollaston made the simple improvement of replacing the round entrance hole by a narrow slit. By orienting the slit perpendicular to the direction in which the prism bent the light, he avoided the overlap of images. The resulting spectrum was purer and clearer (Fig. 2.4).

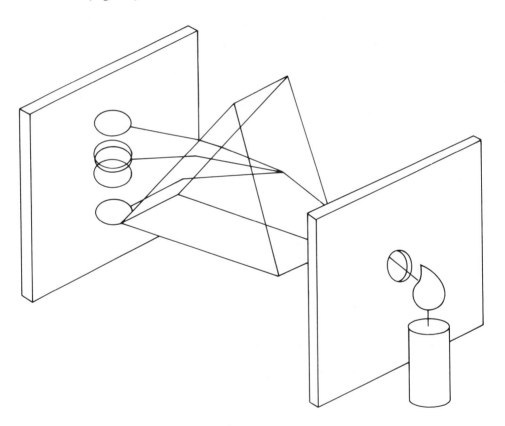

Fig. 2.3 — Schematic diagram of the spectroscope of Melvill, and the quality of his spectra.

Wollaston's improved instrument was still very simple and rather crude. By using just an entrance slit and a prism to disperse the light travelling through it, the rays of light struck the face of the prism at a range of angles. This meant that some rays of the same colour were refracted (bent) more than others, and caused the resulting

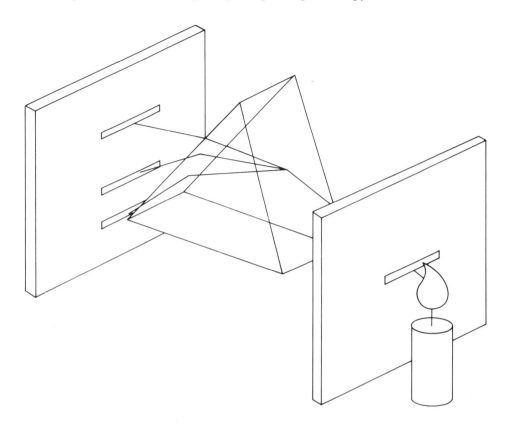

Fig. 2.4 — Improvements to the spectroscope by Wollaston, and the quality of his spectra.

spectrum still to contain overlapped images. In addition, it was difficult to see the details of the spectrum spread out on a white screen. The weak band of colours was small, and appeared washed-out by any room light and irregularities on the surface of the screen. Despite these difficulties, Wollaston observed that the spectrum of sunlight was not a continuous band of colour as Newton had thought, but was crossed by four or five dark bands. Without his slit, he would have missed these bands as had Newton.

Despite these unexplained observations, the pace of investigation remained slow. It was not until 1814 (over a decade later) that Joseph Fraunhofer improved the spectroscope further: he added a telescope to view the light coming from the prism directly. By dispensing with the observing screen, he was able to observe much brighter images in greater detail. This modest improvement opened up a new world that had only been hinted at by the observations of Melvill and Wollaston.

Fraunhofer discovered that the spectrum of sunlight was not crossed by just a few bands as Wollaston had seen, but by hundreds of narrow lines. These spectral lines corresponded to specific colours that were absent from the light. Fraunhofer also found that he could see similar lines in the spectra of a few of the brighter stars, and from the light of planets. The positions of the dark lines never changed, but were different for different stars. Fraunhofer produced a different type of spectrum — consisting of bright lines on a dark background — by heating substances in flames or by electric sparks. Instead of absorption spectra, these were "emission spectra": particular pure colours in isolation. For example, the salt flame that Melvill had seen to give a blurred oval turned out to be resolved into two closely spaced yellow lines. Fraunhofer had assigned identification letters to the dark lines he saw in the solar spectrum, and found that the bright yellow emissions from a salt flame corresponded to his solar "D" lines. Despite this match, he had no idea what the discovery meant, or why some lines should be dark and others bright.

A decade later (1823) Sir John Herschel used the spectroscope to examine the light passing through coloured glass. He found that entire bands of light, and not narrow lines, were absent from the spectrum. Another ten years further on, Brewster extended these observations and found other "absorption spectra" in the light passing through certain types of gas. Brewster realized that some of his gases gave absorption lines similar to those in the solar spectrum, and was able to match up one set for "nitrous acid gas". He was apparently the first person to relate the absorption spectrum of the sun to the presence of particular materials. Later, he found that emission spectra measured in his laboratory also corresponded to the spectral absorption lines of the sun. He was certain that there was a connection between these two classes of light.

The spectroscope obtained its final essential improvement in 1839, when Simms and Swan independently introduced a "collimator" — a lens to make the rays from the slit parallel before they reached the prism. The collimator ensured that all rays entering the prism had the same orientation, and so were refracted in the same way. This gave a further incremental improvement in the clarity of the spectrum.

By the middle of the nineteenth century, then, an accurate instrument had evolved to observe the phenomena of coloured light. The "line spectra" identified by the spectroscope were used by physicists without too much interest in their origin, or curiosity about the characteristic pattern for different substances. For most investigators, the fact that the emissions of particular substances were monochromatic (pure colours) was enough to make them ideal for many experiments.

Not until the late 1850s did the work of Robert Bunsen and Gustav Kirchoff (professors of chemistry and physics at Heidelberg, respectively) show that chemical analysis was possible by analysis of emission spectra. They were the first to demonstrate that the bright lines of the spectrum occupy the same positions independent of the temperature of the flame, and that the line positions were not altered by different combinations of the same metals in the flame.

Chemists, actively seeking an alternative to the tedious analytical methods of the day, welcomed the new technique. The science of optical spectroscopy was born. A textbook of the day touted the great sensitivity of the method.

> The spectrum method of analysis is distinguished from ordinary chemical methods by its extreme delicacy. The three-millionth part of a milligramme of a salt of Sodium, an imperceptible particle of dust to the naked eye, is yet capable of colouring the flame yellow and of giving the yellow line of Sodium

in the spectroscope…On account of this almost constant presence of Sodium chloride, it is scarcely possible to obtain a flame which does *not* exhibit the yellow line of Sodium. (Lommel 1875)

The new science was for many years called "spectrum analysis". The term "spectroscopy", probably coined in the early 1860s, was still little used, even by specialists, in the late 1880s (Dingle 1963). The nomenclature should refer only to measurements that can be made with the eye — "spectrometry" is the more general term for spectrum measurement. "Spectroscopy" is today used to refer to any technique that examines portions of a range of measurements, from subatomic particle energies to nuclear magnetic resonance. The original definition in terms of visual observations of light has been lost. We will not quibble about linguistic purity. It is enough that the word is accepted and understood by the majority.

Despite the possibilities opened up by spectroscopy, it remained an inconspicuous branch of physics and chemistry practiced by very few workers. Even for the practitioners, it represented only an adjunct to their main research interests. Spectroscopy as a science was not embraced by physicists until it began to explain atomic theory in the early twentieth century.

The technique was slightly more popular with chemists, but still represented a very specialized tool. At the end of the nineteenth century, spectrum analysis was proving useful for chemical identification of materials that could be burned in flames. Molecular spectroscopy did not yet exist.

2.5.2 Emission spectra

Substances emitting light generate emission spectra of various types. Emission is caused by the change in energy state of an atom or molecule. Because of the discrete nature of atomic energy levels, transitions between them yield distinct, isolated emission frequencies. The spectrum appears as a series of distinct lines, usually in the near infrared to ultraviolet portion of the spectrum.

Simple atoms that have few electrons, such as hydrogen, have a particularly simply populated energy level arrangement. This leads to a spectrum consisting of distinct series of spectral lines. The regularity of the line frequencies led to attempts to find a simple mathematical formula for them: the so-called Balmer, Lyman, Paschen and other series of hydrogen lines are examples.

In atomic emission spectroscopy, unknown substances are heated to raise electrons to higher energy levels, from which they decay to emit light. Heating can be carried out in a flame, plasma or electric arc.

2.5.3 Absorption spectra

Absorption spectroscopy is performed by providing a continuous spectrum of light to a substance, which then absorbs characteristic frequencies. The "missing" frequencies show up as dark lines in the otherwise continuous spectrum. The requirement is that the substance be cooler than the emitting source, so that the atoms of the sample substance are raised to excited energy levels by absorptions of particular frequencies of light.

The dark lines in the solar spectrum first noted by Fraunhofer were subsequently explained as absorption by the gases in the cooler outer envelope of the sun's atmosphere.

2.5.4   Molecular spectra

The energy levels of atoms are of relatively high energy: transitions between them lead to emission of light at visible or ultraviolet wavelengths. Other energy states exist for collections of atoms: for example, the stretching, vibrational and rotational states of atoms associated into molecules are quantized. Transitions between energy states are produced by the emission or absorption of light of the appropriate frequency. Molecular energy states are generally weaker than the binding energies of electrons to nuclei. They are also more closely spaced, because proximity of atoms in molecules causes a splitting of the atomic levels. As a result, molecules absorb and emit light principally at the lower energy of infrared frequencies. These transitions are usually so closely spaced that they appear as spectral bands in spectrometers having low resolution. As for atomic spectra, the infrared absorption bands are unique spectral fingerprints identifying molecules by their characteristic functional groups which stretch, vibrate and rotate as nearly independent units on the larger complete molecule.

The nineteenth century was a time of ferment in science; perhaps more so than even today. Fundamental discoveries had enormous practical consequences: steam power accelerated the growth of industry; the discovery of the basic characteristics of electricity and magnetism transformed industry towards the end of the century; the consolidation of higher mathematics made calculus and statistics useful tools for engineering. The discoveries in optical science paralleled these changes, and caused comparable turmoil in physics and chemistry.

Fifty years of optical research had led to instruments capable of analysing the colour of light. Photography was now available to record light phenomena directly. Completely new effects such as polarization and interference of light had been discovered and fitted into the new undulatory theory of light. In tune with other branches of science and technology in the nineteenth century, the pace of advance increased.

As an outgrowth of the studies into the nature of light, convenient optical instruments were invented for investigating interference effects. These "interferometers" were soon found to have practical applications, particularly by Albert A. Michelson while a young instructor at the US Naval Academy.

REFERENCES

Cantor, G. N. (1983), *Optics After Newton: Theories of Light in Britain and Ireland,* Manchester University Press, Manchester.
Connes, P. (1984), Early History of Fourier Transform Spectroscopy, *Infr. Phys.,* **24**, 69.
Dingle, H. (1963), A Hundred Years of Spectroscopy, *Brit. J. Hist. Sci.,* **1**, 199.
Home, R. W. (1985), Post-Newtonian Optics, *Hist. Sci.,* **23**, 207.
James, F. A. J. L. (1985), The Creation of a Victorian Myth: The Historiography of Spectroscopy, *Hist. Sci.,* **23**, 1.
Lommel, E. (1875), *The Nature of Light, With a General Account of Physical Optics,* Henry S. King & Co., London.

Mallik, D. N. (1912), *Optical Theories,* University Press, Cambridge.

Newton, I. (1704), *Opticks, Or A Treatise Of The Reflections, Refractions, Inflections and Colours Of Light,* William Innys at the West End of St. Paul's, London. Fourth Edition reprinted by G. Bell & Sons, Ltd, London, 1931].

Ronchi, V. (1956), *Histoire de la Lumière,* transl. by Taton, J., Librairie Armand Colin, Paris.

Sutton, M. A. (1986), Spectroscopy, Historiography and Myth: The Victorians Vindicated, *Hist. Sci.,* **24**, 425.

Young, T. (1802), An account of some cases of the Production of colours, not hitherto described, *Phil. Trans.,* 387.

3

The birth of interferential spectroscopy

Albert Abraham Michelson first published a brief note on the measurement of the speed of light in 1878, while a 26 year old instructor at the American Naval Academy at Annapolis. He had become interested in the problem while preparing a lecture demonstration for his class. Over the next three years, with financial assistance from his father-in-law, Michelson concentrated on improving his experimental technique.

A natural extension of this work was an experimental verification of the existence of a luminiferous aether. This medium, thought to pervade all space, was believed necessary by proponents of the undulatory theory of light to support light waves, in much the way that water is the medium that permits water waves to propagate.

It was reasoned that, were an aether present, it would move with respect to an observer. The rotation of the earth, its movement about the sun, and the motion of objects on the earth would all be with respect to a fixed aether. The speed of light propagating through this medium should therefore vary with direction.

While studying at the University of Berlin in 1880, Michelson designed an instrument, which he called an interferometer, to detect the aether drift.

3.1 THE INTERFEROMETER

The interferometer is an optical device used to generate and control an interference pattern. Thomas Young's screen with a double slit amounted to an interferometer having a fixed path difference: the slit separation determined how far out of step light waves would be. Many configurations of adjustable interferometer are possible, but one of the simplest is the type invented and used by Michelson.

The Michelson interferometer consists of three essential elements (Fig. 3.1):

(1) a beamsplitter to divide the beam from the light source into two parts;
(2) a fixed mirror to reflect one of the two beams back towards the beamsplitter;
(3) a movable mirror to reflect the other beam back towards the beamsplitter.

The two mirrors are aligned to exactly recombine the two beams at the beamsplitter, where they leave the interferometer (one half going back towards the source, and the other leaving at 90 degrees to it, where it can be observed by eye or a detector).

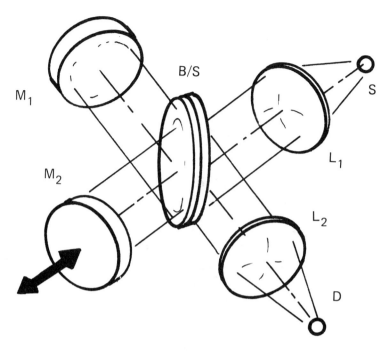

Fig. 3.1 — Elements of Michelson interferometer. S: source; B/S: beamsplitter and compensator plates; M_1: fixed mirror; M_2: moving mirror; L_1, L_2: collimating and focusing optics; D: detector.

The movable mirror can be moved parallel to the axis away from and towards the beamsplitter. In this way, the optical path length of that arm is increased or decreased. This causes the optical path difference (OPD) to vary: a movement of the mirror by 1/4 wavelength of light causes the OPD to vary by 1/2 wavelength.

Michelson designed an interferometer specifically to measure differences in the speed of light in different directions.

Michelson's interferometer consisted of the three essential parts, plus a mechanical carriage to displace the movable mirror (Fig. 3.2). The carriage was driven by a hand-turned screw, and the entire assembly was rigidly mounted to prevent any shift of the components.

If the aether existed, it should move relative to the two arms of the interferometer; the speed of light along the two arms would differ. Because of this, as the earth rotated and changed its orientation with respect to the aether, the relative speed of light along the two arms would vary, leading to changes in the effective optical path. This in turn would cause periodic variations in fringe position.

It was impossible to observe fringe positions continuously for a whole year to note a daily or seasonal change, but the same effect could be noted by rotating the interferometer. As one arm lined up or was placed perpendicular to the supposed aether drift, the fringe displacements should reach extreme values.

The difficulty of the experiment indicates Michelson's abilities as an experimenter. The apparatus was sensitive to vibrations from footsteps on a neighbouring

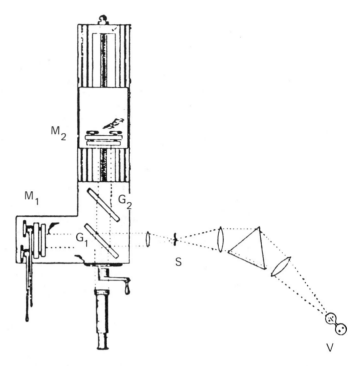

Fig. 3.2 — Michelson's interferometer (reprinted with permission from Taylor and Francis
Ltd).

street. Temperature, air currents (changing the density of air, and hence the speed of
light) and mechanical shifts all masked the effect he sought.

Michelson's work proved that no aether drift existed. This negative result was
instrumental twenty years later in verifying Einstein's special theory of relativity.

Michelson employed the principles of interferometry throughout his professional
career. The applications were diverse, from measuring the diameter of stars to the
development of standards of length, but all involved the extraordinary precision
possible with interferometry. He and E. W. Morley wrote (1887):

> ... it is very easy to estimate tenths or even twentieths of a wave-length,
> which implies that it is possible to find the number of wave-lengths in a given
> fixed distance between two planes with an error less than one part in two
> millions and probably one in ten millions.

In the same publication, he and Morley first published a description of the use of his
interferometer for inferring the spectral nature of light sources:

> ... there are two sets of waves in sodium-light. The result of the superposi-
> tion of these is that, as the difference in path increases, the interference

becomes less distinct and finally disappears, reappears, and has a maximum
of distinctness again, when the difference of path is an exact multiple of both
wave-lengths. Thus there is an alternation of distinct interference-fringes
with uniform illumination.

The method was the same as Fizeau had used some years earlier. Unlike the simple
fringe-counting that Fizeau had been interested in for applications in distance
measurement, Michelson used the technique to study the light emitted by various
materials. He thus made the extension from metrology to spectroscopy, opening up
new possibilities for interference methods.

Later in the same paper Michelson and Morley wrote:

Among other substances tried in the preliminary experiments were thal-
lium, lithium, and hydrogen . . . It may be noted, that in the case of the red
hydrogen-line, the interference phenomena disappeared at about 15,000
wave-lengths, and again at about 45,000 wave-lengths; so that the red
hydrogen-line must be a double line with the components about one sixtieth
as distant as the sodium lines.

They thus discovered that different light sources produced very different
interferograms.

3.2 THE INTERFEROGRAM

The interferogram is the curve of output intensity from an interferometer versus the
optical path difference (OPD) of the two beams.

Consider monochromatic light entering the interferometer, and suppose the two
interferometer mirrors are initially the same distance from the beamsplitter. The
beam will be divided in two, travel down both arms, and recombine at the
beamsplitter. The two halves will arrive back exactly in step (in phase) because the
two arm lengths are identical. As a result, the recombined beam will have maximum
intensity. Suppose the movable mirror is now moved by 1/4 wavelength. Now the
forward and reflected path of its beam will be an extra 1/2 wavelength long; the two
beams recombining at the beamsplitter will be exactly 1/2 wavelength out of phase,
and will combine to yield a minimum of intensity.

As the movable mirror is gradually displaced, this cycle of maximum and
minimum intensity will recur; a plot of the intensity will yield a sine wave having a
period proportional to the wavelength of light passing through the interferometer.

If a second monochromatic light source has a different, shorter, wavelength, the
same sort of modulation pattern will be produced by the interferometer, but with a
smaller scale: the same movement of the movable mirror now corresponds to a larger
wavelength interval, so the maxima and minima occur more frequently.

In general, when the light source contains many wavelengths, each will be
modulated in this way. The output beam from the interferometer will consist of the
superposition of all these wavelengths. Only at the zero path position — the position

when both mirrors are equidistant from the beamsplitter — will all the sine waves be in step. Because of this, the "balanced" position yields a strong peak in intensity. This special position of the interferometer is called the Zero Path Difference (ZPD). The resulting interferogram peak is denoted the ZPD position, "centreburst", or grand maximum.

Away from ZPD, the various components of the light beam fall increasingly out of step; thus, far from ZPD, the interferogram intensity settles down to an average value. At intermediate points, it oscillates about the average value. An example of an interferogram recorded with a modern interferometer is shown in Fig. 3.3.

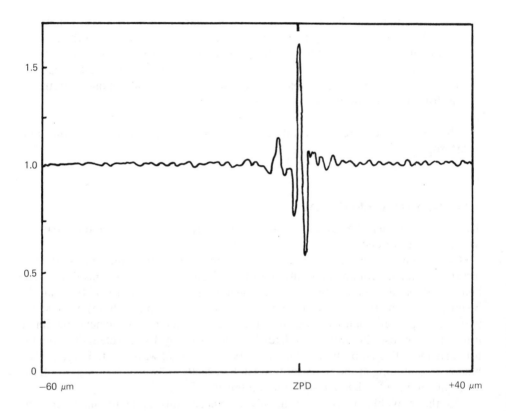

Fig. 3.3 — Interferogram of an infrared source, recorded on a modern instrument. ZPD is zero path difference.

Clearly, the exact shape of the interferogram is intimately connected with the wavelength distribution of the source. In other words, the interferogram is a coded representation of the spectrum. An example of the harmonic analysis of a function was shown in Fig. 2.2. Michelson calculated the relationships between several forms of interferograms and spectra, as shown in Fig. 3. 4.

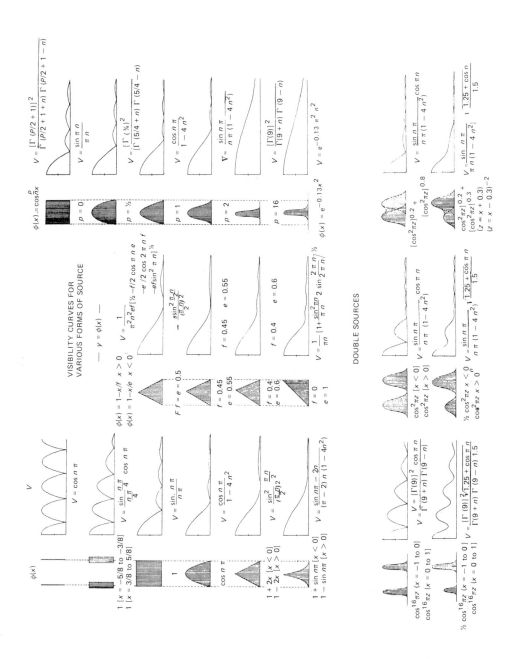

Fig. 3.4 — Relationships between interferograms and spectra as calculated by Michelson (reprinted with permission from Taylor and Francis Ltd).

By 1892 Michelson had thoroughly investigated his new method of interferential spectroscopy, and had published two long and descriptive papers devoted to the technique.

In the first (1891), he pointed out applications of his new method, including investigation of the Doppler broadening of spectral emissions:

> One of the first applications of this method showed that the red hydrogen-line is a very close double; and the same is also true of the green thallium-line. Another instance òf the class of problems which the method may help to solve is the effect of the velocity of the vibrating molecule in the line of sight in broadening the spectral lines.

As Michelson pointed out in the same paper, the validity of his technique was by no means intuitive to everyone:

> This question has been discussed by Ebert, who concludes that the width of the spectral lines due to this cause is not consistent with the results obtained by interference.

Lord Rayleigh, who had quickly taken a strong interest in Michelson's experiments, refuted the critics by providing a solid mathematical foundation. It was he who first related the interference curve to the spectrum by the Fourier transformation.

3.3   THE FOURIER TRANSFORM

The Fourier transformation is a mathematical manipulation which relates a signal, curve or algebraic function to its frequency content. In Fourier spectroscopy, the output signal is known as an interferogram, and is produced by an interferometer. The frequency content curve is simply the conventional spectrum — i.e. intensity plotted versus wavelength or frequency. The interferogram and spectrum contain the same information, but rearranged. The Fourier transform breaks down the interferogram into a set of sine waves which represent the individual wavelength components making up the light. This set of sine waves is then ordered in terms of wavelength to produce the conventional spectrum.

The arithmetic of the transformation requires a computer: to break down an interferogram into n discrete wavelengths takes about n^2 operations of addition and multiplication. A thousand-point spectrum would need about a million operations.

3.4   THE HARMONIC ANALYSER

Calculation of the Fourier transform was a difficult problem for Michelson, and for a long time afterwards. He was able to calculate the exact relationships between a few simple forms of interferogram and spectrum. In practice, however, the observed visibilities (fringe contrast plots) never corresponded exactly with the simple curves. He wrote:

Everyone who has had occasion to calculate or to construct graphically the
resultant of a large number of simple harmonic motions, has felt the need of
some simple and fairly accurate machine which would save the considerable
time and labour involved in such computations. (Michelson and Stratton
1898).

Michelson had been thinking about ways to ease the burden of calculation since he
devised his interferential method of spectroscopy. Some years earlier, he had mused
about an optical method of calculating the spectrum, presaging a technique which
was to be revived in the 1950s. He appears never to have tried out the idea.

Having no better means of calculation at his disposal, Michelson developed with
S. W. Stratton a mechanical calculator for performing the Fourier transform.

The only previously available device for calculating the sum of several harmonic
components (i.e. the superposition of sine waves) was an invention of Lord Kelvin,
who had used it in calculating tidal tables. The instrument consisted of a flexible cord
linked to a series of fixed and movable pulleys. The pulley positions were adjusted to
set the amplitude of the harmonic component to be summed; the motion of the free
end of the cord indicated the resultant of the various sine waves. The device was
limited to adding a small number of sine wave components, because of stretching and
stiffness of the cord. If the number of components were to be increased too far, the
resultant would suffer from large accumulated errors.

Michelson considered several alternate schemes for performing the calculations:
addition of fluid pressures, electric currents, or elastic and other forces. In each case,
he sought a quantity that could simulate the sinusoidal variation in intensity of light
waves. This simulation of a mathematical quantity by another, physical, effect is the
principle of analogue computers.

Michelson and Stratton eventually hit upon a suitable analogue quantity: the
addition of forces by spiral springs. The idea was to alternately stretch and release a
series of springs in a cyclical fashion. Each spring in the series would be pulled at a
specific frequency in order to simulate a light wave of a particular frequency. The set
of springs would pull on a drum so as to rotate it; the rotation was countered by
another large spring acting in the opposite direction. The net rotation of the drum
was indicated by a recording pen, and was the mechanical analogue of the resultant
intensity of superposed sine waves.

A prototype Michelson and Stratton device, which they called a harmonic
analyser, was first constructed using 20 mechanical elements. The results were so
encouraging that they applied for a grant to construct a more complex computer.
This consisted of 80 identical mechanical elements, one of which is shown in Fig. 3.5.
A curved lever, labelled B, is pivoted at the point O. One end of the lever is attached
to the end of an eccentric shaft which revolves as the drum D is turned. As the drum
revolves, the lever bobs up and down in an oscillating harmonic motion: the up-and-
down motion is a very good approximation of a sine wave. A rod, labelled R in the
diagram, communicates this motion up to another lever x. The amplitude of the
motion is adjustable: if the rod is positioned on one side of the pivot, the motion is
positive, while if placed on the opposite side, the motion is negative. The upper lever
x is attached to a drum C by a spiral spring. The other 79 elements of the analyser are

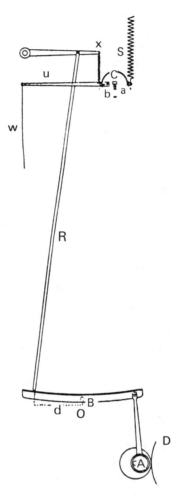

Fig. 3.5 — One calculating element of Michelson's harmonic analyser (reprinted with permission from Taylor and Francis Ltd).

connected in the same way to this drum. The force of the 80 springs pulling on the drum is counteracted by a larger spring S on the opposite side. The drum is also attached to a pen by a linkage (labelled u and w) so that its motion can be recorded.

Each element of the harmonic analyser is arranged to generate a different frequency of sine wave: each eccentric shaft is geared to the rotating drum D with a different number of gear teeth, so that the harmonic oscillations increase from element to element in a regular series. The eccentric nearest the hand-wheel revolves 80 times when that at the opposite end revolves once.

In use, the harmonic analyser would be set so that the 80 adjustable rods indicated a particular form of spectrum. The rods were positioned with an accurate gauge. For example, for a purely monochromatic spectrum, all but one of the rods would be placed at their respective pivot points so that they transmitted no motion to the drum C. The single remaining rod would then act on the drum with a simple sinusoidal motion, which would be recorded on paper. For a more complex spectrum, the rods corresponding to particular spectral frequencies would be adjusted to reproduce their intensities. The resultant would then be a more complex interferogram curve.

The harmonic analyser could sum either sine waves or cosine waves (which are identical to sine curves, but shifted in phase by 1/4 cycle; that is, a cosine wave is maximum when a sine wave has zero amplitude, and zero when the sine curve is minimum). The conversion from sine to cosine summation was achieved by disengaging the conical set of gears and turning all the eccentrics through 90°. Turning the hand wheel rotated the set of gears via a drive chain. The inventors noted that increasing the number of elements might require a stronger operator, or a motor to supply the required force.

Michelson used the harmonic analyser as a synthesizer rather than an analyser: that is, he assumed a particular spectral distribution, set up his device to reproduce it, and then compared the resulting curve with an observed interferogram. Rather than entering the actual measured data (i.e. the interferogram) he tried to simulate it using an assumed result.

The harmonic analyser worked well. Michelson and Stratton believed that they could increase the number of elements to "several hundred, or even a thousand, with a proportional increase in the accuracy of the integrations."

Several harmonic analysers were constructed by Gaertner & Co. of Chicago for various customers. Michelson exhibited his analyser at the Paris Exposition of 1900, for which he won a Grand Prix. Another, now in the Science Museum, London, has found use periodically in the intervening years. It was extensively used by de Havilland Aircraft in 1942 for wartime calculations, and twenty years later for the addition of harmonics in musical tones.

3.5 EXPERIMENTAL LIMITATIONS

Michelson never actually measured interferograms. His detector was his eye. The eye is excellent for measuring contrast, but rather poor at determining the absolute intensity of light. For this reason, Michelson confined himself to measurements of the contrast between adjacent fringes; this quantity, called by him the Visibility, is defined as:

$$(I_{MAX}-I_{MIN})/(I_{MAX}+I_{MIN})$$

where I_{MAX} = intensity of bright fringe, and I_{MIN} = intensity of dark fringe.

The visibility does not depend on the brightness (intensity) of the source, but only on the relative difference in intensity of the fringes.

By limiting his observations to fringe visibility, Michelson was recording the envelope of the interferogram, i.e. the overall character of the oscillations but not the oscillation positions in the interferogram curve; this is illustrated in Fig. 3.6. This loss of information was to restrict the capabilities of his method.

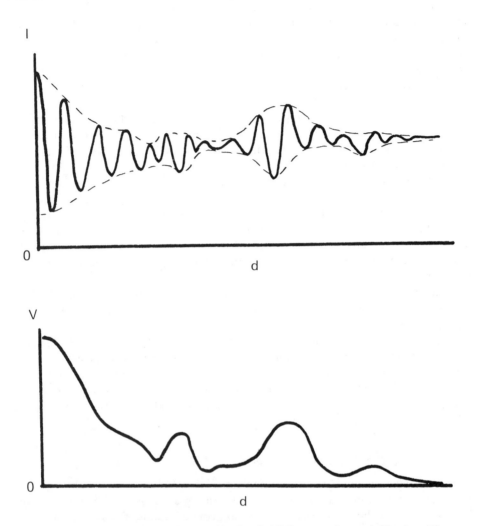

Fig. 3.6 — Comparison of interferogram (top) and visibility curve (bottom). The dotted line shows how the envelope of the interferogram is related to the visibility.

Yet, even before detailed communication with Lord Rayleigh, Michelson seemed to understand the need for something more than visibility measurements:

> In the case of an unsymmetrical source, it is possible to determine the position of the brighter portion by gradually increasing the difference in path from zero. If the fringes are thereby displaced in the positive sense from the position calculated from the mean wave-length, then the brighter edge lies toward the violet. (Michelson 1892)

In a published letter to Michelson, Rayleigh appears not to have reached the same conclusion:

> . . . observations would have to be made not only upon the visibility, but also upon the situation of the bands. You remark that "it is theoretically possible by this means to determine, in case of an unequal double, or a line unsymmetrically broadened, whether the brighter side is towards the blue or the red end of the spectrum". But I suppose that a complete determination of both C and S, though theoretically possible, would be an extremely difficult task. (Rayleigh 1892)

The C and S referred to are the cosine and sine components of the interferogram, containing information about the magnitude (fringe envelope) and phase (fringe position from zero path difference).

3.6 INFRARED AND FAR INFRARED

The research into the nature of light had led quite early to studies beyond the visible. Herschel, in 1801, discovered that a thermometer placed beyond the red end of a spectrum responded to some invisible light; this "Infra-Red" radiation captured the attention of several researchers.

Heinrich Rubens, professor of Experimental Physics at the University of Berlin, was one of the pioneers of infrared research. Over a twenty-year period beginning at the end of the nineteenth century, he methodically studied ways of generating and isolating infrared radiation, discovered substances that absorbed or transmitted it, and invented apparatus to measure it.

In 1900, Coblentz in the US began to accumulate records of the infrared transmittance of various chemical substances. He was able to determine that the infrared spectrum indicated the structural make-up of molecules: particular functional groups (molecular units) absorbed light at characteristic infrared wavelengths. This research was to lead to the use of infrared spectroscopy by chemists for the identification and characterization of chemical products.

3.7 THE MEASUREMENT OF INFRARED RADIATION

Rubens and his contemporaries used a number of instruments for the measurement of radiation beyond the red portion of the spectrum. All measured the intensity of radiation by the change in temperature of a blackened receiver.

The thermocouple is a sensor formed from the junction of two dissimilar metals. The temperature of the junction determines the voltage difference across it. A thermopile is one or more thermocouple junctions thermally connected to the receiver.

A microradiometer measures temperature difference in the same way as a thermopile. In the microradiometer, however, the thermocouple junctions and receiver are attached to the moving system of a galvanometer coil, which is suspended by fine quartz fibre. This has the advantage of omitting long electrical leads between the thermopile and measuring instrument which have a considerable resistance drop. The microradiometer is particularly sensitive to vibration, however.

The bolometer (invented by S. P. Langley in 1880) comprises a blackened metal strip with electrical connections. Change in temperature causes a change in resistance of the blackened receiver. This resistance change is measured by making the strip one arm of a Wheatstone bridge: temperature change alters the balance of the resistive bridge. A sensitive galvanometer is used to regain balance and measure the temperature change.

A classical radiometer is a system comprising an energy receiver and a mirror, all mounted from a quartz fibre in a partially evacuated case. The receiver is blackened on one side so that a beam of radiation causes it to heat more on the absorbing side. The gas pressure inside the case is just high enough to provide enough gas molecules to impart a torque to the suspended assembly without damping its motion: the molecules striking the warmer side recoil with greater momentum than those striking the cooler rear surface. The net twist is eventually balanced by the twist from the torsion of the quartz fibre. The deflection of the system can be monitored by light reflected from the mirror and directed to a distant scale, typically several meters away.

3.8   INTERFERENTIAL SPECTROSCOPY IN THE INFRARED

Nearly twenty years after Michelson's invention of interference methods for spectroscopy, and a decade after his last publications on the method, Heinrich Rubens and coworkers in Germany picked it up.

Rubens had been almost single-handedly extending optical studies into the far infrared since the 1890s. His motivation was to explore the region between light waves and radio waves: James Clerk Maxwell had concluded that both were forms of electromagnetic radiation, and subject to the same laws of reflection, refraction, and absorption. Rubens had discovered efficient infrared light sources, infrared-transmitting materials, and methods of isolating far infrared radiation for measurement.

Rubens had previously used diffraction gratings to disperse infrared radiation, but he appears to have been drawn to interferometry by the prospect of better efficiency. Speaking of the need to use slits in dispersive spectrometers, he wrote:

> In obviating such a diminution of energy, the interference method has a decided advantage over all spectrometric methods, where the use of a slit is unavoidable. A second advantage consists in the evasion of the diffraction grating, which is so uneconomical of energy. (Rubens and Hollnagel 1910)

This reference to better energy throughput is the first mention of what was later to be called the Jacquinot advantage, after the French physicist who rediscovered and generalized it some forty years later.

Rubens and his American graduate student Herbert Hollnagel used an inferior type of interferometer: two quartz plates, without a metallic reflecting surface, having an adjustable spacing. Light was shone directly through the two plates; a small amount was reflected from the first and second plates, and back in the direction of the light source. By this means, two weak beams of equal intensity were obtained, which could be adjusted in phase. If the device were used in transmission instead of reflection, the beams had very unequal intensity: one would be directly transmitted, while the second would be reflected from the second plate to the first, and then back through the second plate to join the direct beam. Because of the unequal intensities, the beams could never exactly cancel, and so visibility of the fringes was rather poor. Another drawback was that the path difference could only be adjusted in one direction: it could never be made zero, because this would require the two quartz plates to touch with no airspace between.

In contrast, Michelson's interferometer of twenty years earlier produced two bright, equally intense beams which could be adjusted in phase symmetrically about the point of zero path difference. The original version thus permitted complete, high-quality interferograms to be recorded.

Despite these disadvantages, Rubens and Hollnagel improved Michelson's method by at least two crucial steps: firstly, they employed an energy detector in place of the human eye. By so doing, they recorded the interference fringes, and not the "visibility" envelope to which Michelson had been restricted. The use of their "radiomicrometer" (more typically referred to as a microradiometer by their contemporaries) was not without its problems, however: .

> The radiomicrometer . . . gave a deflexion of 100 mm for a candle six metres distant with a scale distance of 3 metres and a deflexion period of 10 seconds . . . when the weather conditions were unfavourable, and especially when the wind was high, the zero-point of the instrument varied most irregularly, the variation often attaining several millimetres.

The second advance over Michelson was the use of his method for broad-band radiation measurements: instead of the isolated spectral emissions measured by Michelson, Rubens and coworkers were observing a wide band of wavelengths simultaneously. The principle was, in fact, the same, but it is an intellectual extension that Michelson appears never to have considered.

Disappointingly from the perspective of a modern observer, Rubens and Hollnagel did less with their data than Michelson had done. They were content to extract the barest of information from the curves — principally the average wavelength and spectral widths of their isolated far infrared light. No reference to the Fourier transformation was made. Yet they were aware of Michelson's work:

> The interference curves furnish not only the necessary data for the wavelength computation but also give a probable idea of the homogeneity and energy distribution of such rays. Our problem is one similar to that which Prof. A. A. Michelson had to deal with in drawing conclusions regarding the energy distribution of spectral lines from the visibility curves of the interference fringes obtained by a great difference of optical path.

A year later, collaborating with R. W. Wood, Rubens published the first interferograms obtained with the radiomicrometer (Fig. 3.7). They had added

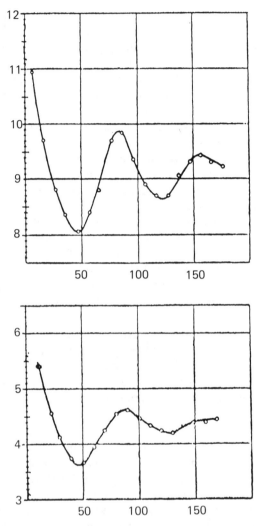

Fig. 3.7 — The first published interferograms recorded by Rubens and Wood (reprinted with permission from Taylor and Francis Ltd).

another key feature to their measurements familiar to later FTIR spectroscopists: the verification of the optical path difference by observing the fringes from a monochromatic light source:

> It was found that the readings of the graduated wheel of the interferometer did not give very reliable indications of the thickness of the air film, especially when the plates were in close proximity. The distance between the plates was accordingly determined in every case, by observing the interference fringes formed by reflecting the light in a sodium flame normally, from the quartz plates. (Rubens and Wood 1911)

By calibrating the optical path difference with an accurately known wavelength, the measurement precision could be extended to unknown wavelengths.

As in his work with Hollnagel, Rubens made no attempt at a systematic analysis of the resulting interferograms. The closest he came was what he admitted was a trial and error method: by making assumptions about the wavelengths transmitted by his materials, and the distribution of his radiation source, he assumed a shape for the spectrum and then checked how well it agreed with the observed interferogram:

> This curve we may now divide into elementary vertical strips, each one of which represents nearly homogeneous radiation. We now draw the interference curves (sine curves) of the various strips, and the superposition of all these curves should give us a curve identical with the curve obtained with the interferometer, if our energy curve has been correctly figured.

In other words, Rubens was doing in a much cruder way by hand what Michelson had been achieving with his 80 point mechanical computer some fourteen years earlier. Had Rubens had access to the harmonic analyser, he could quite conceivably have obtained good quality spectra from his interferograms, without any assumptions whatsoever.

REFERENCES

Bennett, J. M., McAllister, D. T. and Cabe, G. M. (1973), Albert A. Michelson, Dean of American Optics — Life, Contributions to Science, and Influence on Modern-Day Physics, *Appl. Opt. 12.*, 2253.

Connes, P. (1984), Early History of Fourier Transform Spectroscopy, *Infr. Phys.*, **24**, 69.

Connes, P., Smyth, M., Hadni, A. and Gerbaux, X. (1988), Heinrich Rubens, Herbert Hollnagel, and Fourier transform spectroscopy, *Opt. News*, **14**, 6.

Michelson, A. A. (1891), On the Application of Interference-Methods to Spectroscopic Measurements, — I, *Phil. Mag.*, (5), **31**, 338.

Michelson, A. A. (1892), On the Application of Interference-Methods to Spectroscopic Measurements, — II, *Phil. Mag.*, (5), **34**, 280.

Michelson, A. A. and Morley, E. W. (1887) On a Method of making the Wave-length of Sodium Light the actual and practical Standard of Length, *Phil. Mag.*, (5), **24**, 463.

Michelson, A. A. and Stratton, S. W. (1898) A New Harmonic Analyser, *Phil. Mag.*, (5), **45**, 85.

Lord Rayleigh (1892), On the Interference Bands of Approximately Homogeneous Light; in a Letter to Prof. A. Michelson, *Phil. Mag.*, (5), **34**, 407.

Rubens, H. and Hollnagel, H. (1910), Measurements in the Extreme Infra-Red Spectrum, *Phil. Mag.*, (6) **19**, 764.

Rubens, H. and Wood, R. W. (1911), Focal Isolation of Long Heat-Waves, *Phil. Mag.*, (6) **21**, 249.

Part II

Dark ages

4

The decline of interferential spectroscopy

4.1 SPREADING THE WORD

The rejection of Michelson's interferential spectroscopy by the succeeding generation is not surprising in retrospect.

According to Paul Merrill of the Mount Wilson Observatory with which Michelson was associated in later years, Michelson published less than a tenth of what he
knew. He was a cautious scientist, and one who thought in terms of physical models
rather than relying solely on mathematical formulations. Instead of promoting only
the merits of his technique, Michelson was careful to describe what he saw as its
drawbacks.

Co-workers were few. In his early years, at least, Michelson was a difficult
collaborator. He had little success in supervising the thesis projects of his graduate
students. Robert Millikan, a later Nobel prize winner in physics, relates that
Michelson wrote to him:

> What these graduate students always do with my problems, if I turn them
> over to them, is either to spoil the problem for me because they haven't the
> capacity to handle it as I want it handled, and yet they make it impossible for
> me to discharge them and do the problem myself; or else, on the other hand,
> they get good results and at once begin to think the problem is theirs instead
> of mine, when in fact the knowing of what kind of a problem it is worth while
> to attack is in general more important than the mere carrying out of the
> necessary steps. So I prefer not to bother with graduate students' theses any
> longer. I will hire my own assistant by the month, a man who will not think I
> owe him anything further than to see that he gets his monthly check. You
> take care of the graduate students in any way you see fit and I'll be your
> debtor forever. (Millikan 1938)

Michelson's preference for individual research meant that his experimental methods
and belief in interferometry were not passed on. Without the positive energy of a
research group to buoy it, enthusiasm for interference methods foundered.

4.2 AMBIGUITIES

Michelson recognised that his interferometric spectroscopy appeared to have inherent ambiguities. He wrote the preface to the English translation of a 1900 optics text by Paul Drude, in which the German theorist writes (concerning determining the spectrum from visibility curves):

> ...the problem is really not solvable...Michelson...found by trial and error what intensity law $\Phi(m)$ best satisfied the forms of V. It must be admitted, however, that the resulting $\Phi(m)$ is not necessarily the correct one, even though the distribution of intensity and the width of the several spectral lines are obtained from this valuable investigation of Michelson's with a greater degree of approximation than is possible with a spectroscope or diffraction grating. (Drude 1900)

Michelson published *Light Waves and Their Uses*, a popular book on his researches, in 1902. The book was edited from his notes for lectures delivered at the Lowell Institute of Boston in 1899. In it, he voices his own qualifications about his technique:

> The examination of spectral lines by means of the interferometer, while in some respects ideally perfect, is still objectionable for several reasons. In particular, it requires a very long time to make a set of observations, and we can examine only one line at a time. The method of observation requires us to stop at each turn of the screw, and note the visibility of the fringes at each stopping-place. During the comparatively long time which it takes to do this the character of the radiations themselves may change. Besides, we have the trouble of translating our visibility curves into distribution curves. Hence it is rather easy for errors to creep in.

Lord Rayleigh was not an unqualified supporter of interferometric spectroscopy. In a 1912 paper, he echoed Drude's misgivings about determining the spectrum from the visibility curve, saying "...a knowledge of the intensity merely...does not suffice". Towards the end of his career, Michelson reflected:

> While it may be admitted that the analysis of spectral lines by the method of visibility curves is somewhat indirect and not entirely certain, it has nevertheless proved of considerable value, especially in cases where the effects to be observed are beyond the power of the spectroscope. At the time of its inception (1890s) the resolving power of the instruments available was far too small for many of the problems which have yielded to the new method. (Michelson 1927)

4.3 RESTRICTION TO EMISSION SPECTRA

Another practical limitation concerns the visibility curve itself. The interferogram of one or a few emission lines yields high-contrast interference fringes which can be readily discerned by eye. The complementary case — a narrow absorption feature in a continuous background spectrum — yields an interferogram with much poorer contrast (Fig. 4.1). This washing out of the interference features makes absorption spectroscopy by Michelson's method almost impossible. As the majority of applications in infrared chemistry and physics concern absorption spectra, this was an overpowering disadvantage for the method.

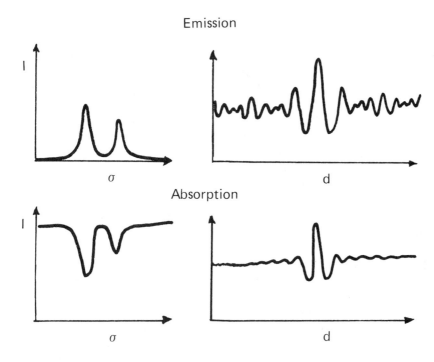

Fig. 4.1 — Spectra (left) and corresponding interferograms (right) for a source emitting only a few frequencies (top) and a broadband source absorbing only a few frequencies. In the absorption case, the interferogram intensity is very uniform away from zero path difference.

4.4   THE MISSING LINK

Michelson, the originator, and Rubens and coworkers, the first to find new applications, came tantalizingly close to developing a valid, unambiguous method of spectroscopy. With the clarity that comes from hindsight, we can see the shortcomings of both.

Michelson restricted himself to visual measurements. Throughout his long career, he never once used radiation detectors to measure light intensity. By observing only the envelope of the interferogram, he missed vital information: the phase of the oscillations, which prevented a complete Fourier transformation from being calculated. The Fourier transform of the "visibility", without this phase information, cannot correctly assign wavelengths and intensities when more than one frequency is present; the calculated spectrum is ambiguous.

A second factor contributing to the unpopularity of Michelson's technique was that it was not amenable to photographic recording. Photography had become the predominant method of recording observations in visible spectroscopy and astronomy by the turn of the century. It allowed straightforward recording of all the information and could be analysed at leisure after the experiment by the use of a densitometer. The laborious, sequential measurement in Michelson's method was too time-consuming for routine work.

Michelson never developed a clear understanding of the limitations of his method. For example, what was the ultimate factor in determining resolution? His work hinted that resolution depended on the maximum optical path difference, i.e. on the total displacement of the interferometer mirror. However, he never stated this fact in so many words.

Another example of incomplete understanding during this period is the answer to the question: what determined the spectral range? Michelson clearly limited himself to what were nearly monochromatic lines; first, because the visibility curves were often fairly simple and capable of intuitive interpretation; second, because his approach of synthesizing a trial interferogram from an assumed spectral distribution had to start with informed guesses. The ability to produce nearly the same interferogram from various spectral distributions probably convinced him to stay with simple problems.

Michelson recognised the relationship between the Fourier transformation, the interferogram and the spectrum. The critical missing link for him was how to resolve the ambiguities of phase. Rubens had inadvertently solved this problem by measuring the actual interferogram intensity, and not its envelope.

The work of Rubens and coworkers provided the complement to Michelson's studies, but had its own deficiencies. Rubens and Wood appear to have had a murkier understanding of the connection between the interferogram and the Fourier transformation. This appears not to have been true of Herbert Hollnagel, who correctly described the interconnection of interferogram and spectrum in his doctoral dissertation. Hollnagel may have attempted the laborious calculations involved in converting his interferograms into spectra, but the task was almost impossible for more than a handful of spectral points.

Ironically, Michelson's harmonic analyser could have performed a relatively high resolution Fourier transformation on Hollnagel's data, providing a far-infrared spectrum superior to anything available by other types of spectrometer at the time.

Hollnagel never published his thesis work. It has been suggested that he may have felt cowed by Rubens' disdain for elegant mathematics, or convinced of the futility of performing the time-consuming calculations for routine research (Connes *et al.* 1988). What is certain is that Rubens paid no attention whatever to Hollnagel's work, and stuck doggedly to his cut-and-try method of interferogram interpretation with R. W. Wood. In the same year as his work with Wood was published, Rubens collaborated and published with O. Von Baeyer, using identical methods. Von Baeyer appears to have contributed nothing to the instrumental arrangements, but the two managed to extend their crude spectral measurements to 300 μm, about $1\frac{1}{2}$ octaves further towards radio waves.

4.5 FINAL DECLINE

Bridging the gap between optical and radio waves continued for another decade. E. F. Nichols and J. D. Tear (1923) reproduced Rubens' method, but with a "Hertzian oscillator" instead of heated infrared sources or mercury lamps. The oscillator was a very short wavelength microwave generator, emitting at 1.8 mm (1800 μm, or 5.6 cm^{-1}).

Their interferometer was considerably more efficient than that of Rubens. It consisted of two flat brass plates mounted side by side, one of which could be shifted backwards by a micrometer screw (Fig. 4.2). Microwaves incident on this "divided mirror" were reflected back as two parallel beams with an optical path difference equal to twice the plate separation. The beams were focused and combined on the detector, where interference fringes could be measured. This so-called "Boltzmann interferometer" reflected each beam much more efficiently than the uncoated quartz plates employed by Rubens.

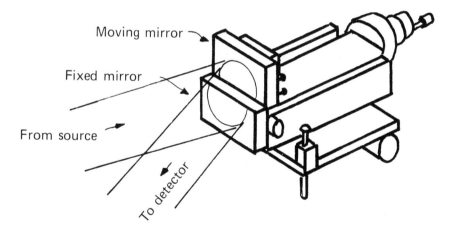

Fig. 4.2 — Boltzmann interferometer used by Nichols and Tear.

Nichols and Tear make no mention of Michelson, Rayleigh or Fourier transforms in the paper, but were clearly well aware of the experiments of Rubens and his collaborators. They recorded interferograms of several different oscillator sources, noting a considerable difference between them. In addition to their spectral differences, the oscillators fluctuated in intensity:

A Hertzian oscillator, especially a short wave oscillator, because of its rapid wearing away and constant need of readjustment, is very erratic and unsteady in action. It can in no sense be called either a constant source of radiation or even a uniformly varying source. Consequently the experimental procedure followed by earlier short wave experimenters has led at best to results which were only in the roughest sense quantitative. In the present experiments, a check was kept at all times on the emission of the oscillator by the "check receiver"...

By using a reference detector in this way, the investigators compensated for source fluctuations. This concept of a "sample" and "reference" beam was to be reapplied in spectrometers in the following decade, and in subsequent interferometers.

Nichols and Tear analysed their interferograms as Rubens had done: by inspection, trying to fit two or three sine waves to them. This amounted to an imprecise Fourier transformation of two or three points, and just hinted at the actual spectra of the oscillator sources. These researchers understood even less than Rubens had about the relationship between interferogram and spectrum. They designed their oscillator-receiver (i.e. light source-detector) system to be tuned to a specific wavelength of radiation. They did not even try to measure its spectrum, but instead wanted to isolate a dominant wavelength (as long as possible) and measure its period by its interference fringes:

> The method of securing homogeneous radiation has been to use a selective receiver to which the oscillator was carefully tuned. The interference curves for five of the six wave-lengths used in the present experiments are shown...The form of the curves affords a basis for estimating the purity of the radiation and the accuracy of the wave-length measurements. (Tear 1923)

Nichols and Tear greatly extended infrared research with their work, but took a step backwards in the interferential method. Their use of interferometers for spectral analysis retrogressed beyond Rubens and Michelson to Fizeau, who had measured a single wavelength by fringe counting some seventy years earlier.

Just prior to the First World War, then, the situation for interferential spectroscopy was unpromising: a clever technique, certainly; useful, for certain problems, undoubtedly; but, in the opinions of the few researchers who were aware of it and understood it, superseded by easier methods.

REFERENCES

Connes, P., Smyth, M., Hadni, A. and Gerbaux, X. (1988), Heinrich Rubens, Herbert Hollnagel, and Fourier transform spectroscopy, *Opt. News*, **14**, 6.
Drude, P. (1902), *The Theory of Optics*, Riborg Mann, C. and Millikan, R. A. (translators), Dover Publications Inc., New York.
Lord Rayleigh (1912), Remarks concerning Fourier's Theorem as applied to Physical Problems, *Phil. Mag.*, (6), **24**, 864.
Michelson, A. A. (1902), *Light Waves and Their Uses*, The University of Chicago Press, Chicago.

Michelson, A. A. (1927), *Studies in Optics,* The University of Chicago Press, Chicago.

Millikan, R. A. (1938), Biographical Memoire of Albert Abraham Michelson 1852–1931, *National Academy of Sciences of the United States of America: Biographical Memoires,* Nat. Acad. Sci., Washington, **19**, 121.

Nichols, E. F. and Tear, J. D. (1923), Short Electric Waves, *Phys. Rev.,* **21**, 587.

Rubens, H. and Hollnagel, H. (1910), Measurements in the Extreme Infra-Red Spectrum, *Phil. Mag.,* (6) **19**, 764.

Rubens, H. and Von Baeyer, O. (1911), On Extremely Long Waves, emitted by the Quartz Mercury Lamp, *Phil. Mag.,* (6) **21**, 689.

Tear, J. D. (1923), The Optical Constants of Certain Liquids for Short Electric Waves, *Phys. Rev.,* **21**, 611.

5

Competing technologies

The interest in atomic spectroscopy and infrared research at the turn of the twentieth century stimulated the development of new forms of spectroscopic instruments. Researchers wanted to measure more quickly, more reliably and with greater detail ever farther through the spectrum. The new applications led to standardization of spectral units and the way instruments were described.

5.1 SPECTRAL UNITS

Dispersive spectrometers are conventionally calibrated in terms of wavelength, with microns (or more properly, micrometres μm) the natural unit for infrared work, and nanometres (known formerly as millimicrons) or Ångströms ($10\,\text{Å} = 1\,\text{nm} = 0.001\,\mu\text{m}$) the preferred units in the visible.

The spectral units used today began life in the nineteenth century. The first spectroscopes were calibrated on completely arbitrary scales: Fraunhofer, mapping the solar spectrum for the first time, simply assigned letters to the absorption lines he saw. Kirchhoff did the same, but added the reading of the angular scale of his prism spectroscope. Other workers, using their own spectroscopes, used these published values to calibrate their instruments. Each instrument had a distinct calibration curve, because the different angles of prisms and the glasses from which they were made caused light to be refracted by different amounts.

Ångström, in 1869, measured spectral line positions by using a different type of spectroscope based on a diffraction grating (described in Section 5.5.2 below). This device had the characteristic of dispersing light at an angle proportional to its wavelength, which prisms do not do. Ångström's "normal" spectral scale only slowly displaced Kirchhoff's arbitrary version. Near the end of the nineteenth century, though, the Ångström scale became the accepted reference, despite corrections made by interferometric measurements.

The Ångström was called the "tenth-meter" in its early days by Johnstone Stoney (because it is $10^{-10}\,\text{m}$). The exact definition of the unit has varied slightly in the twentieth century, being termed successively the "Ångström Unit" and then the "Ångström".

Frequency units are natural for Fourier spectrometers, normally expressed in reciprocal wavelength (cm^{-1}) and termed wavenumbers. The "wave-number" was introduced by Rydberg, an important contributor to the theory of spectra, and represents the number of waves per centimeter of the wave-train of light.

As wavenumbers are units inverse to wavelength, the choice of units alters the appearance of the spectrum. For example, $1\,\mu m = 10\,000\,cm^{-1}$; $10\,\mu = 1000\,cm^{-1}$; $20\,\mu m = 500\,cm^{-1}$; and $50\,\mu m = 200\,cm^{-1}$.

5.2 SPECTRAL RANGE

The electromagnetic spectrum is conventionally divided into regions having distinct physical effects and measured by specific techniques.

The visible portion of the spectrum is approximately 0.4—$0.7\,\mu m$ (400—$700\,nm$, or about $25\,000$–$14\,000\,cm^{-1}$). The ultraviolet lies at higher energies and shorter wavelengths, and extends to about $0.1\,\mu m$ ($100\,000\,cm^{-1}$). Beyond lie X-rays. On the longer wavelength side, the infrared covers the range from about 0.7 to $1000\,\mu m$ ($25\,000$–$10\,cm^{-1}$) with microwave techniques being used for wavelengths much beyond 1 mm.

The infrared spectrum itself is usually divided into three regions: the near infrared (above about $5000\,cm^{-1}$), the far infrared (below about $500\,cm^{-1}$) and the mid infrared in between.

5.3 SPECTRAL RESOLUTION

Resolution, the minimum distinguishable spectral interval, is a characteristic of the spectrometer, and can be expressed in various terms. "Halfwidth", the apparent width of an infinitely narrow spectral emission, is today more precisely termed FWHM — Full Width at Half Maximum. Resolving power is the usable spectral range divided by resolution.

For example, a spectrometer operating between $2\,\mu m$ ($5000\,cm^{-1}$) and $25\,\mu m$ ($400\,cm^{-1}$) with constant resolution of $4\,cm^{-1}$ has a resolving power of 1150 and a wavelength resolution of $0.0016\,\mu m$ at $2\,\mu m$, or a wavelength resolution of $0.25\,\mu m$ at $25\,\mu m$.

5.4 MULTIPLE-BEAM SPECTROSCOPIC INSTRUMENTS

5.4.1 The echelon spectroscope

Michelson, like his contemporaries, really wanted an instrument with which he could observe the structure of spectral lines directly, instead of performing an unsatisfactory mathematical analysis. After working for some time with his interferometer and harmonic analyser, he designed a new type of spectroscopic instrument which he called the echelon spectroscope.

The echelon consisted of a stack of parallel flat plates of precisely equal thickness, arranged like stair steps (Fig. 5.1). Viewed on a slant, the stair steps formed coarse, but precise, grooves. As the inventor explained it (Michelson 1902):

> Suppose that the light came in the direction indicated nearly normal to the surface of the groove. The light would be reflected back in the opposite direction, and that which came from each successive groove would differ in phase from that from the adjacent grooves by a number of waves corresponding to double the difference in path. The retardation, instead of being one wave, would be twice the number of waves in this distance. If the distance between the grooves were very large, the number of waves in this distance would also be very large, so that the order of the resulting spectrum would be correspondingly high. Further, almost all the light returns in one direction, so that the spectrum we are using will be as bright as possible.

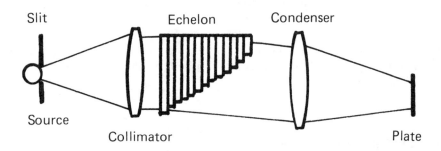

Fig. 5.1 — Essential elements of the echelon spectrograph. The stacked plates of the echelon introduce large phase shifts that depend on the angle of incidence, causing interference of light and producing a spectrum focused on the photographic plate.

Light waves reflected from the various steps of the echelon combine to produce constructive interference at a particular angle. The angle depends on the wavelength, so the colours in the light beam are spread into a spectrum.

Michelson found that he was unable to make the faces of the echelon steps equal in height to better than about three wavelengths, which was some fifty times worse than required. The instrument was unsatisfactory for reflection but provided good precision for use with transmitted light.

The echelon suffers from one complication: for thick steps, which provide very high resolution spectra, different orders of spectra overlap severely. The angles at which a particular wavelength is constructively reinforced are related to integer multiples of the wavelength. For thick plates, the integer is a very large number (over 30 000 for a set of thirty 1-cm thick plates with visible light). This causes overlap of the 30 000th and 30 001th spectrum to inextricably mix over all but a narrow spectral region. By pre-dispersing the light with a prism before it reaches the echelon, however, the light can be made sufficiently monochromatic to yield an unmixed spectrum.

The result is a spatially resolved spectrum of emission lines from substances such as cadmium or sodium. In effect, the combination of multiple plates provides the physical analogue of a narrow-range Fourier transformation, without the need for laboriously observing fringe intensities and performing a mathematical analysis.

With the echelon spectroscope, Michelson was able to obtain high resolution spectra directly as he had done indirectly nearly a decade earlier with his interferometer. For spectroscopists already familiar with prism spectrometers, the echelon provided an easy transition towards slightly more complex technology with much improved spectral resolution.

5.4.2   The Fabry–Pérot etalon

Another spectroscopic technique based on the interference of multiple beams came to prominence at the turn of the century: Fabry–Pérot spectroscopy. In 1897, Fabry and Pérot published details of a new form of interferometer for spectroscopic measurements. It is, in many ways, equivalent to Michelson's echelon spectroscope, and gives comparable results.

A Fabry–Pérot interferometer consists of two highly reflective parallel mirrors known as an **etalon**, positioned with a small gap between (Fig. 5.2). The coatings, not perfectly reflective, allow a small amount of light to enter from the outside and leave.

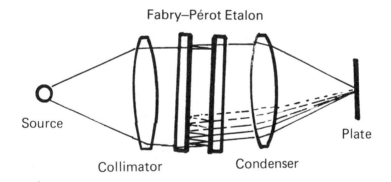

Fig. 5.2 — Elements of the Fabry–Pérot interferometer (etalon tilted and spacing exaggerated for illustration). Multiple reflections between the etalon plates interfere to create a circular narrow-band spectrum at the photographic plate.

A beam of light entering from one side of the assembly is partially transmitted to the interior, where it is repeatedly reflected. At each reflection, a portion of the light is transmitted to the exterior. Because the two mirrors are parallel, the rays of light escaping at each reflection are also parallel. These multiple rays interfere to form a net resultant ray. The intensity of the resultant depends on wavelength and the angle of reflection through the interferometer. Only when the angle is such that the wavelength is a multiple of the plate separation does the resultant have a strong intensity; at all other angles it is weak. The Fabry–Pérot interferometer therefore produces a direct spectrum from an incoming beam of light. Each wavelength is intense at a particular angle from the axis, and so a coloured ring pattern is formed. This circular pattern can be photographed and analysed. The distance from the centre of the ring is related to the wavelength of light and the etalon spacing, and the intensity of the ring at any angle corresponds to the emission intensity at that wavelength.

As with Michelson's echelon spectroscope, the Fabry–Pérot is troubled by closely-spaced spectral orders which overlap and confuse the resulting spectrum. The order overlap depends on plate separation: a larger gap allows more combinations of angles for the same wavelength. This gives a narrower "free spectral range".

A second characteristic is that the reflectivity of the mirrors of the Fabry–Pérot plays an important part in the quality of the spectrum. Highly reflective mirrors prevent much of the light from entering the interferometer to be analysed. However, highly reflective mirrors allow more internal reflections before the beam intensity decays, and so produce more interfering output beams. The number of interfering beams determines the spectral resolving power. So, high resolving power with a Fabry–Pérot interferometer requires weaker total intensity (i.e. longer photographic exposure times).

5.4.3   The Lummer–Gehrcke plate
In 1903, the Lummer–Gehrcke interferometer, another device for producing multiple-beam interference, was introduced. The Lummer–Gehrcke plate is something like an all-glass Fabry–Pérot interferometer turned on its side (Fig. 5.3). When a ray

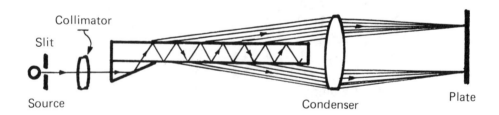

Fig. 5.3 — Elements of the Lummer–Gehrcke interferometer. Rays escaping the plate on either side interfere to form two narrow-band spectra on the photographic plate.

of light travelling through a plate of glass reaches its surface at a large angle, most of the light is reflected back into the glass. For an angle of incidence larger than a critical angle, the light is totally internally reflected. The Lummer–Gehrcke interferometer consists of a plate of glass polished on two opposite surfaces. A small prism attached to one end of the plate is used to "launch" parallel rays of light into the plate at an angle so that the ray strikes the polished surfaces at almost the angle of total internal reflection. Most of the light is reflected back into the plate to strike the opposite surface, but a small amount escapes nearly parallel to the surface. As the remainder of the light bounces inside the glass plate, a weak ray escapes at each reflection. Each succeeding ray is retarded with respect to the previous ray by a large amount: the amount of retardation depends on the plate thickness, refractive index, and angle of the reflected ray. The Lummer–Gehrcke plate thus produces a series of rays that are out of phase by increments, the same result as was achieved by the Fabry–Pérot etalon and the Michelson echelon. As in the other instruments, these multiple rays interfere to yield a narrow-band spectrum that can be focused onto a photographic plate.

The Lummer–Gehrcke interferometer is slightly more complicated than the Fabry–Pérot etalon in that the number of interfering rays depends on the length of the plate (in the Fabry–Pérot, the number depends on the reflectance of the etalon mirrors). In addition, the passage of the rays through glass complicates the analysis: the refractive index of glass (unlike that of the air between the Fabry–Pérot mirrors) varies significantly with wavelength, causing the optical retardation to vary as well. However, the Lummer–Gehrcke interferometer benefits from a broader non-overlapping spectral band (referred to again as the free spectral range) than the F–P. It does not require any optical coatings, which can degrade with time. Plates constructed of quartz can be used for ultraviolet spectroscopy, which is not as easy with Fabry–Pérot interferometers because of the lack of good reflective coatings that do not absorb ultraviolet light.

Lummer–Gehrcke plates, like the Michelson echelon and Fabry–Pérot etalon, demand high manufacturing precision. In a Michelson interferometer, only two beams interfere. In the Fabry–Pérot and Lummer–Gehrcke plate, the beams are multiply reflected from the same surfaces, and so any error in the reflecting surfaces is magnified. The surfaces must be flat to better than 1/80th wavelength, and the glass must be homogeneous. The need for a highly uniform material implies that the glass must be manufactured with extreme care, and also that the plate must be supported without strain and maintained at temperature of the order of 0.01°C; each of these factors affects the refractive index.

The echelon, Fabry–Pérot etalon and Lummer–Gehrcke plate interferometers appeared to have all the advantages that Michelson's two-beam version lacked. They could yield very high resolution measurements of spectral emissions; they were unambiguous in interpretation (provided that the overlap of spectral orders was avoided by a suitable filter); and, they were capable of rapid photographic recording, allowing storage of the data, subsequent analysis, and publication of the photographs in interpretable form.

The drawback to the general application of multiple-interference spectroscopy was its narrow spectral range and the rather critical dependence of performance on the condition of the interferometer mirrors or the accuracy of manufacture of the echelon or Lummer–Gehrcke plates.

These three multiple-interference spectrometers provided the highest-resolution direct spectroscopic methods at the turn of the twentieth century. Unlike two-beam interferometry with the Michelson interferometer, these methods were relatively straightforward and gave fast, easily interpreted results. They were to be the most widely used methods for high-resolution visible spectroscopy for the following forty years.

The alternatives to these forms of interferential spectroscopy were dispersive techniques: prism spectrometers and diffraction grating spectrometers.

5.5 DISPERSIVE SPECTROSCOPIC INSTRUMENTS

5.5.1 Prism spectrometers

Spectroscopy began with prism spectroscopes, as sketched in Chapter 2. A conventional prism spectrometer consists of a slit to admit light from the source, a collimating lens to make the light parallel, one or more prisms to refract the light into its component wavelengths, and a telescope to refocus the image of the slit (now dispersed into a band of colours, or spectrum) for viewing by the eye, a photographic plate or a detector (Fig. 5.4). If a detector is employed to measure the intensity of a

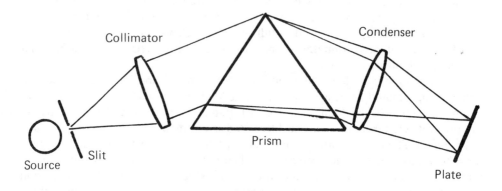

Fig. 5.4 — Essential elements of a prism spectrograph. Light is refracted by the prism into a spectrum on the photographic plate.

portion of the spectrum, a second slit is used to restrict the spectrum to the wavelengths of interest, and scanned with the detector by rotating the telescope.

The dispersion (the angular separation of wavelengths) of a prism spectrometer can be increased by using two or three stages of refraction. A double-pass arrangement is commonly used, in which the dispersed light is reflected back into the prism to retrace its path. Near the entrance slit, a flat mirror "picks off" a small range of wavelengths from the doubly-dispersed spectrum.

The device is known as a "spectroscope" if it is used to observe the spectrum by eye without precise calibration for wavelength, a "monochromator" if it simply restricts the output wavelengths, a "spectrometer" if it is used to measure wavelength (by calibrating the angle of refraction with respect to wavelength), a "spectrograph" if it records an image of the spectrum, or a "spectrophotometer" if it measures both wavelength and intensity. Infrared prism spectrometers are similar in every respect to visible-light instruments, except for the optical materials, light sources and detectors used.

Optical glass transmits little light beyond 2 microns. A number of alkali halide materials transmit well in the infrared: rock salt crystals (NaCl) were among the first discovered with this property. Other materials commonly used today are CaF_2, KBr, NaI, KI and KCl. Some of these materials are hygroscopic, and become clouded after only a few hours' exposure to moist air.

Prism spectrometers suffer from the disadvantage of not having a constant dispersion — i.e. the angle of refraction is not simply related to wavelength. This means that the spacing of the wavelength scale varies, and that the resolution of the measurement varies across the spectrum. The varying resolution can be partially compensated by adjusting the slit width for different wavelengths to pass a constant spectral interval. In practice, however, lack of energy often prevents slits from being narrowed as much as desired.

The non-linear wavelength scale can be calibrated by using light sources of known wavelength (the wavelength is ultimately calibrated by an interference technique, such as Fizeau's fringe counting method described in Chapter 2). Prism spectrometers generally have a relatively unreliable wavelength calibration: the mechanical drive linkages needed to rotate the prism for spectral scanning are prone to backlash, wear or temperature-induced errors.

Prism spectrometers were the instrument of choice for visible spectroscopy by the late 1800s, and used also for infrared studies to as long a wavelength as transmitted by the prisms. John Strong, as part of his thesis work in the early 1930s, developed a method of growing large potassium-salt prisms, and used these in mid-infrared spectrometers.

5.5.2 The diffraction grating

The diffraction grating is a reflective or transparent plate scribed with fine, parallel lines. The line density is typically a few dozen to several thousand lines per millimetre.

Diffraction gratings disperse light to produce a spectrum like a prism's, but by the process of diffraction rather than refraction. Each line acts as a source of divergent waves as the incoming wavefront is diffracted around objects of the order of a wavelength. These waves diverging from each line of the grating interfere in the same way that the multiple beams of an echelon, Fabry–Pérot etalon or Lummer–Gehrcke plate do. The amount of bending produced is proportional to the wavelength: blue is less diffracted than red light.

Diffraction gratings produce a spectrum having a smooth variation of wavelength versus angle, unlike prisms. Unfortunately, they produce less intense spectra, because the energy is diffracted into several orders of interference: the light reflected or transmitted through the diffraction grating is diffracted into several spectra on either side of the slit image, with each succeeding spectrum dispersed into a wider range of angles. This effect can be minimized by blazing, i.e. angling the grooves of the grating with a profile that causes most radiation to fall into one particular range of output angles. Blazed gratings are sometimes referred to as echelette gratings.

Echelettes are designed with groove density (known as the grating constant) and profile suitable to provide the desired angular dispersion with adequate efficiency.

The first diffraction gratings were made by Fraunhofer to study the solar spectrum, and consisted of fine wire looped around pins. Most later versions were made by a "ruling engine", a highly precise scriber. John Rowland at Johns Hopkins University, in about 1890, was the first to successfully rule a relatively large high quality grating. The production of diffraction gratings requires extreme precision: typically, the scribing element is moved with an accuracy of 0.01 μm over the several centimeter length of the groove. This requires temperature control of the entire ruling engine to better than 0.01°C for a period of days or weeks.

Blazed (echelette) gratings were introduced by Wood and Trowbridge in 1910, and by 1918 efficient diffraction grating spectrometers were being used. Despite their superior resolution to prism instrumentation, they did not come into wide use owing to the shortage of good gratings and the difficulty of covering a wide spectral range. Reflective gratings ruled on speculum metal tended to tarnish, and all gratings are easily damaged by scratches and dirt.

Normally, the modern master grating is not used directly in the spectrometer; instead, replicas are made by moulding a negative from the master in a material such as plastic. Errors in groove spacing introduce "ghost" lines into the dispersed spectrum. With conventional ruling engines, these are almost impossible to avoid. Modern gratings are often made by holography, which generates interference fringes on the surface of a photographic plate by an optical variant of the interferometer. The plate is then chemically etched so as to approximate the desired blaze profile. Holographic gratings have the advantage of much more regular groove spacing, thereby avoiding ghost lines, but are more difficult to produce with the desired blaze angle. They thus tend to be less efficient than the best ruled gratings.

Diffraction grating spectrometers can be laid out in a number of optical configurations having advantages of lower aberrations, simpler mechanical design, etc. (Fig. 5.5). Some of the more popular mountings are known as the Paschen, Littrow, Czerny–Turner and Fastie–Ebert designs after their inventors.

The manufacturing tolerances and operating characteristics show that the diffraction grating spectrometer is a close kin of the multiple-interference instruments described earlier in this chapter. Each makes a different compromise of free spectral range, resolution, and manufacturing precision.

Through the 1920s and 30s spectroscopy with prism and grating spectrometers was becoming popular not only with analytical chemists, but also for the more mundane fields of quality control in the paint and fabric industries. Colorimetry demanded routine spectra of batch samples. At the time, spectra were obtained by time-consuming techniques.

5.6   A TYPICAL SPECTROSCOPIC IMPLEMENTATION IN THE LATE 1920s

The prism spectrometer was designed and constructed by the experimenter, and usually consisted of a single prism and lenses to first collimate and then condense the beam. The detector output was amplified by a mirror galvanometer: the weak signal

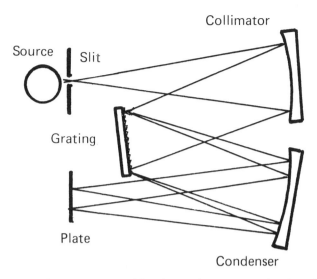

Fig. 5.5 — Essential elements of a diffraction grating spectrograph. The reflective grating diffracts light into a spectrum focused on the photographic plate.

rotated a meter coil which supported a mirror (Fig. 5.6). A narrow beam of light was reflected from the mirror and illuminated a scale placed some distance away. This "optical lever" made small rotations of the coil visible.

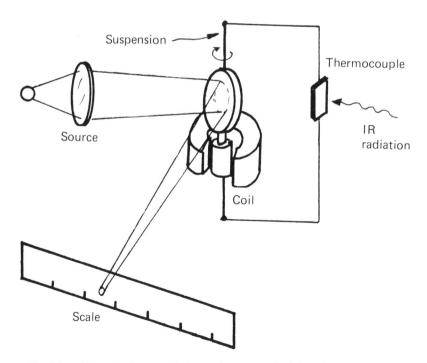

Fig. 5.6 — Schematic diagram of mirror galvanometer for infrared measurements.

The spectrometer operator adjusted the wavelength, usually by rotating a table on which the prism was mounted, read the calibrated scale, and observed the displacement of the reflected spot of light on the galvanometer scale. A reading was taken with the sample both in and out of the beam; the ratio yielded the sample transmittance or reflectance.

The procedure was repeated in small wavelength steps until the spectral range of interest had been covered.

Spectroscopy after the first World War was advancing at a constant pace as investigators methodically extended the spectral range and applications for their techniques. Instrument design progressed with developments in optical layout, materials, and electronics. Although Fabry–Pérot interferometers and prism spectrometers were by now being commercially produced by optical instrument manufacturers such as Hilger, spectrophotometers (to measure spectral intensities) were not commonly available. By far the most-used technique for intensity measurements in the visible was to make observations by eye. Various "visual photometers" were devised which relied on comparing the light source to a reference intensity; Albert Michelson had used just such a scheme for measuring visibility curves.

For infrared measurements, detection was severely limited by drifts in temperature. Developing stable and sensitive detection methods was to occupy the next decade. By the time Michelson died in 1931, such efforts had just begun.

REFERENCES

Brugel, W. (1962), *An Introduction to Infrared Spectroscopy,* Katritzky, A. R. and Katritzky, A. J. D. (translators), Methuen & Co., London.
Fabry, A. and Pérot, Ch. (1899), Méthodes Interférentielles pour la mésure des grandes Epaisseurs, et la Comparaison des Longueurs d'Onde, *Ann. Chim. Phys.*, (7) **16**, 115.
Michelson, A. A. (1902), *Light Waves and Their Uses,* The University of Chicago Press, Chicago.
Tolansky, S. (1947), *High Resolution Spectroscopy*, Methuen, London.
Potts Jr., W. J. and Smith, A. Lee (1967), Optimizing the Operating Parameters of Infrared Spectrometers, *Appl. Opt.*, **6**, 257.
Wood, R. W. and Trowbridge, A. (1910), The Echelette Grating for the Infra-Red, *Phil. Mag.*, **20**, 770.

6

Commercial dispersive spectrometers

6.1 IMPROVEMENTS TO CLASSICAL DETECTION METHODS

6.1.1 The Pfund resonance radiometer

The state of the art in sensitive measurement systems in the 1920s combined an infrared detector with a mirror galvanometer — essentially the same system as for Ruben's earlier experiments. The constant direct current (DC) output signal varied not only with the infrared energy incident on the detector but also with the temperature of the surroundings. The magnitude of the problem can be understood when it is realized that the infrared radiation caused temperature changes as small as a few millionths of a degree Celsius in an ambient background stable to, at best, a few hundredths of a degree. Cartwright and Strong (1938) noted that "just as much time is required for controlling the zero position of the galvanometer as for determining the deflection produced by the energy being measured".

A. Pfund (1929) devised a "resonance radiometer" which was insensitive to the slow drift in signal. The system employed two mirror galvanometers and a pendulum shutter which could periodically block ("chop") the infrared beam. All three components had identical periods of oscillation.

By regularly interrupting the beam with the pendulum shutter, the resulting signal drove the galvanometer mirrors to set up a resonance condition. The resonant frequency was thus amplified, but frequencies in the signal away from the tuned frequency were much reduced. The system therefore responded only to the "modulated" light, and not to background fluctuations.

While this aided the problem of signal drift, it still amplified the effects of Brownian motion on the mirror movement: molecular collisions buffeted the mirror and introduced random errors. Moreover, in order to build up the galvanometer oscillations to stable resonance, some 140 seconds were required for a single observation.

6.1.2 The Firestone amplifier

Detection of weak signals was further aided by the invention in 1931 of an improved drift-insensitive recording scheme by F. Firestone. As Firestone noted (1932):

Whenever an experimenter attempts to measure a very minute amount of radiant energy by its heating effect, as in infrared spectroscopy, his progress is continually slowed by the presence of drifts as well as Brownian motion and mechanical vibration of the indicating system. Drifts arise from continuous changes of temperature which, by causing a continuous change in the amount of radiation falling on the thermopile, give rise to a steady motion of the indicating galvanometer in one direction. This motion makes visual observations of deflections inaccurate or impossible and in the case of a recording system may cause the spot of light to pass off the record entirely.

Firestone devised an extension of the Pfund resonant galvanometer by adding a simple capacitor circuit, tuned to the galvanometer deflections, to more precisely tune the output signal. The oscillating detector signal was, in effect, supplied to an electrically filtered amplifier which passed only the AC component of the signal. Firestone's system was essentially an amplifier which responded to the frequency at which the light beam was chopped, and a galvanometer tuned to the same frequency. Oscillations at this frequency were reinforced, while any fluctuations at other frequencies were gradually damped out.

By eliminating the large-scale signal drifts and reducing the effect of Brownian motion, the ultimate sensitivity was significantly increased. For the first time, users of grating spectrometers could benefit from automatic recording: instead of waiting up to three minutes to make a single visual observation of galvanometer deflection — a process which could require weeks to record a single high-quality spectrum — equally good spectra could be recorded automatically in less than an hour.

Despite this major improvement, spectral observations were still far from easy:

On careful records, the observer watches in the reading microscope the passage of the lines on the grating circle and presses a key which flashes a lamp to give an angle coordinate on the record. If the circle has a carefully designed driving system, then the driving system itself may periodically flash a lamp to mark out the coordinates.... (Firestone 1932)

6.1.3   Electronic amplifiers

At the end of the nineteenth century, electrical signals could not easily be amplified. One method, employed in telephone circuits, was to use "microphone relays" consisting of microphones placed in front of earpieces. The current produced by the microphone could be much larger than that produced by the earpiece. This arrangement gave a net amplification, or "gain".

Electronics as an engineering discipline can be said to have begun with the invention of the triode by Lee de Forest in 1903. This was a vacuum tube consisting of three internal electrodes. It was another decade before researchers began to use vacuum tubes to amplify electrical signals. Tetrodes (four electrodes) and pentodes (five electrodes) were invented in 1916 and 1928, respectively, and gave further improvements.

By the 1920s electronics experimenters had invented a number of circuits for stable amplifiers, electrical filters and modulators. Most applications were initially for radio communication; only gradually were electronic amplifiers used in instrumentation. Firestone's amplifier was a crude example of a tuned high-gain amplifier with an electromechanical filter. Its successors dispensed with pendulum galvanometers and relied solely on electronic components.

Probably the first successful AC amplifier for use with thermopiles was developed by L. Roess (1945). As Pfund and Firestone had done, Roess modulated the light beam by interrupting it with a chopper, and then tuned the amplifier to the modulation frequency to preferentially reinforce the signal frequencies.

The amplifier was designed to amplify the low-frequency signal from a rapid-response thermocouple, which was interrupted at a frequency of 1 to 5 Hz. The electrical noise produced by the amplifier was less than the thermal noise of the thermocouple. This was achieved by using a high-gain input transformer, careful selection of vacuum tubes, operating the vacuum tube heater at low current, and by using two isolated power supplies. Finally, an electrical filtering network was used to tune the amplifier response to the chopping frequency.

Roess treated the output from the amplifier much as Firestone had done: it fed a short-period galvanometer, the entire swing of which was recorded photographically as the spectrometer was very slowly scanned in wavelength. The resulting record had the appearance of a broad band of changing width, instead of the single line plotting intensity *vs.* wavelength that is familiar to modern spectroscopists.

The Roess amplifier was quickly accepted by workers in spectroscopy, and used with thermistor bolometers (invented in 1946).

6.2 RECORDING SPECTROPHOTOMETERS

To relieve the tedium of point-by-point measurement, several investigators designed self-recording spectrophotometers between 1900 and 1930. Those of Arthur Hardy from 1928 were eventually developed to become the first commercial instrument, manufactured by the General Electric Company.

Hardy had decided to investigate problems in the field of colour printing soon after joining the faculty at the Massachusetts Institute of Technology (Hardy 1938). Realizing that "a great mass of spectrophotometric data would be required", he sought an alternative to visual spectrophotometers, which typically were used to make measurements at thirty discrete wavelengths in the visible spectrum. The available "Thalofide" photoresistive cells that were available gave erratic results. Hardy noted that "this erratic behavior was not altogether unexpected. Neither was it a great disappointment because of the almost certain necessity of employing vacuum tube amplifiers, which at that time were almost as erratic".

Hardy's first instrument yielded good visible-range spectra in as little as 30 secs, despite a necessarily primitive detector amplifier which was used to directly drive a recording pen. He observed that users were enthusiastic:

> The first few months of operation of this instrument were very exciting. We
> measured the color of everything within sight and then went out to look for

more samples. The instrument was found to operate with such rapidity that it generally took less time to make a measurement than it did to decide whether such a measurement would be significant.

The prototype was soon being used for recording as many as 3000 spectra in a single month.

Hardy's instrument included features that presaged designs of the following thirty years, including an automatically cam-adjusted exit slit to maintain constant resolution, a speed suppressor to allow the slowly moving recording pen to accurately trace regions in which the signal changed rapidly, and a mechanical integrator (Fig. 6.1).

In 1930 and 1931, Harrison Randall and his graduate student, John Strong,

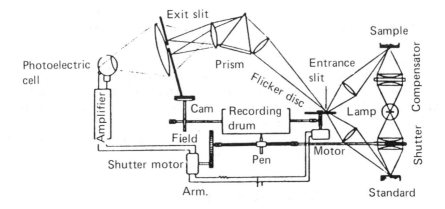

Fig. 6.1 — The Hardy recording spectrophotometer.

produced infrared recording spectrometers employing salt prisms that Strong had grown. The recording system was somewhat simpler than Hardy's servomechanism:

In a recording spectrometer, where it is necessary to use a thermopile receiver, a procedure similar to that used in the recording microphotometer may be employed, the spectrum being passed over a thermopile and the resulting galvanometer deflections being recorded photographically.

In common with many instrument designs of the period, limitations were expressed qualitatively:

The necessity for proper exposure places a limit upon the speed of recording. Another limit also exists, for the spectrum must not be moved over the thermopile so rapidly that the galvanometer will fail to follow accurately the variations of energy density and so to trace out the true spectrum.

The use of the new KCl, KBr and KI prism materials extended the range to 40 μm in the infrared.

Until about 1940 most infrared instruments were custom-made by the laboratories that used them. During the Second World War, however, the instruments proved useful for monitoring the production of essential materials such as synthetic rubber and gasoline. Applications broadened in the following years, and the demand led to several commercial instruments within a decade.

Through the 1930s and early 1940s, spectrometer designs proliferated, clearly indicating a wide need. The design of E. Baker and C. Dean Robb (1943) anticipated features of commercial instruments thirty years hence:

> For routine work of a very special nature a fixed wave-length instrument would often serve the purpose more economically and reliably, but, for general analysis, flexibility is necessary. By having the spectrum appear on an oscilloscope screen, and by providing means of rapid selection of interesting portions of the spectrum at optimum resolution, general analysis can be greatly expedited.

6.3 SERVOMECHANISMS

The automatic control of instrumentation is a special application of servomechanisms. A servo system is a combination of elements for the control of a source of power in which the output of the system or some function of the output is fed back for comparison with the input. The difference between the input and the actual output is used in controlling the power. By comparing the actual action with the desired action, servos overcome practical limitations of hardware and make it behave more ideally. The term servomechanism is normally reserved for feedback systems that involve mechanical parts. For example, an audio amplifier, which uses electronic feedback to produce a stable output, is not referred to as a servo system.

The theory of such systems was developed during the Second World War, when there was a need for automatic-tracking radar systems. This problem caused particular difficulties, because the signal to be used in tracking could be seriously distorted by interference, fading, and receiver noise. It was necessary to develop a theory of feedback control in the presence of noisy signals — in other words, to extend the common-sense laboratory demonstrations to real-world problems.

With the spread of servo-mechanisms during and after the war (e.g. James *et al.* 1947, Brown 1948), more spectrometers incorporated automatic recording, automatic slit programs and other automatic mechanisms. Wood (1947) described an infrared spectrometer typical of several designed in the post war period. It employed a commercially available servo-amplifier (the Brown "Electronick" pen recorder) to plot directly the transmittance of an infrared sample. An automatic sequencer, consisting of a motor-driven shaft supporting eight actuating cams, controlled the wavelength drive motor, servo-controlled slit width adjustment, two servo-motors for balancing the sample and reference channel preamplifiers, and the electromechanical shutter of the spectrometer.

6.4 FOURIER TRANSFORMATION BEFORE COMPUTERS

As described in Section 3.4, Michelson's harmonic analyser was the most convenient means of calculating the Fourier transform at the turn of the twentieth century.

By the 1930s, interferential spectroscopy was forgotten, but other scientific techniques were using Fourier transforms. Probably the most important was X-ray crystallography (invented by William Bragg), in which the X-ray radiation reflected by crystals can be analysed to infer crystal structure. The pattern of reflected dots recorded on film is the two-dimensional Fourier transform of the crystal lattice.

C. A. Beevers and H. Lipson (1934) at the University of Liverpool had begun using Bragg's technique, but "it was feared that the work...would be very long, and an attempt was therefore made to devise a short method of calculation".

Their calculation method relied on constructing trigonometric tables of sine functions of various amplitudes and phase shifts. To synthesize a Fourier transform, they selected the appropriate row of the tables for each sine wave component, and then summed the results for twenty-five points on the wave. The advantage of the technique was that the sine tables were calculated only once; thereafter, only selection and addition were required. Beevers and Lipson were pleased to report that "By expanding $\cos 2\pi(hx+ky)$ the longest double Fourier synthesis can be accomplished by two workers in about two days".

Two years later, the researchers proposed preparing strips listing rows of the sine tables for each amplitude and phase (Lipson & Beevers 1936). The strips were mounted in a mechanical sorting device which allowed selection of the proper strip. The chosen strips were then lined up and the columns were summed on a mechanical adding machine. The idea was adapted by A. L. Patterson a few months later:

> These strips are mounted on a rack, vertically above one another, in order of their indices h. One of a set of stencils is then set accurately over the rack, so that the openings in it select the correct values of $A\cos h(nx_0)$ for a given point (nx_0). Certain openings are surrounded by white borders, or are otherwise marked, to indicate that the values read through them are to be given negative signs.

Although a decided improvement over straight calculation, the method was still laborious. Three years later, Beevers (1939) proposed an electronic digital computer to do the job:

> ...the fundamental sine curve of any amplitude may be represented by a number of sets of impulses. A switch can arrange these sets of impulses to correspond to a wave of any wave-number, and the sets of impulses then go into counters. Successive operations of the generator and arranging-switch

result in the addition of Fourier terms, the terms being added for all values of the variable at the same time.

This seed does not appear to have borne fruit, because the manual "Lipson–Beevers strips" were still being used by researchers a decade later.

6.5 THE GROWTH OF COMMERCIAL SPECTROSCOPY

The Hardy–GE spectrophotometer was in use in at least 150 laboratories, a dozen of them outside the US, fifteen years after its introduction. By 1950, it employed a phototube sensitive from 400 to 1200 nm, i.e. into the near infrared. However, true infrared instruments were more common than either visible-range or ultraviolet (scanning) spectrometers.

The outstanding advance that permitted commercialization was, according to S. S. Ballard (1951), the substitution of stable electronic amplifiers and pen recorders for the less satisfactory galvanometers.

By the 1950s there were at least a dozen manufacturers of dispersive infrared spectrometers. These ranged from large desk-size research-grade instruments to simpler benchtop spectrometers. Research models (e.g. the Beckman IR-3, Grubb-Parsons GS2, Hilger H 800, Leitz Infrared Spectrograph, and Perkin–Elmer Model 21) usually incorporated a double-pass monochromator, double-beam sampling arrangement (see below) and automatic recording of transmittance by a pen recorder.

6.6 DOUBLE BEAM *vs.* SINGLE BEAM INSTRUMENTS

The simplest spectrometer design employs a single beam from light source, through monochromator, through sample, and to detector. The intensity of beam varies dramatically with wavelength: the light source intensity decreases rapidly above 2 μm; the monochromator efficiency varies with wavelength (owing to varying prism dispersion or diffraction grating blaze); light scattering from rough surfaces increases as the fourth power of wavelength; and, transmitting windows have characteristic absorption curves. Because of these influences, the intrinsic response of the spectrometer is not constant across the spectrum. This requires the response with no sample present to be measured just prior to or following the sample scan, and to be used to correct the sample spectrum intensity manually. One of the first popular commercial instruments of this type was the Perkin–Elmer Model 12.

One method used to produce a flat 100% line was to vary either the gain of the signal amplifier or the slit width of the monochromator so that a constant amount of energy reached the detector when the sample is absent. The necessary slit width was supplied by a memory device such as a mechanical cam linked to the prism rotation, or by magnetic tape. When the sample was inserted in the light path, the cam or tape recording adjusted slit width appropriately.

A double beam spectrometer gets round the tedium of manual correction by using two beams, one travelling through the sample and the other close by but avoiding the sample. The beams travel nearly the same path through the monochromator (except for a few mirror surfaces) and so most contributions to spectral difference are compensated. The two beams are either measured by two separate detectors or fall alternately on the same detector. In the latter case, a chopping mirror is used to alternately reflect the source light to the sample and reference path. The two signals, electronically separated, can be divided ("ratioed") to yield a value proportional to sample transmittance or reflectance.

6.6.1 Optical null instruments

In some spectrometers, this signal was used to drive a pen motor to make a permanent record, while at the same time inserting a partially-transmitting "comb" or wedge of absorbing material into the reference beam to reduce its intensity to that of the sample beam. The scheme is shown schematically in Fig. 6.2. The position of the comb attenuator or wedge is calibrated so that the pen position indicates either transmittance or absorbance on a linear scale. The optical null principle was introduced about 1942, and was adopted by all infrared spectrometer manufacturers.

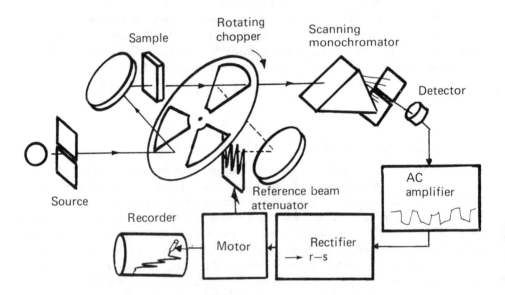

Fig. 6.2 — Schematic diagram of an optical null dispersive spectrometer. The difference in intensity of the sample and reference beams is used to drive a motor to insert an attenuator in the reference beam to obtain a balance, while simultaneously recording the position on chart paper.

There are at least three major faults with optical null systems. First, they lose sensitivity in regions of high sample absorbance. Since the reference beam is occluded to match the sample, there is no signal at all when the sample absorbs. This lack of gain in the system leads to gross errors. Furthermore, the mechanical combs and wedged plates used as attenuators are frequently quite non-linear below a few percent transmittance, further increasing the error. This effect can be alleviated somewhat by never fully blocking the reference beam, so leaving a few percent of the energy for beam balancing.

A second fault is that the beam is modulated between the sample and the spectrometer: the chopper used to direct light to either the sample or reference path precedes the monochromator. This means that any radiation coming from the sample itself (by heating or fluorescence, for example) is modulated and appears in the final spectrum. This effect is increasingly noticeable at longer wavelengths, where the sample emission becomes a larger fraction of the source intensity.

The third problem with optical null systems is their stability. Because the system relies on mechanical linkages to produce an intensity measurement, factors such as sticking, dirt on the movements, dust on the optical comb, etc., all influence the measurement.

The limitations of the technique were recognized, and attempts to get around them were made by several investigators such as Wright and Herinscher (1947), Savitzky and Halford (1950), and Hornig *et al.* (1950).

6.6.2   Energy control

The output of an infrared source shows a large drop in intensity from 4000 to $600 \, cm^{-1}$. In order to accurately record transmittance of a sample, it is important that the energy received by the detector be reasonably constant. Two schemes were used to ensure this: slit control and electrical gain control.

In slit control, a servo-actuated spectrometer slit is employed. The energy in the reference beam is constantly monitored and used to servo-adjust the slit to maintain constant energy. This has the drawback of reducing the spectral resolution in regions of low intensity. The servo-slit gives increased slit widths due to energy fall-off with decreasing frequency.

The alternative is electrical gain control. In this scheme, the gain of the signal amplifier is boosted to maintain a nearly constant value. The gain can be either programmed by a cam that rotates with the wavelength drive, or servo-controlled similarly to the slit servo scheme. Gain control usually leads to unacceptably high measurement noise.

Later recording spectrophotometer designs usually reverted to a cam for slit programming and a constant gain that could be set by the operator.

6.6.3   Electronic null instruments

Optical null instruments have the disadvantage of relying on accurately manufactured mechanical parts for the accuracy of the intensity scale. An alternative, first used commercially in the early 1950s, is the electronic null principle. A block diagram of the scheme is shown in Fig. 6.3.

In this method, the imbalance between the reference and sample path signals is used directly to operate the pen recorder. The degree of imbalance is related electronically to transmittance by taking the ratio of the two signals, and amplifying this to operate the pen recorder.

This simpler system avoids most of the disadvantages of the optical null system. The chopper disk can be placed after the monochromator, so emission from the

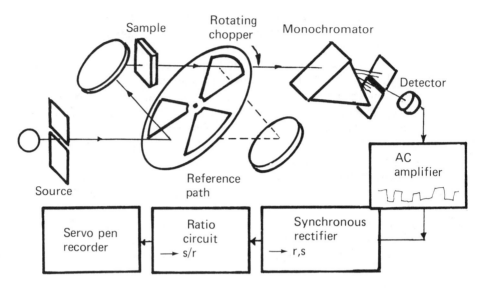

Fig. 6.3 — Schematic diagram of an electrical null dispersive spectrometer. The reference and sample signals are separately measured, and then ratioed and plotted.

sample has no effect. Even at low transmittance, the reference channel is unblocked and provides adequate gain for the servo electronics. And, the long-term stability of even vacuum-tube based electronics was found to be superior to mechanical systems.

6.6.4 Recording systems
The photographically-recording galvanometers of the 1930s gave way to servo-controlled pen recorders by the late 1940s. Such mechanisms were built into the commercial spectrometers of the 1950s. Normally, an ink pen traced the spectrum on chart paper previously imprinted with spectral intervals. Either the pen moved on an axis scanned along a flat bed holding the chart paper, or (more commonly) the chart paper moved on a rotating drum linked to the wavelength drive. The wavelength axis, which was decidedly non-linear for prism spectrometers, was calibrated by observing spectral features of known wavelength, such as gas absorption lines. Ammonia and water vapour were frequently employed, with polystyrene film later used as a convenient and stable sample. Calibration of the vertical (transmittance) scale was less commonly performed: there were no generally accepted standards, and accurate values of transmittance were not important for qualitative work. The intrinsic errors of optical null spectrometers made quantitative analysis difficult.

6.6.5 The dispersive infrared laboratory
By 1960 the infrared spectrometer was an established tool in the analytical chemistry laboratory. Operators had determined the critical factors in obtaining reliable spectra.

Atmospheric fluctuations could cause deterioration of optical surfaces by the absorption of excessive humidity. Variation in temperature caused the refractive index of the prism (and hence the spectral dispersion and wavelength scale) to change. The presence of atmospheric water vapour and carbon dioxide caused large absorption and loss of measurement precision in portions of the mid infrared spectrum. These problems were controlled by totally air-conditioning the spectro-photometer room, thermostatting the monochromator above room temperature, keeping the optical system under vacuum, or liberally using desiccants to absorb atmospheric water.

The reproducibility of spectra was degraded by temperature variations of the instrument. Several hours were normally required for temperature equilibration after interchanging prisms. In diffraction grating instruments, thermal expansion of the grating substrate and wavelength drive caused similar problems.

After the Second World War, Michelson's interferential spectroscopy was remembered, if at all, as an obsolete early method of high-resolution atomic spectroscopy which involved laborious measurements and uncertain analysis. The efforts of instrument designers and researchers focused almost exclusively on the improvement and use of dispersive spectrometers, for which a rapidly increasing market was developing.

REFERENCES

Baker, E. B. and Robb, C. Dean (1943), High Speed Automatic Infra-Red Spectrometer, *Rev. Sci. Instr.*, **14**, 362.

Ballard, S. S. (1951), Spectrophotometry in the United States, in *Proc. of the London Conference on Optical Instruments*, Chapman & Hall, London, Chapter 13.

Beevers, C. A. and Lipson, H. (1934), A Rapid Method for the Summation of a Two-Dimensional Fourier Series, *Phil. Mag.*, (7) **17**, 855.

Beevers, C. A. (1939), Machine for Rapid Summation of Fourier Series, *Phys. Soc. Proc.*, **51**, 660.

Brown, G. S. and Campbell, D. P. (1948), *Principles of Servomechanisms*, Wiley, New York.

Cartwright, C. H. and Strong, J. (1938), Vacuum Thermopiles and the Measurement of Radiant Energy in Strong, J. *Procedures in Experimental Physics*, Prentice-Hall, Englewood Cliffs, New Jersey.

Coor, T. and Smith, D. C. (1947), Automatic Recording Spectrophotometer, *Rev. Sci. Instr.*, **18**, 173.

Cross, A. D. and Jones, R. A. (1968), *An Introduction to Practical Infra-Red Spectroscopy*, Butterworths, London.

Edlén, B. (1966), Frontiers in Spectroscopy, *J. Opt. Soc. Am.*, **56**, 1285.

Firestone, F. A. (1932), A Periodic Radiometer for Eliminating Drifts, *Rev. Sci. Instr.*, **3**, 163.

Hardy, A. C. (1929), A Recording Photoelectric Color Analyser, *J. Opt. Soc. Am.*, **18**, 96.

Hardy, A. C. (1935), A New Recording Spectrophotometer, *J. Opt. Soc. Am.*, **25**, 305.

Hardy, A. C. (1938), History of the Design of the Recording Spectrophotometer, *J. Opt. Soc. Am.*, **28**, 360.

Hornig, D. F., Hyde, G. E. and Adcock, W. A. (1950), A Ratio-Recording Double-Beam Infra-Red Spectrophotometer with Automatic Slit-Control, *J. Opt. Soc. Am.*, **40**, 497.

James, H. M., Nichols, N.B. and Phillips, R. S. (1947), *Theory of Servomechanisms*, Dover Publications, New York.

Lipson, H. and Beevers, C. A. (1936), A Numerical Method for Two-Dimensional Fourier Synthesis, *Nature*, **137**, 825.

Marzin, P. and J. Le Mézec (1966), Electricity and Electronics, in: Taton, R. (ed.), *Science in the Twentieth Century*, Pomerans, A. J. (trans.), Thames & Hudson, London.

Patterson, A. L. (1936), A Note on the Synthesis of Fourier Series, *Phil. Mag.*, (7) **22**, 753.

Pfund, A. H. (1929), *Science*, **2**, 69.

Randall, H. M. (1954), Infrared Spectroscopy at the University of Michigan, *J. Opt. Soc. Am.*, **44**, 97.

Randall, H. M. and Strong, J. (1931), A Self Recording Spectrometer, *Rev. Sci. Instr.*, **2**, 585.

Roess, L. C. (1945), Vacuum Tube Amplifier for Measuring Very Small Alternating Voltages, *Rev. Sci. Instr.*, **16**, 172.

Savitzky, A. and Halford, R. S. (1950), A Ratio-Recording Double Beam Infra-Red Spectrophotometer Using Phase Discrimination and a Single Detector, *Rev. Sci. Instr.,* **21**, 203.

Strong, J. (1932), Apparatus for Spectroscopic Studies in the Intermediate Infrared Region — 20 to 40 μ, *Rev. Sci. Instr.,* **3**, 810.

Wild, R. F. (1947), Automatic Ratio Recorder as Applied to Infra-Red Spectroscopy, *Rev. Sci. Instr.,* **18**, 436.

Wright, N. and Herscher, L. W. (1947), A Double-Beam, Percent Transmission Recording Infra-Red Spectrophotometer, *J. Opt. Soc. Am.,* **37**, 211.

Part III
Renaissance

7

Post-war developments

Several factors made FTIR ripe for exploitation by 1950. That they came together from independent sources can be ascribed more to luck than the outcome of a dedicated research programme. The Second World War led to three developments important to Fourier spectroscopy: computers, instrument science, and information theory. The need for automatic spectrometers was discussed in the last chapter. Routine applications for spectrometry had grown in the inter-war years.

7.1 COMPUTER DEVELOPMENT

Computational machines of all kinds had been developed during and after the war for calculating mathematical tables and performing engineering calculations. Two forms were of equal importance by 1950: analogue and digital computers.

Analogue computers calculated by employing physical effects which mimicked the desired numerical relationship. For example, mechanical analogue computers could be constructed in which the rotation of disks were analogues of the mathematical processes of integration or differentiation. Michelson's Harmonic Analyser had used spring forces as analogues of sine wave intensities. Electronic analogue computers performed similar functions using particular arrangements of capacitors and variable resistors. Digital computers, usually electronic, instead began as sophisticated counting mechanisms working in powers of two, or binary arithmetic. This scheme was implemented by dealing with on/off states using components such as relays and, later, vacuum tubes.

7.1.1 Optical processing

An idea that developed in parallel with electronic computers in the 1950s was optical computation. Systems of lenses can transform information represented as images into other mathematical forms. The usefulness for Fourier spectroscopy had been recognized by Michelson himself in 1892:

> It may be readily shown that the formula $V^2=(C^2+S^2)/P^2$ for the *visibility-curve* due to a distribution of light $y=\Phi(x)$, is identical with that of the

intensity-curve at the focus of a telescope provided with apertures which produce this distribution in the light passing through. Accordingly, if a telescope be provided with apertures adjustable in width (or length) and distance apart, the diffraction-image of a distant illuminated slit will give, at once, a representation of the whole visibility-curve; and by adjustment of intensities and distances any particular visibility-curve may be more or less accurately copied, thus furnishing a means of studying the relations between V and $\Phi(x)$, which, while giving perhaps only a rough approximation to the truth, may prove more convenient than analytical or graphical methods. (Michelson 1892)

In more modern terms, the image plane and collimated plane of a lens are Fourier conjugates of each other. If the interferogram is represented as a linear pattern of regions varying in transparency in a collimated beam of light, the focused image represents its Fourier transform.

Optical processing is attractive because it provides essentially instantaneous calculation. Its drawbacks are the precision of calculation: neither input nor output intensities can be defined to better than a few percent.

Optical computation methods were intensively investigated through the 1950s, and were suggested for calculation of the Fourier transform by Lawrence Mertz (1956) and others.

7.2   INFORMATION THEORY

By 1950, electronic communication networks had reached a level of sophistication requiring careful analysis for further improvements: the telephone system and radio transmission at many broadcast frequencies needed to transmit more information using congested resources. Communication theory, developed initially by Claude Shannon, gave a mathematical foundation to the concepts. This theory also detailed the requirements of data sampling, which were to be vital to the data analysis methods of Fourier spectroscopy.

7.3   INSTRUMENT SCIENCE

These developments just happened along at the right time. But the important driving factor in their combination, as Peter Fellgett (1984) has written, was the development of the concepts of "instrument physics":

In most cases, a scientific instrument is devised in the first place as a means to the end of making some physical phenomenon or quantity susceptible to observation or measurement, and once it has served this purpose nobody thinks very deeply about it again. Consequently, it is often tacitly accepted that "in theory" an instrument should have a particular performance, but "in practice" it does not. This however is not good science, which demands that if theory and practice differ, then one or both must be improved. Had

Adams and Le Verrier been content to say that "in theory" Uranus moves in a particular orbit but "in practice" in a slightly different one, the planet Neptune would never have been discovered.

 Instrument science has become a motivating force of much of modern technology, not merely FTIR design. The idea that understanding the details of a scientific instrument is as worthy of study as the phenomena that the instrument is meant to measure gained credence during the Second World War. Scientists in great numbers applied their abilities not to questions of pure research, but to the more mundane problems of a wartime economy. By optimizing existing instruments and developing new technology for specific real-world applications, researchers gained a new image in the public's eyes — and their own. The idea of instrument science would likely have been welcomed by Albert Michelson, who made a career of getting the most out of simple instruments:

> What would be the use of such extreme refinement in the science of measurement? Very briefly and in general terms the answer would be that in this direction the greater part of all future discovery must lie. The more important fundamental laws and facts of physical science have all been discovered, and these are now so firmly established that the possibility of their ever being supplanted in consequence of new discoveries is exceedingly remote. Nevertheless, it has been found that there are apparent exceptions to most of these laws, and this is particularly true when the observations are pushed to a limit, i.e. whenever the circumstances of experiment are such that extreme cases can be examined. Such examination almost surely leads, not to the overthrow of the law, but to the discovery of other facts and laws whose action produces apparent exceptions ... these will suffice to justify the statement that "our future discoveries must be looked for in the sixth place of decimals". It follows that every means which facilitates accuracy in measurement is a possible factor in a future discovery. (Michelson 1902)

The importance of optimal design is behind the two key concepts of the revived interferential spectroscopy: Fellgett's "multiplex advantage" and Jacquinot's "throughput advantage".

7.4 THE MULTIPLEX ADVANTAGE

From 1948 to 1951, Peter Fellgett was attempting to measure the infrared spectra of stars for his doctoral studies. The poor sensitivity of the available detectors made spectral measurements impossible, even on the brightest stars. Fellgett had, during the war, been part of a group analysing aviation fuels for their molecular species, using infrared "rock salt" spectrometers. At that time, he says,

> I had become interested in why infra-red detectors (we used home-made evacuated thermocouples à la John Strong) were so relatively insensitive;

or, more generally, whether it were possible to identify some physical limit
of radiation detectors ranging from photoemissive cells to radio antennae.
(Fellgett 1991)

He was able to show that the fundamental limitations of all detectors was the ambient
thermal background: spontaneous fluctuations in the thermal radiation received
from the surroundings and radiated from the detector itself. Random variations in
electron motion in the detector materials masked the small additional signals caused
by absorbed light. No significant improvements were possible without cooling the
device to lower the effects of the background.

Considering how well visible light spectrographs seemed to work compared to
infrared versions that used a single detector to measure a narrow band of wavelengths at a time, Fellgett realised that a photographic plate received light of each
wavelength during the entire exposure, whereas the infrared scanning instrument
received light of each wavelength only during $1/n$-th of the exposure, where n is the
number of spectral intervals measured. The conventional visible spectrometer
benefited from a "simultaneity advantage", because the photographic emulsion was
acting as a multi-element detector.

Conventional dispersive spectrometers record information from each spectral
element sequentially, whereas a multiplexed detector records information from each
interval simultaneously, during the entire spectral measurement.

The observing time is important, even if the measuring medium is not a
photographic plate; with another type of detector, such as a thermopile, the principle
remains the same. If a signal is integrated over a time interval t, its magnitude will be
proportional to t; however, if random noise is integrated over the same time interval
t, the final magnitude will be proportional to the square root of t, because the noise
signal fluctuates downwards as often as upwards. The net signal quality is determined
by the ratio of signal to noise, or S/N: this quantity varies as the square root of t.
Thus, the longer the time spent observing the signal (i.e. integrating it) the higher the
signal quality. Fellgett showed that when measuring a spectrum with M individual
spectral elements, a dispersive spectrometer records a signal for each element for
only $1/M$ as long as a multiplex spectrometer, so the S/N ratio will be $M^{-1/2}$ poorer.
For example, a spectrum consisting of 10 000 individual points will have a signal to
noise ratio 100 times better when measured by a multiplex spectrometer than by a
sequential spectrometer. The term "multiplexing" is borrowed from communications theory, and is used to describe the transfer of two or more independent signals
on a single information channel. For Fourier spectroscopy, these "signals" are the
different optical frequencies measured simultaneously by the detector. They are
"encoded" by the interferometer so that they can be combined, measured by the
single detector, and subsequently unraveled by the process of Fourier
transformation.

Fellgett was at first unaware of interferometers as a solution to his problem. He
attempted to find schemes that would allow all the infrared frequencies in the
spectrum to be "multiplexed" onto a single infrared detector during the exposure,
and somehow separated out from the data afterward. His initial thoughts, described
in his thesis (Fellgett 1951), were for a rather complicated arrangement of coded

chopping disks, but before building anything he hit upon an interferometer as solution:

> I then realized that if a two-beam interferometer were to be placed in the original undispersed radiation, and its path difference scanned at a uniform rate, each spectral element would pass through one cycle of modulation of intensity every time the path difference changed by one wavelength. Of course the wavelength is, by definition, different for each spectral element. (Fellgett 1984)

However, his solution to practical multiplexing was broader even then than Fourier spectroscopy:

> It is important to realize that my objective was simply to gain the multiplicity advantage by means of multiplexing and it was entirely incidental that the method I proposed happened to use an interferometric device and to give rise to the necessity of Fourier transformation of the interferogram directly observed. It is particularly important to emphasize this because an interferometer may display the multiplex advantage ... without being either Fourier or interferometric.

7.5 THE JACQUINOT ADVANTAGE

The second key advantage of Fourier spectroscopy relates to the energy "throughput" or "étendue" of the instrument. A dispersive spectrometer employs an entrance and exit slit to restrict the component wavelengths reaching the detector; if spectral resolution is to be increased, the slits must be narrowed, thus reducing throughput further. By contrast, the interferometer has an unobstructed circular aperture; its resolution depends on the optical path difference, which does not significantly change the amount of light passing through it. The interferometer can therefore transmit a much larger solid angle of light for the same spectral resolution.

Although this advantage had been alluded to by Rubens in 1910, it was rediscovered and explained quantitatively by Pierre Jacquinot in the late 1940s, and published in accessible form in 1954.

Jacquinot had initially worked with large dispersive spectrographs which provided high spectral resolution. Upon moving to a smaller provincial French university, however, he had to look for a cheaper means of doing high-resolution spectroscopy. He initially considered Fabry–Pérot interferometers. Like others before him, he was troubled by the limited spectral range and the dispersion, which is not linear.

Jacquinot tried to use the Fabry–Pérot as a spectrometer instead of a spectrograph: rather than recording the circular fringes photographically and subsequently tracing the density pattern on the film with a microdensitometer, he directly scanned a portion of the fringes with a photoelectric cell. This process would have been very inefficient, because only a small portion of the circular rings was accessible to the detector at any time. However, Jacquinot realised that better efficiency could be achieved by recording only the central fringe as the Fabry–Pérot spectrometer was scanned. In this way, the luminosity advantage of the F-P was maintained; a large cone of light was accepted instead of a narrow slit.

Considering the disadvantage of narrow spectral range, Jacquinot reasoned that a Fabry–Pérot interferometer having low-reflectance plates (producing only two strong interfering beams instead of many) would create a "coded" version of the spectrum which could be interpreted by performing a Fourier transformation. This arrangement was precisely what Rubens and coworkers had used about thirty years earlier.

Thus, trying to improve instrument throughput, Jacquinot had independently discovered the principle of interferometric spectroscopy. However, he was not convinced of its practical utility:

> The precision requirements to obtain good spectra were so severe that it was almost unbelievable, at that time, that they could ever be met. One must realize that obtaining an interferogram with the required precision is equivalent to ruling a good grating each time. (Jacquinot 1984)

7.6 OTHER CONTRIBUTIONS

Fellgett and Jacquinot independently discovered the two complementary advantages of Fourier spectroscopy. Others were thinking about similar problems during the same period, however.

Grechushnikov *et al.* (1963) claimed that Fourier spectroscopy "was developed independently of foreign work by the authors at the [Soviet] Institute of Crystallography during the early fifties." Their discussion does not mention either the throughput or multiplex advantages, though, and the development appears to be little more than the realization that the interferogram and spectrum were linked by the Fourier transformation.

Marcel Golay (1951), inventor of the pneumatic infrared detector, developed prism spectrometers employing multiple entrance and exit slits. He presented his technique as an alternative to sequentially-scanned spectrometers; his motivation was the rapid measurement of infrared spectra.

Golay's approach was complex and unintuitive. The slit mask of the Golay spectrometer consisted of four quadrants, two serving as input slit arrays and two as output slit arrays. The slit positions in the entrance quadrants were selected at random so that half the area was removed. The two exit quadrants were then punched out so that one (identical to the first entrance quadrant) allowed the images of the slits to pass through, while the other (the complement of the second entrance quadrant) blocked its images. As in a conventional spectrometer, the prism was rotated to scan the spectrum of an entrance slit across the output slit. Instead of a single detector, however, two detectors were used to monitor the two entire quadrants of exit slits; the difference of the two signals was recorded.

This complex arrangement could measure a spectrum directly. For any position of the prism, the first quadrant of entrance slits produced a random set of output wavelengths which were transmitted to the detector at the first exit quadrant. However, the wavelengths produced by the second entrance quadrant were blocked by the exit mask in front of the second detector. As the prism was rotated, other wavelengths were transmitted through the exit slits of both quadrants. The net effect was that the difference in the two detector signals as the prism was scanned provided a measure of the spectrum.

Because half of the slit mask was open, this arrangement always transmitted half of the incident light. This was considerably more than the throughput of a conventional spectrometer. The multislit design thus gave a stronger signal, as expected of its multiplex nature.

Golay appears to have trod the same ground as Fellgett. However, he never clearly discussed the throughput advantages of his multislit technique, and devoted his efforts to finding its optical and practical limitations. His was a particular case of Fellgett's generalization.

Through the 1950s, Jacquinot and his group continued to investigate other forms of high-throughput spectrometers. None were as elegantly simple as the Michelson interferometer. Yet, despite the undoubted importance and clarity of the work of Fellgett and Jacquinot, they did not change spectroscopy overnight. In fact, the slow rebirth of Fourier spectroscopy was to occupy the following decade.

REFERENCES

Ash, R. (1965), *Information Theory*, Interscience, New York.
Fellgett, P. (1949), On the Ultimate and Practical Performance of Radiation Detectors, *J. Opt. Soc. Am.*, **33**, 970.
Fellgett, P. (1951), Theory of Infra-Red Sensitivities and its Application to Investigations of Stellar Radiation in the Near Infra-Red, *Thesis*, University of Cambridge, U.K.
Fellgett, P. (1952), Multi-Channel Spectrometry, *J. Opt. Soc. Am.*, **42**, 872.
Fellgett, P. (1958), A Contribution to the Theory of the Multiplex Spectrometer, *J. Phys. Radium*, **19**, 187.
Fellgett, P. (1984), Three Concepts Make a Million Points, *Infr. Phys.*, **24**, 95.
Fellgett, P. B. (1991), *personal communication*, Jan. 18–30.
Golay, M. J. E. (1951), Multislit Spectrometry and its Application to the Panoramic Display of Infrared Spectra, *J. Opt. Soc. Am.*, **41**, 468.
Grechushnikov, B. N., Distler, G. I. and Petrov, I. P. (1963), Fourier Spectrometer for Working in the Near-Infrared Region of the Spectrum, *Sov. Phys. Crystallog.*, **8**, 369.
Jacquinot, P. (1954), The Luminosity of Spectrometers with Prisms, Gratings or Fabry–Pérot Etalons, *J. Opt. Soc. Am.*, **44**, 761.
Jacquinot, P. (1984), How the Search for a Throughput Advantage Led to Fourier Transform Spectroscopy, *Infr. Phys.*, **24**, 99.
Mertz, L. (1956), Optical Fourier Synthesizer, *J. Opt. Soc. Am.*, **46**, 548.
Michelson, A. A. (1902), *Light Waves and Their Uses*, Univ. of Chicago Press, Chicago.
Shannon, C. (1949), *The Mathematical Theory of Communication*, University of Illinois Press, Urbana.

8

Experimental interferometric spectroscopy

.

8.1 FELLGETT'S DEMONSTRATION

Peter Fellgett is almost certainly the first person to have derived an actual spectrum by Fourier transformation of the measured interferogram. Owing to discouragement from his director, Fellgett performed and described only a rudimentary demonstration of the technique in his thesis. Indeed, most of his publications during this crucial early period in the rebirth of FTIR are difficult to obtain in the open literature.

Instead of using a Michelson interferometer, Fellgett scanned the interference pattern formed by two wedged plates (Fig. 8.1). Because the plate separation was small, this amounted to an interferogram over relatively small optical path difference. He transformed the observed interferogram by hand, with use of Lipson–Beevers strips, a calculating tool that still represented the only alternative to mechanical calculators such as Michelson's harmonic analyser at the time (over half a century after Michelson's work). Somewhat later, he wrote a program to calculate the Fourier transformation on the EDSAC II computer built by the Mathematical Laboratory at Cambridge University.

The spectra, of a filament lamp and a mercury discharge lamp, eventually impressed his director sufficiently to obtain a grant for Fellgett that allowed him to build an interferometric spectrometer based on a Michelson interferometer. Some of the features of this device (notably the use of a cube-corner mirror, single beamsplitter with two coated surfaces, and two outputs) were still being rediscovered over thirty years later in commercial spectrometers. The evolution of interferometer design will be more fully discussed in the following chapters.

Because of the tradition of visual or, at best, photographic observations, the technical resources available to build these first instruments at an astronomical observatory were very limited:

> For some time the only test-gear I had for doing electronics was an old pair of headphones which I connected in series with a small capacitor, and judged

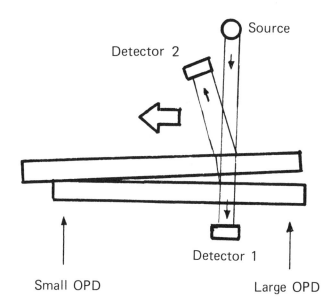

Fig. 8.1 — Schematic diagram of Fellgett's original demonstration of multiplex spectroscopy. Detectors 1 and 2 measure complementary signals, and are electrically connected push–pull to yield a net signal of double intensity.

voltage by the loudness of a click when the capacitor was touched on the point in question. (Fellgett 1991)

As Fellgett's thesis was never published, and publications at first were limited to a few brief notes, his method spread mainly by word of mouth among those who could make use of improvements in efficiency: infrared physicists.
One of the first easily accessible references was a 1952 meeting abstract:

> ... Suitable modulation can be obtained by substituting a two-beam inter-ferometer for the usual dispersing system. The detailed theory of this method has been investigated, and a practical demonstration has been made.

The Optical Society meeting at which these results were presented apparently held a receptive audience. By early 1953, the engineering department of the Perkin–Elmer Corporation in Norwalk, Connecticut, was discussing Fellgett's results, and considering practical interferometer designs (Scott and Scott 1953). The company apparently thought these ideas were premature, because the design, later patented, appears never to have been built (Ford 1991).

8.2 THE JOHNS HOPKINS GROUP

In a visit to England in 1949, John Strong of the Johns Hopkins University, Baltimore, saw Fellgett's spectra of a carbon arc source and mercury lamp, which had been obtained on the "air-wedge" interferometer. His published notes (1957) are more complete than Fellgett's. Fellgett had used two bolometers, measuring reflectance and transmittance, to observe 100 fringes from zero path difference. His spectra extended up to 2 μm in the near infrared. Over 30 years later, Strong related:

> After returning home, I did get the inspiration to introduce interferometric modulation, or chopping. This was accomplished by means of a variable-groove-depth lamellar grating. The depth was varied to produce a fundamental-frequency modulation of the FIR radiations emerging from the exit slit of a grating spectrometer. Thus, the higher grating orders were modulated at harmonic frequencies, as well as scattered radiation. This provided isolation of the desired detector response by means of electrical filtering, rather than by ineffectual optical filtering. (Strong 1984)

This was not an interferometric spectrometer: it was a means of modulating the output of a regular infrared spectrometer to minimize the effect of overlapping spectral orders and stray light. Interestingly, though, it contained the seed of the central idea later to be exploited by rapid scanning FTIR: namely, the modulation at high enough electrical frequencies to permit electrical filtering of the signal.

The lamellar grating spectrometer had been designed by Strong and K. McCubbin, and used by two of Strong's graduate students as a dispersive instrument. Nevertheless, the device could be turned into an interferometer (Fig. 8.2). George

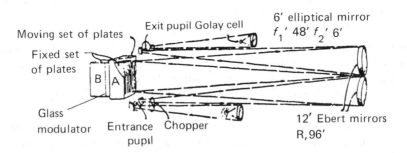

Fig. 8.2 — Lamellar interferometer used by Strong, Gebbie & Vanasse (reproduced by permission of The Optical Society of America).

Vanasse, another of Strong's students, following a visit by Peter Fellgett to Johns Hopkins University in 1950, understood and rekindled interest in Fellgett's original idea. His plan was to employ the lamellar interferometer to record interferograms, and then to convert these into spectra by using a conventional sound analyser. The interferogram, formed into an endless loop, would be played back at a speed that would produce electrical frequencies in the acoustic range. A sound analyser would then separate this waveform into a small number of frequencies by electrical filtering. In this way, a crude spectrum could be rapidly achieved. The principle was published in a brief note by Strong in 1954.

Strong, sharing a common interest in infrared measurements of the atmosphere, asked H. Alistair Gebbie to join his group in late 1954.

Gebbie had been considering improved far infrared techniques, but was unaware of Fellgett's work until joining Strong's group. By all accounts, it was Gebbie who first suggested using a digital computer to perform the Fourier transformation, rather than the analogue frequency analyser that Vanasse had in mind.

Strong arranged for an IBM 605 computer at Binghampton, New York, to be programmed for the Fourier transform. The apparent impracticality of Gebbie's suggestion is not obvious today, but the cost of computation by this method was enormous:

> I recall that computing one point on an IBM 650 computer for each of 250 spectral elements cost about $100 and took more than an hour. (Gebbie 1984)

It is little wonder that only a single far infrared spectrum was published until 1956 (Fig. 8.3). As late as 1959, that same single spectrum had been published in at least four articles, and highlighted by a 1958 book by Strong which brought the technique to a wide audience for the first time.

8.3   LAWRENCE MERTZ AT BAIRD ASSOCIATES INC.

According to Mertz (1965), the work of Strong's group was preceded by his own demonstration of a far infrared Michelson interferometer. This device was developed under an Army Signal Corps contract to Baird Associates in 1954. Mertz credits Bruce Billings and Dave Robinson of Baird Associates with foreseeing the merits of Peter Fellgett's ideas, and nurturing his development.

Mertz's interferometer employed wire-grid polarizers (polarization interferometers are discussed in detail in Section 17.4). Although interferograms were successfully recorded with it — Mertz presented stellar interferograms at a 1957 conference in Bellevue, France — the lack of computing facilities prevented these from being transformed into spectra. Janine Connes relates that Mertz hoped to make an empirical classification of star types based on interferograms without resorting to awkward Fourier transformations (Connes 1961). In his 1965 book, Mertz shows an interferogram of a mercury arc source. This was finally transformed in 1964, but proved to provide a spectrum masked by channel fringes caused by window reflections. Despite his early lack of computing facilities, Lawrence Mertz was central in influencing commercial FTIR designs through the 1960s.

8.4   THE ROAD TO TRANSFORMATION

At this point, it is perhaps a good idea to pause to consider the options open to researchers in the 1950s. Although nowadays digital computation dominates over other calculation methods, this was not the case when the first Fourier spectrometers were being designed.

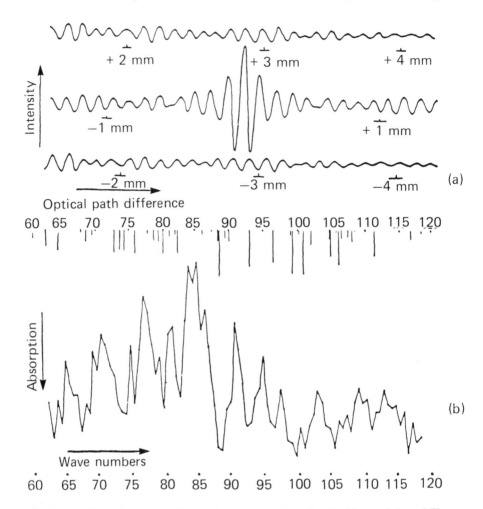

Fig. 8.3 — First spectrum transformed by computer (reproduced with permission of The Optical Society of America).

There were three options available to researchers for transforming their interferograms into spectra: digital computers, analogue computers, and frequency analysers. Each of these was used and evaluated by various investigators.

As already described, the Johns Hopkins group initially began with the idea of employing a wave analyser to yield the intensities of a few dozen frequencies contained within their interferograms.

The wave analyser is a narrow-band, tunable electrical filter. A waveform presented to this passive filter is reduced to a narrow band of frequencies at the output. An analogue voltage, measured on a dial or plotter, indicates the magnitude of this frequency element. The advantage of the wave analyser is that it is easy to use: the interferogram can be applied to its input by, for example, recording it on an endless-loop magnetic tape and playing back the tape at high speed to generate the appropriate electrical frequencies.

One version (Firle 1956) consisted of the following elements:

(1) A recording system, which records the function to be analysed as a variable-area modulation on photographic film advanced uniformly in time during the recording process;
(2) A play-back system, which permits the film recording to be played back at a greater linear speed than the recording speed. The film modulates a light beam which falls on a photocathode; and
(3) A suitable electronic spectrum analyser for the audio-range, into which the signal from the play-back system is fed.

The disadvantage of the wave analyser is that it is rather coarse in its frequency selection. More than a few hundred discrete elements would be difficult to measure, owing to the relatively broad electrical filtering possible. In spectroscopic terms, this amounts to poor spectral resolution.

The second alternative, analogue computation, had in fact been the method chosen by A. A. Michelson for his work. The interferogram, translated into the form of a mechanical amplitude, voltage, or similarly measurable quantity, is applied to the analogue computer, which then yields another measurable output.

Disadvantages of analogue computers are principally their lack of accuracy: spectral intensities better than a few percent are difficult to obtain. On the other hand, the advantage is, as with the wave analyser, rapid analysis.

The digital computer, although recognised at the time as a good choice in principle, suffered from high cost, difficult access, and unfamiliarity. One of its secondary advantages was its ability to be programmed for other useful tasks, such as the computation and plotting of ratios of spectra, strengths of absorption lines, and attenuation coefficients.

8.5 JACQUINOT'S GROUP

Jacquinot, with his research students, formed the third research group seriously investigating Fourier spectroscopy in the 1950s. Janine and Pierre Connes began work on a Michelson interferometer to be used in the near infrared and visible regions of the spectrum. The group tackled Fourier spectroscopy, and other efficient techniques, from both a theoretical and experimental point of view. The first widely available review of these methods was published by Jacquinot (1960).

8.6 THE 1957 BELLEVUE CONFERENCE

Apart from seminars held by visiting researchers, the first meeting of workers in Fourier spectroscopy was held at the Aimé–Cotton laboratory at the Centre National de la Recherche Scientifique (CNRS) Bellevue, France, in 1957. The conference was entitled "Recent Progress in Interferometric Spectroscopy", and covered a variety of techniques including Fabry–Pérot recording spectrometry: only five papers dealt with Fourier spectrometry. The colloquium was nevertheless described by several of the participants as among the most fruitful they ever attended.

Janine Connes (1958), as part of her thesis work, discussed two hitherto unmentioned points: the effect of a finite solid angle subtended by the detector, and the importance and capabilities of apodization.

George Vanasse, then still a graduate student of Strong's, presented a paper on the group's contributions. Their lamellar interferometer had obtained interferograms to a maximum optical path difference of about 4 mm. To calculate the spectrum, the interferogram intensities had been read by eye, point by point, from a chart record; the numerical list was entered into the remote computer. A young woman was later hired to read off the interferogram data from its record on the strip-chart recorder and to plot the computation results. According to Hajime Sakai (1991), then also a graduate student at Johns Hopkins university, Vanasse "was not fully aware of their breakthrough accomplishment in Fourier spectrometry, for achieving high quality spectrometry, a good spectral resolution with a good signal-to-noise ratio." Vanasse and Strong were working on a much larger lamellar interferometer for far infrared measurements.

Measurements of stars by Fourier spectroscopy were presented by both Fellgett and Mertz (1958). Fellgett obtained the first star spectra in the near infrared at a resolving power of 60 to 100, using an interferometer with cube-corner mirrors. Mertz, having no computing facilities, was able to show only interferograms, but also presented his rapid-scanning scheme.

After obtaining their doctorates from Johns Hopkins University, Vanasse, followed by Ernest Loewenstein and Hajime Sakai, joined the US Air Force Cambridge Research Laboratories. AFCRL was to become a centre for developments and funding for Fourier spectrometry through the 1960s and 70s.

8.7 CONNES' THESIS

In 1961, Janine Connes published her doctoral thesis, which was to remain the most thorough analysis of Fourier spectroscopy for a decade (Connes 1961). In it, she dealt with the numerous practical details necessary for any experimental technique: the effects of beam divergence through the interferometer, imperfections in optical elements and alignment, irregularities of scan movement, errors in correcting phase variations in the interferogram, and conditions for optimal signal-to-noise ratio. Many of the points she discussed were rediscovered years later; for example, numerical filtering of the interferogram to limit the number of points in the interferogram and to limit the spectrum to a well-defined spectral band.

Connes supplemented her theoretical work with experimental demonstrations. Two subjects were measured, both in the near infrared (by no means the easiest spectral region to tackle): the emission of the night sky near 1.6 μm, and the recombination radiation of germanium at about 1.7 μm. The design of Connes' instrument contained most of the features found in succeeding spectrometers. The Michelson interferometer used 20-cm diameter mirrors and a 7×8 cm glass beamsplitter/compensator combination. In order to keep the beamsplitter and compensator plates sufficiently parallel, they were held in contact. This deviated from

Michelson's original arrangement, which placed the compensator plate in one arm, away from the undivided beam. Michelson's configuration has the advantage of involving three, rather than four, transmissions through the beamsplitter/compensator pair. But, provided that reasonably transparent and homogeneous materials are used, this advantage can be outweighed by the difficulty in separately mounting and maintaining the orientation of two separate plates.

Connes noted some difficulties with multiple reflections between the semireflecting beamsplitter surface and the adjacent uncoated compensator surface — all four surfaces of the pair reflect light and create faint satellite interferograms which combine to yield a distorted resultant. This problem can be avoided by "wedging" the plates so that no two surfaces are parallel. In effect, this places the phantom interferograms outside the field of view of the detector.

The detector was a lead sulphide photoconductive cell (the most sensitive detector for this spectral region) cooled to dry-ice temperature. It was mounted directly on the rear surface of a microscope condenser, an arrangement attributed to her husband Pierre Connes and known as an immersed element. For some measurements near 1 μm, the PbS cell was replaced by a photomultiplier.

As a reference channel to determine accurately the optical path difference, Connes used a monochromatic cadmium lamp beam travelling through the interferometer along the same path as the primary sample beam. The two were combined at the entrance end by a beamsplitter, and similarly separated at the output side. The cadmium light was monitored by a photomultiplier tube. The primary and reference channels were separated by optical filters.

The interferometer proper was laid out for 30° incidence on the beamsplitter. The moving mirror was mounted on a carriage travelling on high-precision parallel slides. Parallelism to better than 1/10 of a fringe of red cadmium light was claimed over an 8-mm displacement and over a 5-cm usable mirror diameter. The carriage was driven by a micrometer screw with 0.5-mm pitch. Connes found that even high-precision screws were too imprecise for recording interferograms without the reference channel, and so she employed a screw of mediocre quality, driven by a geared-down synchronous motor. The gear box allowed reduction factors between 1 and 4096, and gave mirror velocities between 60 μm/sec and 15 nm/sec. Despite a desire to use static measurement, i.e. measuring the signal at each optical path difference while the mirror was motionless and then moving immediately to the next, she initially used a slow, constant drive speed and later compromised with a drive that slowed in the region of each measured point.

As in all interferometers before and since, vibration was a problem. The interferometer rested on a concrete block mounted on rubber shock mounts to avoid external vibration. The motor and gearing were interlinked with flexible shafts to avoid direct transmission to the optical elements.

A chopper was used to modulate the incoming light at a frequency of 125 Hz, a frequency at which the PbS detector is particularly sensitive. The amplified output was detected by a synchronous detection apparatus, filtered by an electrical filter, and passed to a recording potentiometer.

Initial measurements of the night sky were hindered by the fact that the blades of the chopper at a temperature of 15°C caused a stronger signal than the radiation from the sky itself. Once the mid infrared emission from the blades was filtered out by optical filters, undistorted sky spectra were obtained.

These first results, obtained in two hours' observations and having resolving power of 900, were far superior to a 5½-hour measurement made with a grating spectrometer having a resolving power of only 150.

The measured resolution, $6.3\,cm^{-1}$, was nearly identical to the value calculated from the maximum path difference (1.96 mm). The spectral range was 1250–$6800\,cm^{-1}$. The 840 point spectrum calculation required 1 hr 20 min to calculate on an IBM 704 computer. A subsequent 1500 point spectrum calculation was performed on an IBM 650 computer at the University of Toronto, a faster model having magnetic drums and fast-access memory.

While the night sky observations verified the resolution of her Fourier transform spectrometer, Connes made laboratory measurements of the emission of germanium cooled to liquid helium temperature to compare FTIR more directly with dispersive methods. Initial spectra were comparable with dispersive results but recorded in 2 rather than 48 hours. In an attempt to improve resolution, a path difference of up to 12 mm was employed; this gave theoretically a resolution of $1\,cm^{-1}$ and a resolving power of 6000.

Connes and the other members of Jacquinot's group continued to press the technique towards near-infrared, high-resolution measurements. The strong theoretical underpinnings and masterful experimental demonstrations made their work the state of the art.

8.8   WORK AT NPL

H. A. Gebbie moved to the National Physical Laboratory (NPL) in Teddington, England in 1957. There, he had access to the "Ace" and "Deuce" electric computers, the latter of which was said to be some 20 times faster than the "high speed" IBM 650. It was nevertheless slow by modern standards: computing the spectrum of 528 interferogram points over the spectral range 125–225 μm took five minutes.

The advantages of beginning with far infrared measurements were clear:

> ... this kept the numbers of entries in the transforms down, but still gave us results that could hardly have been obtained by other methods. This kept the cynics at bay because we were doing something new. If we had started prematurely with NIR spectroscopy we would have been at a big disadvantage and given our critics, of whom there were many, grounds for comparison with existing methods. (Gebbie 1984)

8.8.1   Michelson *vs.* lamellar interferometers
Gebbie, like Fellgett before him, adopted the Michelson interferometer instead of Strong's lamellar type. In principle, the lamellar type was the more efficient. By using a beamsplitter, which divides not only the incoming but also the outgoing beam

into two parts, the Michelson interferometer throws away half of the available energy. The lamellar interferometer avoids this waste by dividing the beam wavefront rather than the beam amplitude. Moreover, like all mirror-based optical systems, the performance of the lamellar interferometer is not limited by the absorption or dispersion (variation in refractive index) of transparent optical elements.

Unfortunately, lamellar mirrors are technically more difficult to manufacture than beamsplitters. A lamellar mirror consists of two interleaved parts positioned like the fingers of two folded hands; all the "fingers" must be flat and parallel to interferometric tolerances. Both the initial fabrication and movement during scanning are difficult to perfect. As a result, lamellar interferometers have never been used at above a few hundred wavenumbers. Other theoretical limitations, and practical instruments, are discussed in Section 13.2.

8.8.2 Early NPL instruments
An examination of two of the first NPL instruments illustrates features that were to be adopted by early commercial instruments. The first, described in conference proceedings (Gebbie *et al.* 1962) was designed for near infrared studies. The second (Gebbie and Stone 1964) was a far infrared instrument for gas measurements.

8.8.3 A near infrared FTIR
This instrument was designed for a maximum path difference of 30 cm. It was a conventional Michelson interferometer employing flat interferometer mirrors. Two features are notable: the optical design of interferometer, and the scan-mirror mechanism.

8.8.4 The compensator plate
As Michelson and others had done, the NPL group employed both a beamsplitter and separate "compensator" plate (Fig. 8.4). The compensator is necessary to provide the same light path through both the two arms of the interferometer. For example, without a compensator, the light path along one arm involves transmission once through the beamsplitter material, and one reflection each from the interferometer mirror and beamsplitter surface. The path along the other arm requires three transmissions and two reflections. The refractive index of the beamsplitter material will therefore cause an additional optical path difference because of the unbalanced path through the interferometer, and this unbalancing will depend on wavelength (because refractive index is wavelength-dependent). This in turn causes the interferogram to be distorted; it is no longer symmetrical about zero path difference. Indeed, the extra path difference will cause a large displacement of the pcak from zero path difference.

The straightforward solution to this problem is to use a compensator plate. In the Michelson version, this plate was positioned in one arm of the interferometer to intercept only the rays travelling along that path. Both arms then undergo three transmissions and two reflections. This arrangement attenuates the beams through the interferometer least, if the beamsplitter material absorbs or scatters light. Another advantage of few transits across the beamsplitter/compensator material is

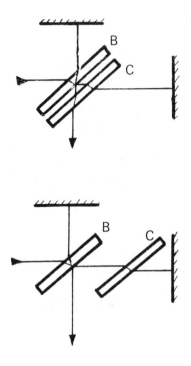

Fig. 8.4 — Compensator plate positions. Top: J. Connes and most successors; bottom: Michelson and Gebbie.

that variations in refractive index have a smaller effect on the optical path difference. However, by mounting the beamsplitter and compensator plates separately, there is a much greater probability of misalignment. This will cause optical path difference offsets on a smaller scale to those produced when the compensator is absent.

Subsequent Michelson interferometers for Fourier spectroscopy have therefore nearly all used a beamsplitter/compensator pair, rigidly mounted together. Both plates are intercepted by both light paths through the interferometer. Because of this, both arm paths undergo four transmissions and two reflections.

The movable mirror of the NPL interferometer was mounted on a carriage that was supported on PTFE pads running along a glass slideway (Fig. 8.5). The pads reduced the stick–slip effect of friction. The glass slideway was ground flat to within a wavelength of light to prevent tilts of the movable mirror.

The mirror carriage was towed along the slideway either forwards or backwards by a glass fibre loop attached to the nut of a leadscrew. The rather elastic characteristics of the towing fibre were minimized by the low-friction guideway. The leadscrew itself was rotated by a motor and reduction gear.

The optical path difference of the interferometer was monitored by employing two channels: one, the sample channel, used most of the area of the interferometer beamsplitter and mirrors; the second, monitor, channel comprised the central

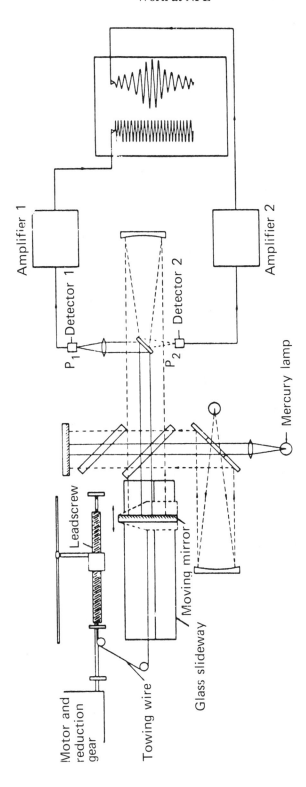

Fig. 8.5 — NPL near-infrared interferometric spectrometer (reproduced with permission of H. A. Gebbie).

portion of the interferometer, which modulated the light from a filtered mercury lamp. This monochromatic light source thus generated sinusoidal fringes of known separation. This method had been used by Rubens and Wood in 1911, and made the results somewhat independent of irregularities of the scan drive. As Gebbie pointed out:

> Since the mirror displacement is measured by reference fringes, no demands on the accuracy of the leadscrew or lack of hysteresis in the connecting mechanism are made, beyond that they should allow the motion to be smooth . . . . An important requirement of the mirror motion is that the average speed over any displacement of $0.25\,\mu$ must not exceed the maximum fringe counting rate . . .

This problem of smooth, regular motion (even with reference fringe monitoring) has continued to plague interferometer designs in the intervening years.

Another publication (Gebbie *et al.* 1964) provided more details about data acquisition and performance. The reference fringe measurements were used to trigger the digitization of the detector signal, with the result punched on paper tape. This tape was subsequently used for input to the ACE computer, which performed the Fourier transformation.

A typical measurement required about 1 hr of recording and 15 min of calculation. A spectral range covering 2 to $12\,\mu m$ was quoted, although results were published to $3400\,cm^{-1}$ (about $3\,\mu m$).

8.8.5   An evacuable Michelson interferometer

The difficulties of accurate scan drives were much reduced in the far infrared. NPL (Gebbie and Stone 1963) produced a simple design which served as a model for later commercial instruments (Fig. 8.6).

The scan drive consisted of a carriage running along two cylindrical rails. Smooth motion was made possible by using thin Teflon sheet as bearing material.

8.9   MOIRÉ POSITION MEASUREMENT

Instead of a monochromatic mercury lamp as the source for reference fringes, the NPL group used a Moiré fringe measurement system. This is essentially a low-precision analogue to monochromatic fringe referencing.

Moiré fringes were probably first observed by textile workers as the shifting patterns of dark lines through overlapping layers of cloth. David Rittenhouse, a 19th century astronomer, noticed the effect through window curtains. Lord Rayleigh was the first to use it scientifically, as a test for checking photographic reproductions of diffraction gratings in the 1870s.

A Moiré pattern is a cyclic variation in transmission or reflection caused by the overlap of two regular scales. Commonly, the two scales consist of identical alternating dark/bright bars of equal spacing — i.e. similar to the variations in amplitude along a light wave — and are often photographic plates reproducing a

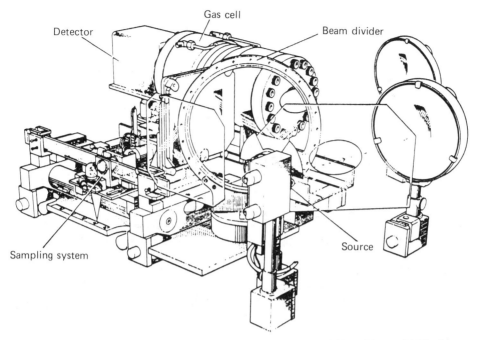

Fig. 8.6 — NPL far infrared interferometer (reproduced from Gebbie and Stone (1964) with permission from Pergamon Press PLC).

large-scale pen-and-ink pattern. The superposition of these scales is analogous to the interference of light rays, and leads to the same large-scale variations in intensity. The effect is illustrated in Fig. 8.7. Movements small compared with the grid spacing are clearly signalled by gross changes in the intensity of light transmitted through the grid.

In practice, a Moiré system consists of a light source, a long fixed scale, a small moving scale having the same pattern size, and an optical detector mounted behind the small scale to measure the light transmitted by the combination. The moving scale, attached to the moving element to be measured, transmits light to the detector when the two patterns line up, and blocks light when the patterns are a half-bar out of phase. The resulting detector output is equivalent to the output when observing a fringe pattern from a scanning interferometer. The only practical differences are that the Moiré pulses are triangular in shape (because a "square wave" intensity variation, rather than a sinusoidal variation, is used) and that the scale of movement is an order of magnitude larger (owing to the larger scale of the Moiré fringes). The advantage of the Moiré technique is that the system is robust: it does not depend on interference of light, but rather on large-scale alignment of two transparent patterns. The disadvantage is that the precision available by Moiré measurement is some ten times lower than with optical interference. However, for far infrared work, where wavelengths (and hence the necessary precision) are also an order of magnitude longer than in the mid infrared, Moiré systems are perfectly adequate.

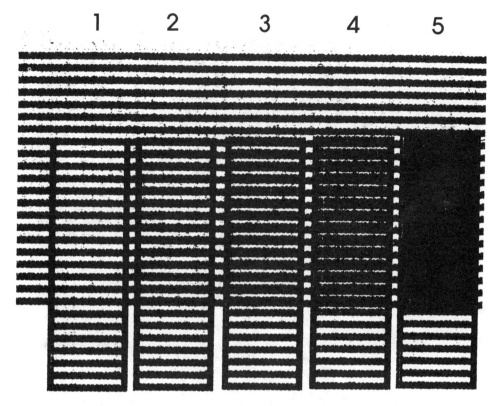

Fig. 8.7 — Moiré position measurement. A fixed grid and moving grid are located between a light source and detector. As the moving grid is displaced, the amount of light transmitted varies cyclically. In this example, the small grid in positions 1 to 5 has been successively displaced by 1/10 the grid spacing, resulting in a change of transmittance from 50% to 0%.

8.10   ADVANCES IN DETECTORS

8.10.1   The Golay cell

The first fundamentally new type of radiation detector to appear since thermopiles and bolometers was the pneumatic detector invented by Marcel Golay of the American Signal Corps Engineering Laboratories (Golay 1947, 1948).

This device is based on the expansion of heated gas. It consists of a small cell filled with gas; radiation, modulated by an external chopper or similar device, enters through an infrared-transmitting window and strikes an absorbing film a few millimeters in size (Fig. 8.8). The periodic warming of the absorbing film is transferred to the gas in the cell, which expands and distorts a flexible mirror forming the back face of the cell. This flexible mirror is part of an optical system which includes a focused light source and line grating. The light passes through the grating, onto the mirror, and back through the grating again in such a way that the shadow of the grating is imaged on the grating itself, blocking most or all of the light from exiting (the arrangement is equivalent to a Moiré system using a single grid). Minor changes in the mirror angle cause the amount of light reflected out through the

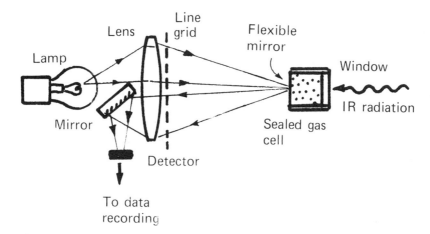

Fig. 8.8 — Schematic diagram of Golay cell infrared detector.

grating to vary dramatically. The reflected light is measured by a photocell, amplified, electrically filtered, and applied to a gauge or recording instrument.

The Golay cell gives a linear signal over a wide range of intensity, and can be used for wavelengths as long as microwaves (i.e. beyond the far infrared). It is typically modulated at 10 Hz, and it has a response time of a few milliseconds. They are surprisingly robust detectors, but tend to lose gas pressure and their sensitivity over a period of months or years.

8.10.2 Photoelectric infrared detectors

Research during the Second World War, carried out principally in Germany toward infrared aircraft-detection instruments, led to the development of semiconducting photoconductive detectors. The first of these, the lead sulphide (PbS) detector, is sensitive from the visible region to about 3 μm in the near infrared. Lead selenide (PbSe) and lead telluride (PbTe) detectors were subsequently developed for the 1–5 μm and 1–6 μm regions, respectively.

Photoconductive detectors are more sensitive than the thermocouple and bolometer in their regions of peak sensitivity, but cover narrower spectral regions. They also have a higher electrical frequency response, and can be modulated to thousands or tens of thousands of Hz.

8.10.3 Photomultiplier tubes

The photoelectric effect was intensively studied at the turn of the twentieth century, and explained theoretically by Albert Einstein. His analysis was strong evidence that light consists of photons, or discrete corpuscles as Newton had believed, and earned Einstein the Nobel prize.

When certain types of surface are bombarded by electrons, each electron can expel several secondary electrons. If this cluster of electrons is captured in an electric field and directed to another surface, the process can be repeated. This electron multiplication can also be started by an energetic photon of light: a single photon can yield a cascade of electrons that can then be further amplified and recorded. Current multiplication of ten million is achievable, making photomultipliers useful for measuring extremely weak sources of light. The first photomultiplier tube was described by Zworykin in 1936. Initially, the performance was poor: the sensitivity was low, and background noise was very high. Subsequent work developed better photoemissive surfaces and improved cathode designs for the tubes.

The photoelectric effect is of use for ultraviolet, visible, and near infrared light. Longer wavelengths cannot be detected, because the energy of infrared photons is inadequate to expel electrons from solids. Photomultiplier detectors are thus seldom encountered by infrared spectroscopists.

8.11 THE STATE OF THE ART: THE CONNES' PLANETARY SPECTRA

Towards the end of 1965, Janine and Pierre Connes of CNRS in France submitted a paper to the Journal of the Optical Society of America. The contents of the paper had already been circulated to others in the field: Mertz referred to them in his book (1965) and a review paper by Ernest Loewenstein (1966) highlighted them.

The Connes' results (1966) caused a stir both among workers in Fourier spectroscopy and among scientists in general. They had made measurements of the spectra of Venus and Mars that were superior to the best previous data by several orders of magnitude, and exceeding what most suspected was possible. Even four years later, when further results were presented during a conference at Aspen, Colorado, organized by the Air Force Cambridge Laboratories, "their results . . . awed all the participants" (Hajime Sakai).

They had chosen a difficult application for Fourier spectroscopy: near infrared measurements through the atmosphere. Astronomical observations with FTIR instruments were complicated by atmospheric turbulence, fluctuations in transmission, and guidance errors. As the authors said,

> . . . results to date have been few, and either inferior to or, at best, comparable with those given by grating spectrometers. It is not too surprising that under these circumstances doubts have been cast on the validity of the method. To prove that these doubts are unwarranted is the main purpose of this paper . . .

The fore-optics of the interferometer included a servo-controlled guide mirror to keep the light of the planet centred on the instrument aperture. Although this system responded to perturbations within tens of milliseconds, it did not keep the aperture uniformly illuminated. A "scrambler" was therefore added to diffuse the incoming light and render it homogeneous. The original scrambler consisted of a dove prism rotating at 300 rev/sec, but was found to be "very noisy and cumbersome" and introduced "beats" with harmonics of the frequency of the light chopper of the interferometer. Subsequently, a passive scrambler consisting of a reflective tube was used.

The interferometer itself employed "cat's eye" reflectors to return the beam to the beamsplitter, independently of mirror tilt (cat's eyes are discussed further in

Section 13.1.2). The moving mirror was supported on a carriage rolling on three steel balls. The balls rolled on glass plates which were not optically flat, but which were kept free of dust. The carriage was moved by a loudspeaker-type electromagnetic drive, with its speed controlled by a servomechanism. The carriage was driven discontinuously: it was moved by an increment, stopped for measurement of the detector signal, and restarted, about 100 times per second. A complete spectrum with 0.1 cm^{-1} resolution took about two hours to record.

To determine the optical path difference of the interferometer, a monochromatic mercury lamp was shone through a portion of it, and detected by photomultipliers. Movement of the scan mirror by increments of the mercury line wavelength were thus accurately detected.

A second auxiliary channel of the interferometer was devoted to a white light source. The broad-band radiation from the visible lamp produced an extremely narrow interferogram that was used to detect the zero-path position of the interferometer.

The interferograms, containing as many as 12 000 points, were recorded on paper tape. The system stopped automatically if clouds covered the image or if it was lost for any other reason. Data tapes were either transferred by telephone link to a computer (when measurements were made in the USA) or carried by car and aeroplane to Paris (when measurements were made in France) to computer facilities. The interferograms were interpolated and edited to correct for error contributions from various sources, and interferogram asymmetry.

Despite such problems as a mouse's nest in one of the cat's eye retroreflectors, and a rattlesnake in the paper tape punch, the Connes were able to obtain high-quality interferograms at the telescopes of several observatories. The results obtained with this elaborate system were impressive. Measurements of solar spectra confirmed the theoretical resolution of 0.1 cm^{-1}. The spectra of Venus were some 7 times better in resolution than those from previous diffraction grating spectrometers, with similar signal-to-noise ratio. The Connes' telescope captured about five times less energy than the one that had been coupled to the grating spectrometer, so their results were all the more striking.

Spectra of Mars were better still: about ten times better in resolution AND in S/N. The principal complaint by the authors was that atmospheric turbulence limited further improvements.

The first half of the 1960s witnessed numerous experimental demonstrations of Fourier spectroscopy, showing it to be both powerful and practical. Few new discoveries had been made since the 1950s; instead, experimental techniques had been developed. With impetus from the Connes' results, investigators and instrumentation companies began to exploit the new technique. Those at the forefront of the research began to ask themselves what the ultimate limitations to Fourier spectroscopy were.

REFERENCES

Buijs, H. (1969), Fast Fourier transformation of large arrays of data, *Appl. Opt.*, **8**, 211.
Connes, J. (1958), The Field of Application of the Fourier Transform Method, *J. Phys. Radium*, **19**, 197.

Connes, J. (1961), Recherches sur la Spectroscopie par Transformation de Fourier, *Rev. Opt.*, **40**, 45, 116, 171, 231, translated by Flanagan, C. A. (1963) as document AD 409 869, Defense Documentation Center, Alexandria, Virginia.

Connes, J. and Connes, P. (1966), Near-Infrared Planetary Spectra by Fourier Spectroscopy. I. Instruments and Results, *J. Opt. Soc. Amer.*, **56**, 896.

Connes, P. (1978), Of Fourier, Pasteur, and sundry others, *Appl.Opt.*, **17**, 1318.

Fellgett, P. B. (1991) personal communication, 18–30 January.

Firle, T. E. (1956), Low Frequency Power Spectrum Analyser, *Rev.Sci. Instr.*, **27**, 140.

Ford. M. A. (1991), personal communication, 25 January.

Gebbie, H. A. (1984), Fourier Transform Spectroscopy — Recollections of the Period 1955–1960, *Infr. Phys.*, **24**, 105.

Gebbie, H. A., Habell, K. J. and Middleton, S. P. (1962), Michelson Interferometers for Spectrophotometry in the Near Infra-Red Region, *Proc. Conf. on Optical Instruments and Techniques*, London.

Gebbie, H. A. and Stone, N. W. B. (1964), A Michelson Interferometer for Far Infrared Spectroscopy of Gases, *Infr. Phys.*, **4**, 85.

Gebbie, H. A. and Vanasse, G. (1956), Interferometric Spectroscopy in the Far Infra-Red, *Nature*, **178**, 432.

Golay, M. E. (1947), A Pneumatic Infra-Red Detector, *Rev. Sci. Instr.*, **18**, 357.

Golay, M. E. (1949), The Theoretical and Practical Sensitivity of the Pneumatic Infra-Red Detector, *Rev. Sci. Instr.*, **20**, 816.

Jacquinot, P. (1960), Developments in Interference Spectroscopy, *Rept. Prog. Phys.*, **23**, 268.

Loewenstein, E. V. (1966), The History and Current Status of Fourier Transform Spectroscopy, *Appl. Opt.*, **5**, 845.

Mertz, L. (1958), Multichannel Stellar Spectrometer, *J. Phys. Radium*, **19**, 233.

Richards, P. L. (1964), High-Resolution Fourier Transform Spectroscopy in the Far-Infrared, *J. Opt. Soc. Am.*, **54**, 1474.

Sakai, H. (1991), personal communications, 27 January and 20 February.

Scott, L. B. and Scott, R. M. (1953), A New Arrangement For An Interferometer, *Perkin-Elmer Corporation Engineering Report No. 246*, May 22, 1953.

Strong, J. (1954), Interferometric Modulator, *J. Opt. Soc. Am.*, **44**, 352(A).

Strong, J. (1957), Interferometry for the Far Infrared, *J. Opt. Soc. Amer.*, **47**, 354.

Strong, J. (1984), Fourier Transform Spectroscopy Reminiscences, *Infr. Phys.*, **24**, 103.

Strong, J. and Vanasse, G. (1959), Interferometric Spectroscopy in the Far Infrared, *J. Opt. Soc. Am.*, **49**, 844.

Strong, J. and Vanasse, G. (1960), Lamellar Grating Far-Infrared Interferometer, *J. Opt. Soc. Am.*, **50**, 113.

Vanasse, G. A. , Strong, J. and Loewenstein, E. (1959), Far Infrared Spectra of H_2O and H_2S Taken with an Interferometric Spectrograph, *J. Opt. Soc. Am.*, **49**, 309.

Vanasse, G. A. and Strong, J. (1958), Applications of Fourier Transformation in Optics: Interferometric Spectroscopy, in: *Concepts of Classical Optics*, W. H. Freeman & Son, San Francisco, Appendix F.

9

Working out the details

Even after the demonstrations by Strong's group and others, resistance to the interferometric technique was high. Strong himself had, as he said (1984), "...an experimentalist's natural distrust of anything involving such a prodigious calculation".

Respected spectroscopists dismissed the method. Gebbie (1984) writes that S. Tolansky, known for his expertise in high-resolution spectrometric methods, "categorically pronounced that it would be impossible to transform [interferograms]". The mistrust was, in many ways, reasonable. Strong's group initially knew little about numerical methods. L. A. Wigglesworth, a mathematician recommended by Gebbie, was able to instruct them concerning apodization and digital sampling. But even then there were niggling concerns. Gebbie states:

> There was, however, a troublesome problem with these early spectra which gave me doubts for a very long time and caused me to believe that some numerical quirk at low wave numbers remained to be elucidated. It turned out to have a physical explanation but mysteriously plagued many spectra including the first taken in the laboratory... Initially I suppressed all results below $10\,\mathrm{cm}^{-1}$ and anguished for many years about the phenomenon of "anomalous absorption" in water vapour.

Other investigators entertained doubts about the method. F. D. Kahn had published a note in *Astrophysics Journal* (1959) pouring cold water on the multiplex advantage. He showed that Fourier spectrometry was vulnerable to various perturbations generally termed "scintillation noise". Such noise is characterized by fluctuations that vary in proportion to the intensity of the light source. One example is a twinkling star. In such a circumstance, the "multiplex advantage" becomes a "multiplex disadvantage" (the details of the multiplex advantage for various types of noise are treated in Section 17.5.5). As Hajime Sakai (1991) describes:

> The first method tried to combat the scintillation noise degradation was the ratio recording of the interferogram signal against the input signal level. It

was found very quickly that the scheme was ineffective in a practical sense because of the inherent complexity in achieving the expected compensation.

The astronomers at the forefront of Fourier spectroscopy had chosen its most difficult case: a fluctuating light source and near infrared measurements, where tolerances were most critical. Others concentrating on laboratory measurements achieved earlier confirmation of Fellgett's multiplex advantage.

Vanasse and Strong published two new spectra in 1959, along with more experimental details. The path difference of their lamellar grating interferometer was changed manually by setting micrometer screws. The total experiment time for the three published spectra ranged from about one to three hours; they recorded the interferograms on a pen recorder, and then measured the curve to obtain a numerical list of interferogram points to transform. By this time, they were clear about the requirements of digital sampling, apodization and resolution.

9.1 APODIZATION

Apodization is a mathematical compromise which compensates for incomplete data. Strictly speaking, the interferogram should be measured to infinite optical path difference to yield a spectrum. Only in this way can all the frequencies composing the light source be properly recorded. If the interferogram is truncated, the sudden cut-off of data results in oscillations around sharp spectral features such as absorption lines. The effect is illustrated in Fig. 9.1. An abrupt end to the interferogram must be recreated by the Fourier transform, which obligingly calculates spectral frequencies at unrealistic (even negative) intensities. The resulting spectral distortion can be severe enough to mask the true spectral characteristics of the light source.

Apodization or "foot removal" gets rid of the spurious "feet" or sidelobes around spectral features by gradually smoothing the interferogram to zero intensity as the measurement comes to an end. The intensity at zero path difference is not adjusted, but the intensities of interferogram points away from ZPD are progressively reduced to reach exactly zero at the last point. This process is usually done after the interferogram has been recorded.

Apodization has the drawback, though, of worsening the spectral resolution. The spectral resolution depends directly on the maximum optical path difference recorded in the interferogram; by reducing the relative contribution of points far from ZPD, apodization "dilutes" the maximum path difference. There is therefore a trade-off between the reduction in spectral distortion and the worsening of resolution. An apodizing function that smooths only the last few points of the spectrum will alter the resolution and sidelobes very little. On the other hand, smoothing interferogram points beginning near ZPD will have drastic effects, yielding a very regular but low-resolution spectrum.

Various apodization functions have been used to trade off resolution for oscillations. The most intuitive is triangular apodization: with this function, the interferogram intensity is reduced in proportion to the distance between ZPD and the maximum optical path difference (OPD), L. It can be shown that the unapodized

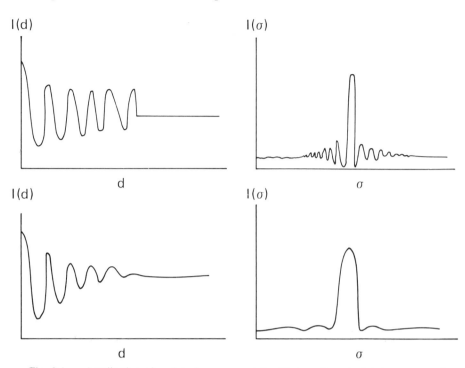

Fig. 9.1 — Apodization of an interferogram and its effect on the calculated spectrum. A measured interferogram (top left) has an abrupt termination at the maximum optical path difference, resulting in spurious sidelobes around spectral features. An apodized interferogram is smoothly reduced to zero intensity, resulting in a smoother, lower-resolution spectrum.

spectrum produced for a maximum optical path difference L is equal to $1.21/2L$. In other words, if an interferogram is measured to a maximum OPD of 2 cm, the spectral resolution (expressed as full width at half maximum of the narrowest spectral feature) is $1.21/4 = 0.30$ cm^{-1}. With triangular apodization, the relationship becomes $1.77/2L$. This amounts to a worsening of resolution by $1.77/1.21 = 46\%$; with an OPD of 2 cm, triangular apodization will give resolution of only 0.44 cm^{-1}. On the other hand, the intensity of sidelobes is considerably reduced. Resolution can always be improved by scanning the interferogram over a longer path difference, but the amount of distortion caused by sidelobes cannot be easily judged. Apodization is therefore universally applied to interferograms.

Finding the best apodization function in the early days of Fourier spectroscopy was a matter of trial and error and personal taste. Each laboratory had its favourite function. A. Filler (1964) suggested various trigonometric functions. More recently, Robert Norton and Reinhard Beer (1976) at JPL investigated a wide variety of apodizing functions for the optimum trade-off. Some of the more commonly used apodization functions are given in Table 9.1. Even today, the apodization functions recommended by various manufacturers can vary significantly in computation time, yet give almost imperceptibly different results on real spectra.

Table 9.1 — Some apodization functions

Optical path difference (OPD) is denoted by δ and the maximum OPD of the interferogram is L. The apodization function for path difference δ is multiplied by the interferogram intensity $I(\delta)$ to yield a new apodized interferogram value $I'(\delta)$

Apodization Name	Function	Resolution (FWHM)
Boxcar or Tophat (i.e. no apodization)	1	$1.21/2L$
Cosine	$\cos(\pi\delta/2L)$	$1.58/2L$
Triangular	$(1 - |\delta|/L)$	$1.77/2L$
Bessel	$[1 - (\delta/L)^2]^2$	$1.91/2L$
Sinc^2	$\mathrm{sinc}^2(\pi\delta/L)$	$2.17/2L$

9.2 DIGITAL SAMPLING

Shannon's work (e.g. 1949) indicated that there are certain requirements that must be satisfied when "sampling", i.e. when making periodic measurements, of a signal. A signal may be any continuous waveform, such as a fluctuating voltage or the varying intensity produced at the output of a Michelson interferometer.

In order to record the signal faithfully, it must be sampled with at least twice the frequency of the highest frequency component it contains. For example, the earth rotates about its axis once per day, and about the sun once per year. If a picture is taken at some point on the earth every 12 hours, the set of pictures will record the daily variations in sunlight; if the pictures are taken a few days apart, it will be impossible to infer how frequently day changes to night; and if the pictures are taken years apart, even the cycle of seasons will not be interpretable.

An analogous effect can be seen in movies of western stagecoaches. The camera captures images of the wheels about 24 times per second. As the stagecoach speeds up, adjacent spokes of the wheels exchange places in exactly 1/24 sec. When this happens, the wheels appear motionless to the film camera. If the wheels turn slightly slower, they appear to turn backwards in the replayed film.

In the same way, if the Michelson interferometer modulates light up to 5000 cm^{-1}, the signal must be sampled twice as fast. Since 5000 cm^{-1} corresponds to a wavelength of 2 µm, it is necessary to sample at 1 µm path difference intervals. If the sampling occurs at larger path increments, the spectrum will be distorted by "folding" the frequencies above the sampling frequency into the lower frequencies, resulting in an uninterpretable overlap. As with the wheels of the movie stagecoach, it becomes impossible to determine what the true frequency is. The folding is sometimes referred to as "aliasing" — i.e. higher frequencies are masquerading or aliased as lower frequencies.

9.3 SURFACE FLATNESS vs. WAVELENGTH

The heart of a Fourier spectrometer is the interferometer. In order to measure a strong interferogram signal, the interferometer must ensure that all the incoming light rays undergo the same treatment.

Consider a light ray traveling through the interferometer. If one of the two mirrors is displaced slightly, the ray component in that arm of the interferometer will be either more or less retarded; when recombined at the beamsplitter, the phase and therefore the intensity of the ray will be affected. For this reason, if the interferometer mirrors are not perfectly flat, rays reflected from different points will leave the interferometer with different phases. This means that the modulation of the light beam (i.e. the extremes of high and low intensity as the interferometer scans) will be compromised. In fact, the efficiency of modulation falls as mirror flatness deteriorates. The same effect occurs for imperfect beamsplitters: surface faults in any reflecting element (and to a much smaller degree, in transmitting elements) of the interferometer lead to poorer modulation. This is true only of the interferometer itself: the ray components must be separately affected to degrade modulation. Because of this, the quality of the two interferometer mirrors and beamsplitter are critical, but other optical elements in the spectrometer such as windows, focusing optics and so on, are relatively unimportant.

In practice, a rule of thumb is that the interferometer mirrors and beamsplitter should be flatter than one-tenth of the shortest wavelength to be examined. Thus for a mid-infrared instrument measuring up to $4000 \, \text{cm}^{-1}$ ($2.5 \, \mu\text{m}$), mirrors should be flatter than about $0.3 \, \mu\text{m}$ to avoid significant loss of efficiency.

From this, it is clear that there is a spectral limit to the use of a Fourier spectrometer: the mirror quality determines the shortest wavelength that can be used. The earliest Fourier spectrometers worked well in the far infrared, where wavelengths are some ten times longer than in the mid infrared. Interferometer optical tolerances were relatively low. FT spectrometers intended for visible or ultraviolet measurements need optics about one hundred times flatter than those of the first commercial Fourier spectrometers.

9.4   THE EFFECT OF BEAM DIVERGENCE IN AN INTERFEROMETER

An interferometer modulates the intensity of any incoming beam of light. The ideal incoming beam consists of perfectly parallel rays of light (Fig 9.2). Because the light source is not a single point of light, though, the incoming beam is never perfectly parallel. This causes the light rays to strike the beamsplitter and the interferometer mirrors at a range of angles. The actual pathlength travelled by a ray through the interferometer depends on its angle; those rays not perfectly parallel to the axis of the interferometer will travel a shorter path (Fig. 9.3). A range of entrance angles causes a range of optical pathlengths, and a range of pathlengths implies a range of ray intensities. Thus imperfect "collimation" (parallelness) of the incoming beam causes a smearing of output intensities: the modulation of the interferometer is degraded.

Viewed at the detector plane, the range of phases caused by the range of ray angles appears as a bulls-eye pattern (Fig. 9.4). The large central fringe is the only portion viewed by the detector; otherwise, it would average over a range of intensities and yield a more constant signal. If the angular range of the incoming beam is above a certain value, the bulls-eye pattern contracts until the detector views more than the central fringe. All interferometers are therefore designed to be used with a predefined input beam. If the detector is too large, or if the input beam too divergent, the modulation efficiency will be compromised, and measurement precision will fall.

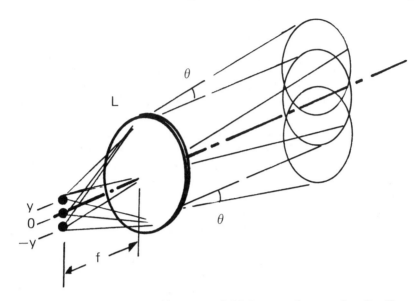

Fig. 9.2 — Beam divergence caused by an extended light source. Lens or mirror L collimates
light originating at its focal position f. For source points a distance y off-axis, the collimated
beam is tilted by an angle $\theta=\arctan(y/f)$ with respect to the axis. A broad source thus produces a
divergent beam.

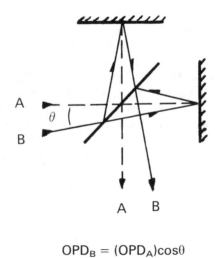

$$OPD_B = (OPD_A)\cos\theta$$

Fig. 9.3 — Effect of angle of incidence on optical path difference.

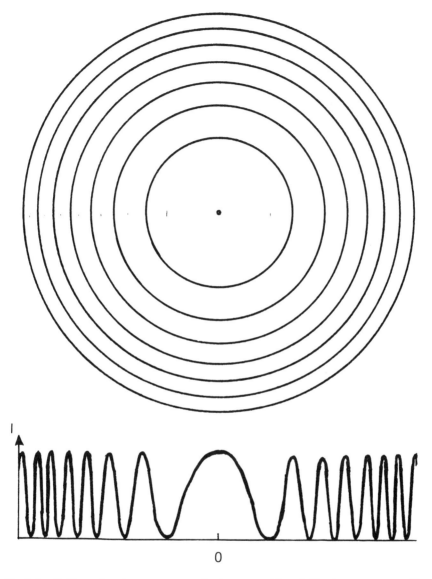

0

Fig. 9.4 — Bull's-eye interference pattern at the detector position of a Fourier spectrometer. To integrate over a region of nearly constant phase, the detector must cover only the central spot of the pattern, which contracts with longer optical path difference and higher frequency.

By the early 1960s, most of the crucial relationships in Fourier spectroscopy were understood and applied by the majority of investigators. The results obtained in various laboratories were sufficiently encouraging for instrument manufacturers to sense a potential market.

REFERENCES

Connes, J. (1961), Recherches sur la Spectroscopie par Transformation de Fourier, *Rev. Opt.*, **40**, 45, 116, 171, 231, translated by Flanagan, C. A. (1963), as document AD 409 869, Defense Documentation Center, Alexandria, Virginia.

Connes, J. and Connes, P. (1966), Near-Infrared Planetary Spectra by Fourier Spectroscopy, *J. Opt. Soc. Am.* **56**, 896.

Gebbie, H. A. (1984), Fourier Transform Spectroscopy — Recollections of the Period 1955–1960, *Infr. Phys.*, **24**, 105.

Filler, A. H. (1964), Apodization and Interpolation in Fourier-Transform Spectroscopy, *J. Opt. Soc. Am.*, **54**, 762.

Katti, P. K. and Singh, K. (1966), A Note on the Surface Accuracy and Alignment of the End Mirrors in a Michelson Interferometer, *Appl. Opt.*, **5**, 1962.

Mertz, L. (1965), *Transformations in Optics*, Wiley, New York.

Norton, R. H. and Beer, R. (1976), New Apodizing Functions for Fourier Spectrometry, *J. Opt. Soc. Am.* **66**, 259.

Sakai, H. (1991), personal communication, 27 January.

Shannon, C. (1949), *The Mathematical Theory of Communication,* University of Illinois Press, Urbana.

Strong, J. and Vanasse, G. (1959), Interferometric Spectroscopy in the Far Infrared, *J. Opt. Soc. Am.* **49**, 844.

10

The Industrial Revolution

At this point, the narrative must change style somewhat, shifting from individuals to groups of individuals and companies. There are two reasons for this: first, two or three decades is a dangerously recent period to discuss objectively, particularly when workers still active in the field are concerned. Second, the growth of interest in FTIR in the 1960s meant that research groups and companies soon took a leading role in development. The combination of more investigators, collective development and improved communications between groups make it difficult to unravel who did (or thought of, or talked about) what first. Although in most cases the industrial teams were guided by the ideas of one or two key individuals, commercial secrecy tended to make their contributions anonymous.

10.1 THE STATUS IN 1962

After the 1958 publication of John Strong's optics textbook describing interferometric spectroscopy, the 1957 Bellevue conference on the subject at CNRS in France, and Jacquinot's review article in *Reports of Progress in Physics,* the technique began to be known to the outside world.

Researchers using Fourier spectrometry were still primarily physicists interested in far infrared measurements. There were at least four "seed" groups with more experience than the others: that of Strong and Vanasse in Minnesota, Gebbie and co-workers at NPL in England, Jacquinot, the Connes and others in France, and Lawrence Mertz at Baird Associates.

10.2 SLOW-SCAN FTIR

This technique, common to all first-generation commercial spectrometers, is also known as the step-and-integrate or static method. The arrangement is shown schematically in Fig. 10.1. The idea is straightforward: the intensity of the interferogram is measured as a succession of individual readings at increments of optical path difference. The scan mirror is moved to beyond the zero path difference; a drive

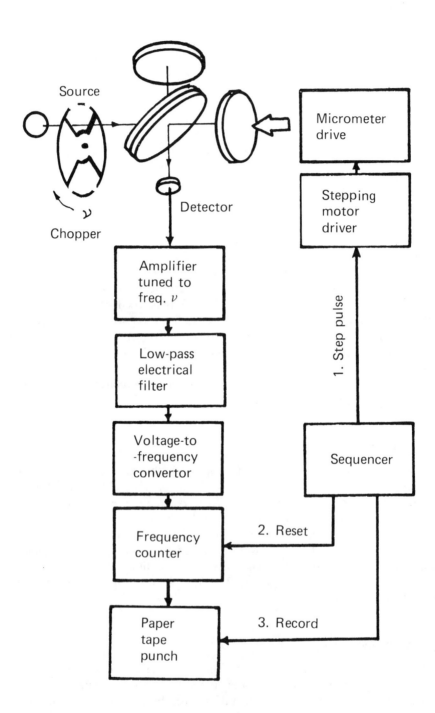

Fig. 10.1 — Schematic arrangement of slow-scanning interferometer system.

mechanism moves it forward an increment and stops to let it settle. The light from the infrared source, modulated by a rotating chopper disk, passes through the interferometer. The detector, following the interferometer, is tuned to the chopped signal by a narrow-band amplifier (usually a phase-locked synchronous amplifier, or "lock-in").

By observing the fluctuations occurring at the chopping frequency, and filtering out all variations of other frequencies, noise is considerably reduced. The filtered signal is integrated for a fixed "gate time", (this further reduces the noise in the measurement) and is then transmitted in digital form to a paper tape, punched card, or on-line computer. The integration is sometimes performed by a digital counter. Strong and Vanasse originally measured the interferogram intensity from a chart recorder trace, and then typed the list of numbers into a computer.

The electrical filtering often requires several seconds for weak signals. This removes most extraneous noise sources such as signal fluctuations caused by the mains frequency. As the electrical filtering can be made to pass only an extremely narrow range of frequencies, it has an advantage over rapid-scan Fourier spectroscopy, which must use a broad passband, particularly at high speed and broad spectral ranges (rapid-scan FTIR will be discussed in Chapter 11).

The slow-scanning technique is well adapted to measuring very small signals, e.g. far-infrared measurements, where sources are weak, optical losses high, and physical effects subtle.

There are drawbacks to slow-scan FTIR. First of all, it is slow. The need to wait for mechanical settling usually restricts samples to, at most, a few per second. Interferograms seldom exceed a few thousand points, because the slow recording makes it sensitive to drifts. Temperature change, mechanical shock (e.g. doors closing or heavy footsteps), electrical changes, variations in the infrared source — all lead to drifts in the signal and hence distortion of the interferogram. Interferogram distortion leads in turn to deformations of the final spectrum.

Slow-scan FTIR is also relatively inefficient. The use of a chopper disk, which alternately blocks and passes the infrared beam, prevents 50% of the available radiation from being used.

10.3   THE FIRST COMMERCIAL FOURIER SPECTROMETERS

Companies that had traditionally supplied the spectroscopic equipment to infrared physicists began to see the shift in emphasis. Quite rapidly, they prepared to market commercial versions of the instruments being constructed in several laboratories. The speed of commercial response was due in part to the proselytizing effect of a few key individuals.

10.3.1   Grubb-Parsons (Newcastle upon Tyne, UK; now a part of NEI Parsons, Ltd, and inactive)

Sir Howard Grubb-Parsons and Company Ltd introduced the first commercial interferometer in 1962, based on a design supplied by the National Physical Laboratory (Teddington, England). The Grubb-Parsons infrared spectrometers, both dispersive and Fourier, are well described in a book by the head of their infrared department (Martin 1966).

The first interferometer was large and heavy. The optical components were mounted on a rigid steel baseplate, which was itself contained within a large steel vessel that could be evacuated.

The IS3 spectrometer covered the far infrared range (10–675 cm^{-1}) with good resolution (0.1 cm^{-1}). It was designed to be a versatile instrument, and was available with various sampling kits for solids, gases, liquids, and microsampling. The electronics system consisted of a lock-in amplifier, an analogue-to-digital converter, and a paper-tape punch. A Moiré fringe system was incorporated to measure the optical path difference accurately. The paper-tape punch recorded a reading at each increment of path difference, signalled by a Moiré pulse. The Fourier transformations and subsequent analysis were to be carried out by off-line computers.

From about 1965, a newer, modular design was developed. Like the early designs, the Mark II spectrometer was developed by H. Gebbie and J. Chamberlain of the NPL. It had an optimum resolution of 0.2 cm^{-1} and a spectral range of 10–675 cm^{-1}. To make the interferometer as simple as possible, no collimation optics were used: the interferometer was traversed by slightly divergent beams (Fig. 10.2). A polyethylene doublet lens was used to focus the modulated output onto the Golay cell detector. The sample could be placed immediately between it and the lens. The lack of collimation has a negligible effect in the far infrared, but would cause loss of resolution at higher wavenumbers.

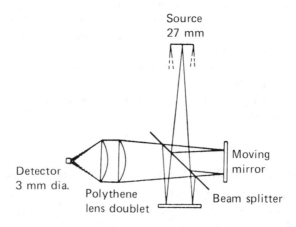

Fig. 10.2 — Grubb-Parsons interferometer (reproduced by permission of NEI Parsons Ltd).

The Moiré fringe system was not employed in the Mark II. Instead, the mirror carriage was connected directly to the spindle of a micrometer, and the sensing of the movement was achieved simply by noting the amount of rotation of the micrometer thimble. A stepping motor making 200 steps per revolution was used to drive it. This determined the optical path difference between each measurement, and thus the maximum spectral range: the sampling theorem gives this as $1000\,\mathrm{cm}^{-1}$. Although the Fourier transform could be calculated over this range, the available beamsplitters and limitations in the precision of the micrometer screw thread limited spectra to below $700\,\mathrm{cm}^{-1}$.

10.3.2 Beckman-RIIC (originally of London, England; now Fife, Scotland)

The Research and Industrial Instrument Company (RIIC) followed Grubb-Parsons with a commercial interferometer system in 1964. With initial consultation from H. Gebbie, they manufactured two families of Michelson interferometer, the FS-820 and FS-720. These employed Mylar beamsplitters and were evacuable. The FS-820 was a large Michelson interferometer covering the 10–$200\,\mathrm{cm}^{-1}$ spectral range and having $0.2\,\mathrm{cm}^{-1}$ resolution. The range could be extended to higher wavenumbers by replacing the quartz detector window with a diamond window. A polyethylene lens was used as a condenser in front of the Golay cell detector.

The FS-720 was very similar in mechanical construction to the Grubb-Parsons Mark II and NPL cube interferometers (Thorpe *et al.* 1970). It was modular in design and allowed evacuation (Fig. 10.3). The three-inch (7.6-cm) diameter optics were

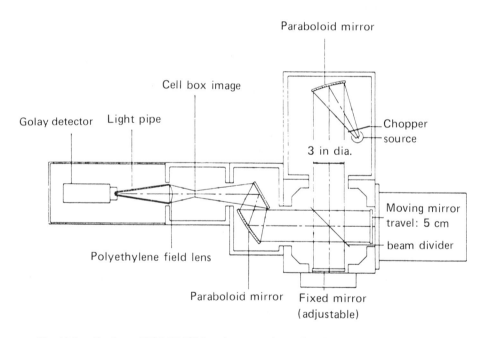

Fig. 10.3 — Beckman-RIIC FS-720 interferometer (reproduced by permission of Beckman-RIIC Ltd).

completely reflective, and the instrument used a Golay cell detector. The 10–$500\,\mathrm{cm}^{-1}$ range was covered with $0.1\,\mathrm{cm}^{-1}$ resolution. Unlike the Grubb-Parsons instruments, the Beckman designs included a separate sample compartment and optical filter wheel for selective filtering. The beam through the interferometer was also collimated instead of divergent.

R. Milward joined the company in 1963 and developed a lamellar interferometer system, the LR-100 (Milward 1969). The interferometer is shown in Fig. 10.4. The

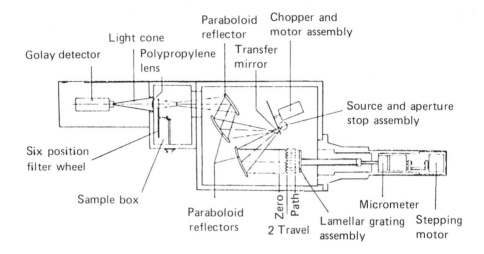

Fig. 10.4 — Beckman RIIC LR-100 lamellar interferometer (reproduced by permission of Beckman-RIIC Ltd).

LR-100 operated in the 3–80 cm^{-1} range, where Michelson interferometers are relatively inefficient: a Michelson configuration requires two or more beamsplitters to modulate the energy efficiently over this range, and wastes at least 50% of the input radiation by transmitting it back out of the entrance port. As Strong's group had found, the lamellar interferometer is limited at high frequencies by the quality of the lamellar mirrors, which are difficult to make flat, by errors in mirror parallelism during scanning, and diffraction effects.

Fourier transformation of the interferogram was performed by the FTC100 Fourier transform computer. This hybrid analogue–digital computer could handle up to 1024 interferogram points in 12-bit words, and could calculate the ratio of the sample to reference spectrum.

Together, Beckman-RIIC and Grubb-Parsons sold some 300 instruments world-wide by the time they ceased manufacture in the late 1970s. Many of the spectro-meters, updated with newer computers or specialized optical arrangements, are still in use today.

10.3.3 CODERG (Clichy, France; now disbanded)
CODERG (Societé de Conversions des Energies) manufactured a few models of far infrared spectrometer, based on designs of R. Milward.

The first, known as the MIR-2, comprised two cylindrical chambers. One contained the Michelson interferometer, and the second enclosed a configurable sampling optics system.

The later Model 2000, or "Fourierspec" instrument, was also contained within two evacuable chambers (Fig. 10.5). The interferometer section, comprising a Mylar beamsplitter, mercury source, chopper, and flat mirror Michelson interferometer, occupied one chamber. A spectral range of about $10–800\,\mathrm{cm}^{-1}$ was possible. The interferometer could be moved in $10\,\mu m$ steps or continuously scanned, with the mirror position being monitored by a Moiré system.

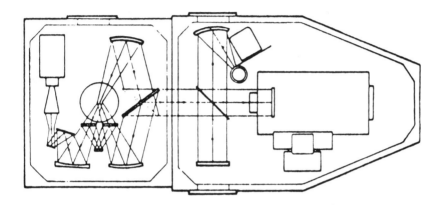

Fig. 10.5 — Coderg interferometer (reproduced by permission of Elsevier Press).

The second chamber contained a sample compartment that could be rearranged by adjusting mirror positions to provide for three types of measurement: reference scans, reflection, and transmittance scans, respectively.

The Model 2000 could be computer-controlled, a feature unusual in commercial instruments of its generation. A particularly innovative characteristic was the capability of real-time observation of the spectrum as it was collected: a Varian 620/i minicomputer incrementally calculated a classical Fourier transform of the interferogram as it was gradually extended through the scan, showing the result on an oscilloscope. Up to 1500 spectral points could be transformed in 1.9 sec. This sort of real-time improvement in resolution has not been employed in most other commercial instruments, owing to the much higher data and calculation overhead for modern rapid-scanning spectrometers. Such a real-time display of the spectrum is nevertheless very useful for indicating the quality of the measurement, and also for convincingly showing the relationship between optical path difference and resolution.

The CODERG Model 2000 was controlled by the operator's instructions to the computer for either (1) single or double beam operation; (2) spectral range; (3) interval between spectral points; (4) total number of points; (4) stepped or continuous scanning; and, (5) apodizing function.

For those users who had other means of data reduction, the Model 2000 was available with standard paper-tape output.

A more advanced instrument, the Model 4000, replaced the flat interferometers by "cat's eye mirrors" (consisting of a focusing primary mirror and a secondary mirror to retrace the path); these made the interferometer insensitive to tilt errors. The interferometer beamsplitter was oriented for 30° incidence, instead of 45° as for the Model 2000, and four Mylar thicknesses could be mounted on a rotatable wheel. The sampling chamber was in other respects similar to the Model 2000. Both instruments had a maximum resolution of 0.05 cm^{-1}.

Like its earlier competitors, CODERG ceased manufacture of FTIR spectrometers in the late 1970s.

The technology implemented in these designs was rather similar. Despite the field being so new, the commercial instruments trod nearly the same path. The reason for the similarity was in large part due to the handful of individuals who had seeded these pioneer companies' efforts. The designs nevertheless represented a clear step forward from the systems developed at Johns Hopkins: they employed motor drives for the interferometer movement, and a small dedicated computer for Fourier transformation.

10.4   A TYPICAL LATE-1960s IMPLEMENTATION

A routine infrared spectrum was rather more laborious to obtain by the Fourier transform technique than by the dispersive spectrometers of the day. However, only FTIR provided adequate sensitivity for the best quality far infrared work.

To prevent absorption of infrared light by water vapour, the spectrometer and sample chamber were evacuated by a vacuum pump. "Purging" of the instrument with dry air or nitrogen was seldom adequate to remove all traces of moisture.

10.4.1   Infrared optics and light pipes

For measurements on samples that did not conveniently fit into the commercially designed sample enclosures, experimenters often used "light pipes" to channel the modulated light between interferometer, sample, and detector.

Far infrared wavelengths are intermediate between visible light, for which lenses and mirrors are used, and microwaves, for which waveguides are normally employed. With lenses and mirrors, light is refracted or reflected by components having dimensions much larger than a wavelength. So-called "geometrical optics" is used to calculate the result. However, microwaves have much longer wavelengths (typically of the order of millimetres or centimetres). When the wavelength of the radiation is comparable with the dimensions of the instrument, so-called "physical optics" is used in calculations. This takes into account the interaction of the light wave on the scale of a single wavelength, and includes the contributions of interference, diffraction, and absorption. Far infrared optics is concerned with both regimes.

A light pipe is simply a hollow tube with a polished internal surface. It functions much like an optical fibre: once inside, light is repeatedly reflected from the highly-reflecting surface and channeled from input to output.

Unlike an optical fibre, the interior of the tube is empty space, to prevent absorption of the infrared radiation by water vapour. Also unlike a fibre, the reflections at the polished surfaces are not perfect: in an optical fibre, reflection occurs at the interface between two types of glass, the outer cladding having a lower refractive index than the inner core. For shallow angles of incidence, this results in total internal reflection and no losses. In a light pipe, on the other hand, reflection occurs simply from polished metallic surfaces. Each reflection causes a loss of the order of 1% — often much higher if the surfaces are oxidized, pitted, or coated with a thin layer of contaminants such as oil vapour from the vacuum pump. To achieve the best performance, the walls of the light pipe must have an extremely fine surface finish and high reflectance. A surface finish of about 0.1 μm peak-to-peak is required, which is one-hundredth of the infrared wavelength. A reflecting layer of gold is often applied to the walls of the light pipe by evaporation in a vacuum. Despite their rather high scattering and reflectance losses, far infrared light pipes can channel about the same amount of light as a typical lens or mirror optical system.

A convenient feature of light pipes is that light can be concentrated by tapering the tube diameter. It was shown by Williamson (1952) that a tapering light pipe will increasingly condense the rays of light reflecting down it as the diameter decreases, but will also cause the rays to reflect at angles closer to perpendicular incidence. In fact, for rays entering at too large an angle, a conical light pipe will cause the light to be reflected back out of the entrance aperture. A tapered light pipe thus acts simultaneously as an optical energy concentrator, ray disperser, and component to limit the field of view. Light pipes constructed of copper tubing and light cones formed from moulded alloy on mandrel formers are frequently combined to direct far infrared light into sample and detector cryostats.

10.4.2 Experimental procedure

The slow-scanning interferometer was prepared by verifying the optical alignment. The detector signal, traced on a chart recorder, was used to locate the zero path position (where the signal peak occurs). The alignment of the interferometer mirrors was adjusted to maximize the signal. Next, any other optics used between the interferometer, sample chamber and detector were adjusted to peak the signal. Finally, the moving mirror drive was sometimes adjusted to ensure that one of the mirror steps fell exactly on zero path difference. If this was done, the interferogram was assured of being approximately symmetric, which allowed a simple cosine Fourier transform to be performed. This requires half the computer memory and computation time (both in short supply) of the more general complex Fourier transform (details of Fourier transformation are discussed in the next Section). Once aligned, the moving mirror was set back beyond zero path difference by running the stepping-motor drive backwards. A further few steps forward removed any "back-lash" caused by loosely-meshing gear teeth in the drive.

The interferometer and data collection were operated independently of the computer. A simple mechanical or cam-operated sequencer or interlinked timers would usually be employed for the succession of actions required: to step the moving mirror to a new position (via a pulse to a stepping motor); wait a "dead" time for vibrations to die out; enable a "gating" time in which the electronics integrated the detector signal; record the integrated signal on paper tape; and, finally, move on to the next mirror position, and clear the signal buffer. The operator would monitor the signal on the chart recorder, restrain associates from banging doors in the vicinity, avoid turning on or off any equipment that might introduce a "glitch" in the detector signal, and stop the sequencer when the mirror had travelled the desired distance past ZPD.

The detector signal was usually very "noisy", i.e. obscured by random fluctuations. In order to improve the signal quality, the light source was "chopped" by a rotating disk. The resulting AC signal was then electrically filtered to remove frequencies different from the chopping frequency. In addition, so-called phase synchronous detection was employed to amplify only the portion of the signal in phase with the chopping disk.

The filtered signal from the interferometer detector was converted into digital form and punched on paper tape by a teletype machine. This paper tape was then fed to a paper tape reader for input to the computer memory.

A typical minicomputer used for FTIR spectrometers contained 4K words (four kilowords, or 4096 words) of memory, with which a 1024 or 2048 point spectrum could be calculated.

A simple program loaded the data from paper tape into memory, performed a fast-Fourier transformation, and then plotted the resulting spectrum on an oscilloscope screen. The spectral intensities could also be printed out or punched on paper tape.

Inevitably, mechanical shocks or thermal changes to the light source during the experiment caused the interferogram to have spikes, discontinuities or gradual drifts. Some of these could be edited from the data by altering the numbers in the computer and punching a new paper tape. For subtle distortions to the interferogram, the only solution was to repeat the experiment or to average several interferograms together. This was performed by acquiring the respective paper tapes and loading them one by one into the computer, which used a simple program to sum the corresponding points.

In order to obtain the final spectrum, the measurement process was repeated without the sample in place. The sample spectrum was then divided by the reference spectrum to yield a result independent of instrument characteristics. Unfortunately, the need to make two measurement runs separated by minutes or hours, and including opening and re-evacuation of the interferometer or sample chamber, often allowed only qualitative spectra to be obtained. Over the necessary time period, any number of changes could and did occur, including unequal evacuation pressures, light source fluctuations, misalignment of the interferometer mirrors or step position, and detector changes.

10.5   THE FAST FOURIER TRANSFORM

The practicality of Fourier spectroscopy had, since its inception, been limited by the computation time of the spectrum. Fellgett (1958) continued to use Lipson–Beevers strips, the manual calculation aid for approximating the Fourier transform that was by then twenty years old. Most other investigators through the 1950s preferred analogue computers or frequency analysers, because the few digital computers available were prohibitively expensive. The digital computer, too, was slow. The transition from vacuum tubes to transistors in computers improved reliability and reduced operating cost, but did not significantly change life for the Fourier spectroscopist. Even though the throughput and multiplex advantages allowed the interferometer to make measurements more quickly and with better quality than a conventional spectrometer, the subsequent Fourier transformation was usually much slower than the scanning of the spectrum by a dispersive spectrometer. Experimenters using Fourier spectroscopy were in the incongruous position of making spectroscopic measurements in minutes, but taking hours or days to decode the results.

The Fourier transform seems designed to conspire against high resolution measurements. The algorithm requires about n^2 operations to be performed to calculate an n-point spectrum. Doubling the number of points in a spectrum thus requires four times as many calculations. Spectra of a few hundred points were calculated in the late 1950s; by the early 1960s this had risen to a few thousand points, requiring about one hundred times more calculation. The improvement had been made possible by the increase in computation speed of newer computers. However, extension to spectra of tens of thousands of points was virtually impossible, as the calculations would have required computer time measured in days rather than minutes. Paul Richards (1964), favourably comparing Fourier spectroscopy to dispersive methods, was pessimistic about its usefulness for near infrared measurement:

> We feel that...interferometric spectroscopy with numerical Fourier transformation is currently the best spectroscopic technique in the far-infrared. Except for weak-source experiments, however, this is not necessarily true at higher frequencies. Large computing times are required to obtain resolution comparable with that obtained from grating monochromators in the near infrared...If we choose a sampling interval such that $\sigma_{max} = 10\,000$ cm^{-1}, then it would take ≈ 0.4 hr on an IBM-7094 for our program to compute one resolution width of the spectrum and its normalization. The cost...is of the order of one hundred dollars per resolution width.

The plateau in resolution and spectral range was unexpectedly broken in the mid 1960s when a new way of calculating the Fourier transform was discovered. The so-called "fast Fourier transform" (FFT) is a very efficient mathematical procedure (algorithm) for calculating the discrete Fourier transform.

The algorithm was published by James Cooley and John Tukey in 1965. Historical researches by Cooley and others, and more recently by Heideman *et al.* (1985), have shown that the technique has a long and obscure lineage, having been invented in part, forgotten and reinvented by several independent researchers. An algorithm very similar to the FFT of Cooley and Tukey was originated by Carl Friedrich Gauss in an unpublished manuscript of 1805.

The convoluted path to the FFT may ironically have been aggravated by the specialized popularity of the Fourier transform. Fourier used his technique of "harmonic analysis" from 1807 for problems of heat conduction. Lord Kelvin applied the method decades later for the analysis of daily temperature variations. Others employed it for calculating the variations in sea tides. The various disciplines that used Fourier transformation had poor communication with each other. This remained true even when Cooley and Tukey published their algorithm: it was a year before practitioners discovered the implications of the method for Fourier spectroscopy (Forman 1966).

Instead of the n^2 operations needed previously to compute an n-point spectrum, the FFT needs only about $n(\log_2 n)$ operations. Thus, a 100-point spectrum by conventional methods requires 10 000 operations but only 660 operations by the FFT, a fifteen-fold improvement. The advantage is greater for spectra with more points: a 1000 point spectrum is calculated some 100 times faster, and a 10 000 point spectrum about 1000 times faster. Fourier transformation of an 8000-point interferogram that would have required an hour with the conventional algorithm takes a few seconds on the same computer. By the early 1970s the first million-point spectrum had been calculated by the FFT (Michel 1972).

The FFT provides exactly the same result as the conventional Fourier transform, but has one additional requirement: where the conventional FT can accept and transform any number of input points, the FFT is limited to a power of 2 (this is actually a practical rather than a fundamental requirement: although other powers can be used, the binary system is particularly convenient to program on digital computers, and has been used universally). The FFT must therefore be carried out on interferograms of 16, 32, 64,...2048, 4096..., 2^n points. If the interferogram has a different number of points, it must either be truncated or "filled out" to the next largest power of two. A 900 point interferogram would thus be extended with zeroes (i.e. the average value of the interferogram) to 1024 points, and would yield a 1024 point spectrum. Besides being a necessity for using the FFT algorithm, "zero-filling" had a practical advantage: it gave more spectral points for the same number of observations, and so gave an accurately interpolated spectrum. This interpolation does not increase the spectral resolution, which is determined solely by the maximum optical path difference of the interferogram, but is nonetheless useful when sharp spectral features are recorded. Even with the FFT algorithm, Fourier transformation is a numerically intensive and time consuming calculation, though. Zero-filling is usually kept to the minimum possible, and spectral interpolation is performed by more efficient methods.

10.6 METHODS OF PHASE CORRECTION

The Fourier transform of an arbitrary function is complex: that is, it consists of a real and an imaginary part. The real part corresponds to the symmetrical component of the original function (the portion that can be built up from cosine waves). The imaginary part of the Fourier transform corresponds to the antisymmetrical component (the portion composed of sine waves). In Fourier spectroscopy, an ideal interferometer produces an interferogram that is perfectly symmetrical about the zero path position of the mirror: that is, it looks identical whether the mirror is moved forwards or backwards from ZPD. This implies that it can be decomposed into a series of cosine waves. The amplitude of each frequency of cosine wave in the interferogram corresponds to one frequency in the spectrum. The Fourier transform of such an interferogram has only a real part, (the imaginary part is equal to zero).

In a non-ideal, real-world interferometer, various imperfections lead to asymmetric interferograms (the subject of asymmetric interferometry is discussed further in Section 17.2). The asymmetry is due to the two arms of the interferometer having different characteristics. One arm includes extra transparent material which shifts the phase of light travelling through it. The most common source of this extra material is a beamsplitter and compensator plate of unequal thickness. The result of such phase distortion is that the interferogram consists not only of cosine wave components, but also sine wave components. The complex Fourier transform of the interferogram then has two parts: a real part and an imaginary part due to the antisymmetric components.

As the imaginary part of the Fourier transform is due to imperfections of the interferometer, it contains no useful experimental information about the light source or sample. However, the existence of a non-zero imaginary component means that the real component is distorted; only a perfectly symmetric interferogram can directly provide an undistorted spectrum. Given an imperfect interferometer, it is therefore necessary to correct the data for phase distortion. Three general methods have been used for phase correction: magnitude calculation, and techniques due to Mertz and Forman.

10.6.1 Magnitude calculation

The easiest way of correcting for phase errors is to first calculate the Fourier transform of the interferogram. This will give a complex function having real and imaginary components. In practice, by performing a Fourier transformation of the set of interferogram points digitized by the instrument, two new sets of points, the cosine and sine transforms, will be obtained. These can be denoted $Re(\sigma)$ and $Im(\sigma)$, respectively. The desired phase-corrected spectrum is simply the magnitude of the complex function:

$$\text{Corrected spectrum at frequency } \sigma = \{Re(\sigma)^2 + Im(\sigma)^2\}^{1/2} \qquad (10.1)$$

As to be expected from the easiest method, there are a few drawbacks. Suppose, for example, that the intensity of the light source is zero in some spectral region. The spectrum will then be zero, with some superimposed noise from the measurement process. As shown above, the calculated spectrum is a quantity always equal to or greater than zero. This means that if the measurement results in noise fluctuating around the 0% line of the spectrum, the magnitude spectrum will distort this to appear as noise always greater than zero. Measurements near 0% will thus be shifted to higher apparent values, resulting in poor performance with highly absorbing samples or weak light sources. This nonlinearity of the intensity scale is the most important technical drawback of the magnitude spectrum method of phase correction.

The second criticism of this technique is that it requires the interferogram to be measured on both sides of zero path difference. This double-sided interferogram requires a longer scan mechanism, at least twice the scan time, more memory space, and longer calculation time than a single-sided interferogram. These factors are becoming less important with the availability of cheaper memory and faster computers, but were serious limitations in the early days of the FFT.

10.6.2   Mertz phase correction

Lawrence Mertz (1967) proposed a more efficient scheme for correcting phase errors, involving correction of the distorted amplitude spectrum by the phase spectrum. The process can be itemized as follows:

(1) Measure the interferogram for a short distance on one side of ZPD, and a long distance on the other side. The length of the long side is determined by the resolution desired. The length of the short side is just long enough to calculate a low-resolution phase spectrum.
(2) Calculate the phase spectrum from the short double-sided portion of the interferogram, i.e. calculate the complex Fourier transform from the interferogram points available on both sides of ZPD.
(3) Calculate the amplitude spectrum (i.e. the real, cosine Fourier transform) from the long single-sided portion of the interferogram.
(4) Use the phase spectrum to correct the amplitude spectrum.

The advantages of the Mertz method are that an entire double-sided interferogram need not be measured, thereby saving measurement time; only a real Fourier transform is calculated on most of the data, saving calculation time, and, most importantly, the intensity scale of the spectrum is not distorted as in the magnitude calculation method. The Mertz method uses a simple algorithm giving fast computation. A disadvantage of the technique is that the phase spectrum must be very accurately calculated in order to correct the phase errors properly. If the phase spectrum is too noisy, for example, the resulting spectrum may still be partially distorted. This situation can be avoided by measuring more points on the "short" side of the interferogram. Another possibility (for interferometers that are sufficiently stable over periods of hours) is to measure the phase spectrum by using a bright light source unobstructed by an attenuating sample, and storing this for subsequent correction of weaker measurements.

10.6.3   Forman phase correction

Michael Forman, who first applied the fast Fourier transform to Fourier spectroscopy, also quickly devised a phase correction method still used today. The Forman method is mathematically equivalent to the Mertz method, but has some practical differences.

In the Forman method, the phase correction is done on the interferogram rather than on the spectrum. The steps can be summarized as follows:

(1) Measure an interferogram having one short side and one long side, as in the Mertz method.
(2) Calculate the complex Fourier transform of the points on either side of ZPD to compute the phase spectrum. This step is identical to the Mertz method.
(3) Calculate the inverse Fourier transform of the phase correction.

(4) Convolve the resulting set of data points with the data points of the interferogram. Convolution is a mathematical operation in which two data sets are offset, multiplied point by point, and added together to yield each output point. Each succeeding output point is obtained by offsetting the data by one point and repeating the multiplication and addition process.

(5) Calculate the cosine Fourier transform of the output data set.

The convolution procedure is relatively slow, because it requires repeated multiplications of all the data. The Forman method therefore is usually slower than the Mertz method. The advantage of the Forman technique is that the convolution process can also perform other manipulations on the data. Convolution is the principle behind digital filtering, a numerical method of removing or altering the relative intensities of frequencies in a spectrum or interferogram. By multiplying the phase correction function by another filtering function, spectra can be further tailored. The most important application is to limit the spectrum to a narrow spectral region to reduce calculation time for the FFT. This technique is used, for example, in the Bomem DA3 spectrometer system, in which a purpose-developed "vector processor" is used to perform both the convolution and FFT calculations.

10.7 DISPERSIVE *vs.* FOURIER SPECTROMETERS

The promulgation of the Fellgett and Jacquinot advantages in the early 1950s, followed by experimental demonstrations culminating in the Connes' superb results, did not convince the bulk of practicing spectroscopists of the superiority of FTIR.

Several of the pioneers in Fourier spectroscopy have reported that publication of their work in traditional forums such as *The Journal of the Optical Society of America* was difficult; newer periodicals such as *Applied Optics* (launched in 1960) were much more open to the new technology. The exotic nature of FTIR discouraged many practicing spectroscopists. Gerard Kuiper, of the Lunar and Planetary Laboratory of the University of Arizona, had measured the best planetary spectra using dispersive spectrometers prior to the Connes. In the *Communications of the Lunar and Planetary Laboratory* about 1962, he published a report "proving conclusively" that Fourier spectroscopy could not deliver on its promise even in principle. Lawrence Mertz (1991) relates how Kuiper was converted to the multiplex method:

> Gerard Kuiper...had denounced FTS. In a letter to Kuiper I urged him to reconsider his position. In the meantime Harold Johnson (also of U. Arizona) had Fred Forbes come to visit me to try out my interferometer. Fred borrowed the interferometer and smuggled it on board the Convair 990 that Kuiper was using for planetary IR spectroscopy. When the dispersive instrument malfunctioned Fred substituted the interferometer and the results led to an about-face by Kuiper, who then became a staunch proponent of FTS. It is to Kuiper's credit that he did not stonewall the issue.

Chemists, too, initially ignored Fourier spectroscopy as a practical technique. The editor of the text *Applied Infrared Spectroscopy* (Kendall 1966) made clear his expectations for spectroscopic technology, relegating interferometric methods to a single paragraph:

> With the commercial introduction of gratings as dispersing means (about 1959), their use has come to the fore and they will in time largely replace prisms. Currently, however, a vast amount of "spade work" needs doing to uncover and correlate with molecular structure the "new" absorption bands provided in infrared absorption spectra through the use of gratings. It will be several decades at least before prism infrared instruments are obsolete...
>
> An instrument using the interferometer principle has been developed and is available commercially. The interferometer supplies an interferogram with the data on punched paper tape. A standard transmission spectrum can be derived from this by submitting the punched tape data to the operations of a large size digital computer.

The major spectrometer companies had, over the preceding decade, introduced dispersive spectrometers covering the entire infrared range. The Beckman IR11 worked from 800 to 33 cm^{-1} (12.5–300 µm); the Grubb-Parsons GM3, to 65 cm^{-1} (154 µm); and, the Perkin-Elmer 301, to 14 cm^{-1} (714 µm). These highly-evolved instruments were complex compared with Fourier spectrometers. For example, the P-E 301, introduced in 1961, incorporated five diffraction gratings, two light sources, and over a dozen filters to cover the range from 15 to 400 µm (Martin 1966). Its far infrared coverage was won micron by micron: between 100 and 25 µm, six filter changes were required, with some segments only a few microns wide. Such instruments could be made to work, but were clearly near the limits of technology for dispersive instrumentation. Chantry (1971) summarized the situation:

> Interferometric methods were slow to win general acceptance because of essentially irrational objections to a computer based spectroscopic system. Basically spectroscopists wanted submillimetre spectrometers that had the same comforting shape and type of operation as their familiar mid-infrared instruments. Emotional forces of this type met a response from the instrument manufacturers who produced wonderfully complex feats of engineering that enabled them to manufacture automatic double-beam grating spectrophotometers covering the far infrared to as low as 33 cm^{-1}. Not surprisingly, these instruments are extremely expensive.

As late as 1969, physicists debated the superiority of Fourier spectrometers in a special issue of *Applied Optics*. Pierre Jacquinot (1969) showed that while Fourier spectroscopy was undoubtedly superior for certain classes of problems, there were grey zones of experimentation where either technique might be preferable.

For example, in the far infrared (where Fourier methods first got their start), the lack of beamsplitters having good properties over a wide spectral band limits the number of spectral elements. A similar situation holds for certain studies in the absorption spectra of solids, where transmitting "windows" are narrow.

There were situations where dispersive spectrometers were clearly preferred. For simple problems, the requirements can be so low that even the simplest and cheapest existing instruments are adequate. Fourier techniques are not worth the trouble. Secondly, certain problems call for monochromatic measurements, where a dispersive instrument has the advantage. Where a Fourier spectrometer would be forced to repeatedly measure and calculate a spectrum (albeit perhaps a narrow-bandwidth spectrum), a prism or grating spectrometer could be simply set to a fixed wavelength to obtain a continuous analogue recording of transmittance *vs.* time.

The Jacquinot advantage, too, can be reduced in some situations. In far infrared spectroscopy, high resolution is frequently unimportant. In this case — combining low resolution with small wavenumber — the allowable solid angle through the interferometer becomes much larger than can practicably be used. Experimental results therefore fall far short of theory.

The throughput and multiplex advantages can, of course, be traded for reduced measurement time. Because of this, an experimenter desiring only modest spectral resolution might opt for a much quicker measurement than would be possible by dispersive spectroscopy. But as Jacquinot pointed out, "some people might reasonably think that a gain of a few hours of recording in a quiet laboratory with stable sources is negligible compared with the time devoted to the use of theoretical interpretation of spectra and is not worth making a complete change in their habits and acquiring or building new equipment." Psychology, and not just theory, had a part to play in the choice between dispersive and Fourier spectroscopy.

Alistair Gebbie (1969) discussed arguments against FTIR that were current in the 1960s. Spectroscopists initially complained that "people won't wait for their spectra to come out of a computer", yet many were enthusiastic to digitize their spectra for computer manipulation. This process is inherently less direct and accurate in conventional dispersive spectrometers than in FTIR instruments: dispersives employ some form of mechanical linkage for the wavelength drive, and do not benefit from the "Connes advantage" of an accurate laser-referenced frequency scale.

A second argument against Fourier spectroscopy (and a myth that was current well into the 1970s) was that the technique was deficient in its ability to give intensity information. Chemists and many physicists mistrusted FTIR for quantitative analysis. There were several reasons for this belief. Fourier spectrometers were single-beam instruments. The slow-scanning interferometer acquired separate sample and reference spectra as much as hours apart. During this time interval, the infrared source could vary in output, a mechanical shock could misalign the optics of the interferometer, or electronic gains could change. Any or all of these factors distorted the interferogram and resulting spectrum. The ratio of two such single-beam spectra was usually unreliable in intensity.

Another reason to mistrust FTIR for quantitative analysis was that spectroscopists new to the technique took insufficient notice of the increased energies available. The much increased throughput and dynamic range of the Fourier spectrometer demand that the detector and amplifier combination should have much better linearity than the equivalent signal chain in a dispersive spectrometer. If not, the spectrum will be distorted in intensity and unreliable for accurate transmittance or absorbance measurements.

Gebbie showed that all forms of spectrometer were simply variations on a theme. The two-beam Michelson interferometer represents one extreme, while the prism spectrometer in effect uses an infinite number of beams. The grating spectrometer is an important intermediate case, using a number of beams equal to the number of grooves in the grating surface.

A prism spectrometer directs each spectral frequency to a unique angle, thereby providing a convenient spectral presentation. A grating spectrometer does slightly worse: it separates the spectrum into several orders which must be separated by filters or a pre-monochromator. The Michelson interferometer sorts out the spectral frequencies as superposed cosine waves — an encoded representation. The spectral resolution is poorest in the prism instrument and best in the interferometer, but the amount of data processing required is in the opposite order.

As pointed out by several authors, a diffraction grating is a highly precise device which must be constructed to very high mechanical tolerances. To construct a 25-cm square grating with 4000 lines per cm, a groove over 30 km long must be ruled having a deviation of less than a millionth of an inch (0.025 μm). Once manufactured, the grating could be replicated to make good copies, and needed only to be kept clean. The Michelson interferometer, on the other hand, has to meet high mechanical tolerances for each and every scan.

Kneubuhl (1969), a proponent of grating spectrometry, showed examples where a far infrared Fourier spectrometer fell far short of its theoretical performance. A good grating instrument was able to give comparable results. Nevertheless, he itemized the difficulties of using grating spectrometers in the far infrared:

(1) Large diffraction gratings with at least 15 cm×15 cm size are required;
(2) The optical path must be evacuated to better than 10^{-3} mm Hg;
(3) Golay cells must be replaced by liquid-Helium-cooled solid-state detectors such as Ge bolometers or InSb or GaAs detectors;
(4) Stray light must be avoided in the optical path by proper geometric optics and not by absorbers;
(5) Gaseous and chemical spectroscopy require double beam spectrometers, while for spectroscopy of liquids and solids single beam instruments are sufficient or even advantageous.

Kneubuhl noted several deficiencies of Michelson interferometers:

> The advantages of Fourier spectroscopy over grating spectroscopy are seriously impaired in the far ir and in the submillimeter wave region. The relatively small ratio of apparatus dimension to wavelength, the relatively large dimensions of thermal sources, and the low intensity emitted lead to poor optics for the spectrometers working in this region. The detectors usually possess a small solid angle area product which reduces the Jacquinot advantage. In addition far ir and submillimeterwave beam splitters show narrowband characteristics, which means beam splitters of Michelson inter-ferometers must be interchangeable for every octave. Therefore only lamellar grating interferometers can be applied for broadband spectroscopy.

In spite of such criticism, by 1970 the theoretical superiority of FTIR over grating and prism spectrometers was generally established. The technique was still viewed with great mistrust by chemists, however. FTIR was restricted mainly to far infrared problems; it was suspect for quantitative analysis; and, there was no commercial model as easy to use as a dispersive spectrometer.

A further decade was to elapse before analytical chemists began to warm to FTIR as a competitor and successor to dispersive spectrometers.

Table 10.1 — Features common to Fourier spectrometers of the 1960s

Golay cell detector
Spherical mirror, lens and/or light pipe optics
Scanning by the periodic rotation of a micrometer screw by a stepper motor
Signal filtering by an amplifier tuned to the modulation produced by a light chopper
Paper tape or magnetic tape data recording
Moiré fringe position reference
Minicomputer with 4Kbyte memory for control and analysis
Oscilloscope display of spectrum

REFERENCES

Beer, R. and Cayford, A. H. (1967), An Investigation of a Fundamental Intensity Error in Fourier Spectroscopy, *J. Phys.*, **28**, Suppl. 3-4, 34.
Bell, R. J. (1972), *Introductory Fourier Transform Spectroscopy*, Academic Press, New York.
Chantry, G. W. (1971), *Submillimetre Spectroscopy*, Academic Press, London.
Connes, J. and Connes, P. (1966), Near-Infrared Planetary Spectra by Fourier Spectroscopy. I. Instruments and Results, *J. Opt. Soc. Am.*, **56**, 896.
Cooley, J. W. and Tukey, J. W. (1965), An Algorithm for the Machine Computation of Complex Fourier Series, *Math. Comput.*, **19**, 297.
Dunn, S. T. (1978), Fourier transform infrared spectrometers: their recent history, current status, and commercial future, *Appl. Opt.*, **17**, 1367.
Fellgett, P. (1958), On numerical Fourier transformation with special reference to Lipson–Beevers strips, *J. Sci. Instr.*, **35**, 7.
Finch, A., Gates, P. N., Radcliffe, K., Dickson, F. N. and Bentley, F. F. (1970), *Chemical Applications of Far Infrared Spectroscopy*, Academic Press, London.
Forman, M. L. (1966), Correction of Asymmetric Interferograms Obtained in Fourier Spectroscopy, *J. Opt. Soc. Am.*, **56**, 59.
Forman, M. L. (1966), Fast Fourier-Transform Technique and Its Application to Fourier Spectroscopy, *J. Opt. Soc. Am.*, **56**, 978.
Gast, J. and Genzel, L. (1973), An Amplitude Fourier Spectrometer for Infrared Solid State Spectroscopy, *Opt. Comm.*, **8**, 26.
Gebbie, H. A. (1969), Fourier Transform *vs.* Grating Spectroscopy, *Appl. Opt.*, **8**, 501.
Grechushnikov, B. N., Disler, G. I. and Petrov, I. P. (1963), A Fourier Spectrometer with Filters, *Sov. Phys. Cryst.*, **8**, 367.
Heideman, M. T., Johnson, D. H. and Burrus, C. S. (1985), Gauss and the History of the Fast Fourier Transform, *Archive for the History of Exact Sciences*, **34**, 265.
Hoffman, J. E. and Vanasse, G. A. (1966), Real-Time Spectral Synthesis in Fourier Spectroscopy, *Appl. Opt.*, **5**, 1167.
Jacquinot, P. (1969), Interferometry and Grating Spectroscopy: An Introductory Survey, *Appl. Opt.*, **8**, 497.
Kendall, D. N. (ed.) (1966), *Applied Infrared Spectroscopy*, Reinhold, London.
Kneubuhl, F. (1969), Diffraction Grating Spectroscopy, *Appl. Opt.*, **8**, 505.
Kneubuhl, F. K., Moser, J.-F. and Steffen, H. (1966), High Resolution Grating Spectrometer for the Far Infrared, *J. Opt. Soc. Am.*, **56**, 760.
Loewenstein, E. V. (1966), The History and Current Status of Fourier Transform Spectroscopy, *Appl. Opt.*, **5**, 845.

Martin, A. E. (1966), *Infra-Red Instrumentation and Techniques*, Elsevier, Amsterdam.

Mertz, L. (1967), Auxiliary Computation for Fourier Spectrometry, *Infr. Phys.*, **7**, 17.

Mertz, L. (1991), personal communication, 29 January.

Milward, R. C. (1969), A Small Lamellar Grating Interferometer for the Very Far-Infrared, *Infr. Phys.*, **9**, 59.

Richards, P. L. (1964), High-Resolution Fourier Transform Spectroscopy in the Far-Infrared, *J. Opt. Soc. Am.*, **54**, 1474.

Vanasse, G. and Sakai, H. (1967), Fourier Spectroscopy, in *Progress in Optics VI*, Wolf, E. (ed.), North-Holland, Amsterdam.

Thorpe, L. W., Neale, D. J. and Hayward, G. C. (1970), New instrumentation for far infrared Fourier spectrophotometers, *Aspen International Conference on Fourier Spectroscopy*, Vanasse, G. A., Stair, A. T. and Baker, D. J. (eds), AFCRL-71-0019, p. 187.

Williamson, D. E. (1952), Cone Channel Condenser Optics, *J. Opt. Soc. Am.*, **42**, 712.

Yoshinaga, H., Fujita, S., Minami, S., Suemoto, Y., Inoue. M., Chiba, K., Nakano, K., Yoshida, S. and Sugimori, H. (1966), A Far Infrared Interferometric Spectrometer with a Special Electronic Computer, *Appl. Opt.*, **5**, 1159.

11

Rapid-scanning interferometers

Surprisingly, although the first practical FTIR system had been demonstrated in the United States, commercial designs appeared there relatively late. Block Associates (Cambridge, USA) had produced interferometers under government contract, but brought out the first commercial version only in 1966.

The origins of rapid-scanning interferometry centre on Lawrence Mertz and Block Associates. As described in Chapter 8, Mertz had developed a far infrared polarizing interferometer while at Baird Associates. After military service and some graduate studies (during which his work in Fourier spectroscopy was rejected by Harvard University as a subject unsuitable for a PhD), Mertz joined the fledgeling Block Associates as vice-president. Two of the company founders, Myron Block and Neils Young, had been with Mertz at Baird Associates.

Digilab was later founded as the commercial division of Block Associates; succeeding interferometers appeared under its name. The Block and Digilab interferometers were different from all preceding designs because they used the technique of "rapid-scanning".

11.1 PRINCIPLES

The method of rapid-scan Fourier spectroscopy is considerably different from the slow-scan technique and, in many ways, is more elegant. As Mertz (1969) described it, in justifying patent claims:

> The term "rapid" does have distinct connotations such as the elimination of auxiliary modulators and phase-sensitive amplifiers, the use of standard audiofrequency electronic equipment including tape recorders, and over-stepping atmospheric-scintillation frequencies ...
>
> It is the reciprocal drive to obtain repetitive interferograms that I believed, and still believe, to be the novel patentable feature: the essence of the patent. The words "reciprocal mirror" appear prominently in each and every claim of the patent. Rapid scanning would be impotent without the reciprocable feature.

Perhaps it is a matter of opinion whether the reciprocal drive is an obvious and trivial procedure to apply. It certainly was not obvious to me at the time, since eight years of diligent research had elapsed between Fellgett's thesis and my conception of the reciprocal drive.

The patent, incidentally, was not granted, principally because of a delay of fourteen months (rather than the limit of twelve) between publishing a paper at a 1960 Optical Society of America meeting and in filing the patent claim.

A block diagram of a rapid-scan interferometer is shown in Fig. 11.1. The differences from slow-scan technology can be seen by comparing it with Fig. 10.1. In rapid-scan FTIR, the light source, which is not chopped, passes directly into the interferometer. The interferometer mirror scans so that the optical path difference changes rapidly. As the mirror moves, the fringe intensity on the detector changes quickly. For example, a monochromatic light source would produce a sinusoidally varying intensity; this, in turn, would yield a sinusoidally varying detector signal. The scanning typically generates a detector signal in the audio range (from tens of Hz to hundreds or thousands of Hz). For mid-infrared work, this implies a mirror movement of a few millimetres per second.

Each frequency in the light source modulates the detector signal at a frequency proportional to the speed of mirror movement. The interferogram is scanned in a few tens of seconds (or minutes, for extremely long path differences or low mirror speeds). Because such a rapid scan may not provide adequate measuring time for acceptable signal quality, the scans are usually repeated and averaged. "Co-adding" or coherent addition, consists of summing the corresponding points of successive interferograms, and then performing a Fourier transform on the result.

The detector must respond spectrally to all wavelengths being analysed, but also to all modulation frequencies generated by the interferometer. Electrical frequencies above or below this are generally filtered out so as not to contribute to measurement noise. The need for a relatively large electrical bandwidth (fast-response detectors) contrasts with the situation for slow-scan interferometry, where the detector is used at almost DC frequencies.

The waveform is usually "sampled", i.e. digitized and stored in computer memory, in synchrony with fringe peaks from a laser beam. The end result is identical to slow-scan FTIR: a measurement of the interferogram intensity at regular intervals of optical path difference.

The rapid scanning makes the measurement less sensitive to transitory effects. Anything occurring on a time scale longer than one scan is essentially invisible and does not perturb the measurement.

By omission of the chopper disk and settling time, the observation efficiency is more than doubled, thereby improving S/N or measurement speed.

11.2   THE ANALOGUE-TO-DIGITAL CONVERTER

The ADC is an electronic device used to convert an analogue signal into a digital representation that can be used by a microprocessor.

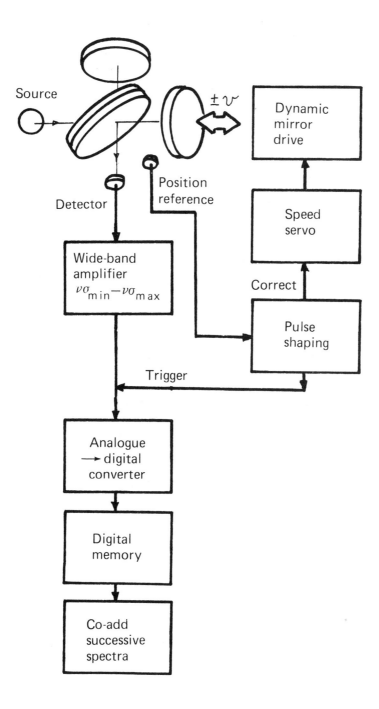

Fig. 11.1 — Block diagram of a rapid-scanning Fourier spectrometer. Note that either raw interferograms or spectra may be co-added.

ADCs are characterized primarily by speed and resolution. Speed, in number of conversions per second, can reach hundreds of kHz, and must be adequate to sample at the highest expected modulation frequency. The relationship between the wavenumber σ of light, the rate of change of optical path difference υ (equal to twice the mirror velocity in most interferometers), and the resulting electrical modulation frequency f is:

$$f=\sigma\upsilon \qquad\qquad\qquad (11.1)$$

The ADC speed therefore determines the maximum scan speed υ_{max} and/or the maximum wavenumber σ_{max} in the spectrum that can be analysed.

ADC resolution determines the precision of conversion, and is expressed in bits. A 10-bit ADC resolves $2^{10}=1024$ levels. A wide dynamic range is needed for FTIR, since the interferogram signal varies from a very intense zero-path peak to weak oscillations far from ZPD. Inadequate ADC resolution causes the weak oscillations to be inaccurately digitized; the resulting distortion appears as noise throughout the transformed spectrum.

There are two general types of ADC. For fast data sampling, the "successive approximation" ADC is normally used. The sampling time is short, and conversion speed is fast enough to allow rates of several hundred thousand readings per second at 16 bit resolution. An alternative method is the "dual ramp" or integrating ADC. This type is slower, and samples for a relatively long time. A rate of a few hundred readings per second is usually possible. The analogue-to-digital converter that performs the digitization must have adequate resolution. The scan speed should be selected so that the measurement noise is equal to the least significant bit of the ADC. If the speed is slower, time is wasted; if it is faster, the system is not being used to its full capacity. By keeping the noise at about the level of the smallest ADC increment, the signal will occasionally fluctuate between two digitization levels and so yield a better average.

Typical FTIRs now employ 15- or 16-bit ADCs, with some high-performance applications demanding 20 to 22 bits. Modern ADCs are usually a single integrated circuit or portion of one.

11.3 GAIN RANGING

An alternative to using expensive ADCs with more than 16 bits is gain ranging. In this technique, the instrument controller keeps track of the position of the scan mirror, and boosts the preamplifier gain at one or more precise positions in the scan where the interferogram amplitude is weak. This has the effect of keeping the signal intensity well above the quantization limit of the converter. There are drawbacks, however: the gain factor must be known precisely, and compensated by exactly the same factor in software. If not, a discontinuity appears in the digitized interferogram, leading to spectral distortion or "ghost features" — variations in spectral intensity around strong absorbances.

11.4 EARLY BLOCK ENGINEERING INTERFEROMETERS

Lawrence Mertz relates that publicizing the technology of Fourier spectrometry was difficult. *The Journal of the Optical Society of America* would not accept his papers. Frustrated by the "conservatism of the academic community", he took out a series of half-page advertisements in *J. Opt. Soc. Am.* between 1960 and 1962. These provide some of the only details available on the first Block Associates (later Block Engineering) instruments.

In the first (March 1960), he described rapid-scanning interference spectrometry, noting:

> This technique provides an extremely compact spectroscopic instrument without entrance or exit slits, chopper or phase-sensitive detector. Even more important, it does not require a digital computer for the data reduction; a tape recorder and wave analyser suffice.

In a subsequent advertisement (December 1960) the Block Associates I3S hand-held FTS was described. This compact instrument consisted of interferometer, telescopic fore-optics and sighting scope, all mounted on a rifle-like grip. It covered the 3 to 12-μm range with 50-cm^{-1} resolution.

Eight months later, an advertisement reported the I-4 spectrometers, having 40 cm^{-1} resolution and near- to mid-infrared spectral ranges. The instruments could measure up to 6 interferograms per second (at lower resolution) and were said to provide a gain "of more than 1000 in sensitivity over conventional dispersion spectrometers when used on extended sources." The price for the interferometer and electronic controller was \$4515.00.

Mertz (1991) credits Niels Young with the mechanical engineering and Gerry Wyjntjes with the electrical engineering of the first Block interferometers. As discussed by him (1965) in an early description of the method,

> The success of rapid scanning interferometry depends principally on the engineering of the interferometer and the drive system. The only presently successful example is basically a Michelson interferometer with one mirror mounted on a loudspeaker type transducer. The traditional hangar type construction of interferometers has been replaced by a cube . . . This integral type of construction of the interferometer gives far greater solidity than older designs.

The original Block Engineering rapid-scanning interferometers from about 1960 used this voice-coil mounting of one mirror, although the group tried other schemes involving cam-type mechanisms; these suffered poorer scan-to-scan reproducibility.

The voice-coil scan arrangement was capable of a few scans per second, generating fringe modulation of a few hundred to few thousand Hz.

The modulation frequencies proved to be variable: a constantly changing voltage applied to the scan drive did not generate a proportional movement of the mirror. Because the mirror speed changed through the scan, the range of fringe frequency varied and necessitated the electrical filtering of the detector signal to be wider than optimal. This in turn led to poor noise characteristics.

The problem was partly resolved by applying a "kinked" voltage ramp to the scan mirror drive. This tailored the rate of change of drive voltage through the scan to maintain a more constant speed.

A subsequent improvement was to employ a speed servo-control. In this approach, a reference channel consisting of monochromatic light is passed through a portion of the interferometer, in the same way as for position referencing. For speed control, the signal generated by the monochromatic fringes is compared with a constant-frequency oscillator. Deviations in mirror speed are indicated by proportional changes in the frequency of the monochromatic fringes. Differences in phase between the monochromatic fringes and the oscillator are used to alter the scan drive signal in the sense needed to reduce the discrepancy. With servo-control, the scan motion can be made more uniform and independent of external vibrations.

The interferograms recorded by the Block interferometer were coherently added, point by point, to yield an averaged interferogram. This co-adding process was performed by specially designed electronic hardware, first by the Block Co-Adder and in later versions by a Fabri-Tek Model 1062 BE signal processor. The Fabri-Tek processor could co-add up to 4096 interferogram points, and incorporated a 10-bit analogue-to-digital converter. The resulting averaged interferogram could then be recorded on magnetic or paper tape, for subsequent Fourier transformation by a large computer.

The first Block Engineering data systems were restricted to 1024 words of 12-bit memory with data input via a 10 to 12-bit ADC. This allowed either 1024 or 4096 intensity levels to be recorded. Put another way, it limited the interferogram measurements to 0.1% or 0.025% precision. As described by Dunn (1978):

> The Fourier transform was performed by repeatedly reading the signal-averaged interferogram from the memory at very high speeds and performing an analog frequency analysis on the repetitive waveform. The frequency analysis was then recorded on an x–y recorder as intensity vs. frequency. These systems suffered from a lack of input and output dynamic range, low resolution (20 cm^{-1}) and poor stability. They also lacked any means for ratio recording. The only case where they could win over dispersive spectrometers was for very weak signals, which did not exceed the dynamic range of any system component.

11.5   FIRST DIGILAB SPECTROMETERS

From 1966 to 1968, three American companies — Block Engineering, Nicolet (then known as Fabri-Tek) and Dunn Associates — combined to improve upon the basic

Block interferometer system. These instruments employed a higher quality ADC, an 18-bit memory, and separate detector and interferometer housings. Some thirty systems were sold, mostly to industrial research laboratories (Dunn, 1978).

In 1968, Digilab, a subsidiary of Block Engineering, was formed to develop a commercial FTIR product line. Digilab instruments incorporated newly available technology, and aspects of their design have been incorporated in most succeeding commercial systems. The new technology included:

— the triglycine sulphate (TGS) detector;
— 15-bit analogue-to-digital converter;
— 16-bit minicomputer;
— He–Ne laser;
— rotating-disk memories.

Experience at Block Associates also led to engineering improvements:

— a laser fringe position reference, for accurate sampling of the interferogram;
— an air-bearing drive, for smooth motion of the scan mirror;
— improved gain range at the ADC, for more precise intensity measurements.

The original Digilab Fourier spectrometers were by far the fastest automatic systems on the market in 1970. Single scans could be performed in as little as one second, and a typical spectrum was computed and plotted in less than 30 seconds. The Digilab designs served as the models on which most subsequent interferometers were based. Initially, three versions were sold:

(1) The FTS-14 spectrometer, operating between 10 and 10 000 cm^{-1} with a range of beamsplitters.
(2) The FTS-12 spectrometer, for research between 200 and 10 000 cm^{-1}.
(3) The FTS-16 far infrared spectrometer, for the 10 to 400 cm^{-1} range.

FTS-14

The FTS-14 was the most popular instrument and the first commercial system manufactured by the company. Designed by Raul Curbelo, its Model 296 interferometer employed a scan drive capable of 4 cm displacement at a speed of 1 cm/sec, providing scans of 2 cm^{-1} in 8 seconds (Fig. 11.2). This was later improved to 0.5 cm^{-1} (Chenery and Sheppard 1978).

The position referencing system used two channels: a helium–neon laser channel for producing monochromatic fringes, and a white-light channel for locating the zero path difference peak. These two channels provided the information necessary for accurate sampling of the interferogram and control of scan motor speed (position referencing is described in detail in Section 13.4).

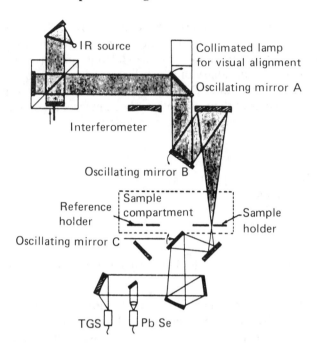

Fig. 11.2 — Digilab FTS-14 Fourier spectrometer (reproduced by permission of Academic Press Inc.).

The optics used a stabilized globar source, maintaining constant output to within 0.2% at $500 \, cm^{-1}$. The beamsplitters were designed for two spectral ranges: the central portion coated for high-wavenumber operation, and the outer annulus for low-wavenumber measurements. Two detectors were employed: a PbSe detector for the near-infrared central portion of the output beam, and a pyroelectric triglycine sulphate (TGS) detector for the mid to far infrared range. The FTS-14 was the first commercial instrument to use this new detector.

After the interferometer, a system of two moving mirrors could be switched to direct the beam to a "sample" area or "reference" area. Between complete scans, the controller redirected the beam to permit either sample or reference interferograms to be recorded.

The interferometer was used with a Data General Corporation Nova minicomputer. The computer did not control the interferometer, which was "free-running". Instead, the operator set the instrument scan conditions such as scan velocity, signal gain, and maximum optical path difference on the optical head controller. The controller managed data collection, sampling and analogue-to-digital conversions. Except for controlling some secondary functions such as setting the diameter of the aperture stop, the computer was relegated to monitoring the scanning process. It verified the intensity of the He–Ne laser and infrared signals, the number of points recorded in the current interferogram, and the number of interferograms scanned. The computer also managed the other aspects of spectral measurement, including:

(1) signal-averaging and storage of single-beam or double-beam interferograms;
(2) calculation of the Fourier transform, including apodization and phase correction;
(3) plotting of spectra in various formats, including an accurate wavenumber scale derived from the laser reference;
(4) secondary analyses such as peak selection or integration of peaks.

The original system did not include a display oscilloscope, so interferograms and spectra could only be viewed by tracing them on a plotter. The system was considerably more automated than previously available Fourier spectrometers, though, and made FTIR simple enough to be considered a practical tool by research chemists.

FTS-12

The FTS-12 was a particularly compact system built around the Digilab Model 196 interferometer, having a 3-cm diameter entrance aperture and high scan speed (as short as 1/8 second for $20\,cm^{-1}$ resolution). The spectrometer was popular for field studies, and was available with an accessory for diffuse reflectance measurements. Data handling was similar to the FTS-14.

FTS-16

The Digilab FTS-16, intended for far infrared use, employed an interferometer design similar to the original Grubb-Parsons Mark II of a few years earlier.

11.6   JPL

Rapid-scanning interferometers did not immediately replace slow-scan types. For example, researchers at the Jet Propulsion Laboratory in Pasadena, California, developed a slow-scan interferometer that operated quickly. Schindler (1970) described their reasons for preferring this scheme to rapid-scanning:

> Although this method of scanning is somewhat more complex, it resolves two major problems inherent with constant speed scanning. It eliminates errors due to driving speed fluctuations; this is a very important consideration in a high-vibration environment, because the optical path difference between the two beams is known, and constant, at every instant in time. With a constant speed system, sampling occurs only once; thus, the position is only known once per monochromatic reference fringe. A second major problem solved by step scanning is the elimination of phase-shift errors due to the ir detectors and to electrical filtering; this is an important consideration at high data rates.

The JPL interferometer moved as quickly as one step per 1.5 msec, with the optical path difference maintained to 20 Å (0.002 μm) during the measurement. In order to achieve these very rapid step-and-integrate measurements, the interferometer incorporated a servo-control system. For the servo, the secondary mirror of one of the cat's eye retroreflectors (described in Section 13.1.2) was oscillated by a piezo-electric transducer at a frequency of 480 Hz. The movement of the mirror was small — about 0.008 μm — but sufficient to modulate the fringe intensity from the reference laser. The phase and intensity of this high-frequency "ripple" on the reference channel were monitored to drive the primary mirror of the retroreflector to the correct position. In order to move the path difference to the next step, a voltage was generated to override the servo, and reference-laser pulses were counted by the digital electronics. Once the desired number of pulses (i.e. laser wavelengths) had been counted, the servo "locked-on" to the new position to damp out movement. The infrared interferogram intensity was then measured. An entire interferogram could be scanned in this way in 1.5 minutes.

Several features of the JPL positioning system were incorporated into commercial rapid-scanning interferometers of the 1980s. No faster step-scanning interferometer has since been made. The problems of the rapid-scanning technique, described above by Schindler, were eventually made manageable by improvements in technology.

11.7 POLYTEC GmbH

Polytec introduced slow-scanning far infrared Fourier spectrometer systems in 1971. The FIR-20, FIR-25 and FIR-30 were some of the last commercial slow-scanning interferometers produced, at least in western countries, and probably the most advanced. The instruments, designed principally by Ray Milward (previously with Beckman RIIC and Coderg) were in many respects advanced versions of the RIIC FS-720 (Fig. 11.3). The three versions were similar, differing mainly in scan displacement.

The FIR-30 incorporated an electrically actuated beamsplitter selector, to choose one of four Mylar beamsplitters (Milward 1972). This avoided the half-hour delay involved in admitting air to the interferometer, mounting a new beamsplitter, and re-evacuating. The instrument also included a reconfigurable sample chamber (like the earlier Coderg spectrometer) permitting reference, transmittance or reflectance measurements by adjusting the position of mirrors. The beamsplitter was used at a 30 degree angle of incidence instead of 45°; this reduced the required beamsplitter size, and also minimized polarization effects.

The FIR-30 was more automated than previous FTIR instruments. Although it allowed manual setting of parameters such as scan speed, sampling interval, time constant and beamsplitter and optical filter choice, all these could be chosen automatically simply by selecting the desired spectral range. The spectrometer covered 10–1000 cm^{-1} at up to 0.05 cm^{-1} resolution.

The FIR-30 was amongst the first FTIR systems aimed at chemists. Until then, a major criticism of FTIR was the long delay between measurement and observation of the spectrum. Dispersive instruments provided a continuous plot of the spectrum as it was measured, allowing the operator to stop if the sample was improperly prepared or the instrument was not optimized. As Coderg had done, Polytec employed a

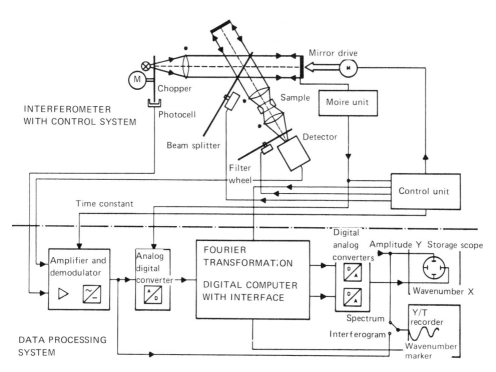

Fig. 11.3 — Polytec FIR-30 spectrometer. The optics, shown as lenses for simplicity, are
actually mirrors (reproduced by permission of Polytec GmbH).

storage oscilloscope to display a continuously updated spectrum (the same program-
mer was, in fact, responsible for both the Coderg and Polytec instruments). The
spectrum was recalculated after every measured interferogram point. As points were
typically measured at a rate of one per second, and the computer could calculate a
complete 1500 point spectrum in 0.4 sec, this "real-time" display carried no penalty.
The appearance on the screen was of a complete spectrum gradually improving in
resolution. This real-time display was unique to Polytec and Coderg spectrometers:
later rapid-scan instruments generally demanded much more intensive control by the
computer, leaving insufficient time for display of intermediate results. By 1973, some
thirty units had been sold, principally in Western Europe.

Despite the growing popularity of pyroelectric detectors such as trigylcine
sulphate (TGS), the FIR-30 employed a Golay cell detector. Those of some
manufacturers had gained a reputation for fragility and unreliability, particularly in
the USA, but the Golay cell is nevertheless superior in noise equivalent power
(NEP) and has a remarkable linear response over a wide range of optical power,
thereby reducing spectral distortion.

Polytec rapid-scanning instruments

In 1974, Polytec marketed the MIR-20, a moderate resolution ($0.5\,cm^{-1}$ unapodized) mid-infrared (4000–$400\,cm^{-1}$) FTIR instrument. It initially employed a

teletype terminal and paper tape punch for communication with the minicomputer, although magnetic tape and disk units were soon made available. It was an evacuable interferometer, a feature not generally available in other mid infrared instruments.

Later versions incorporated a push-button control unit for selection of experimental parameters and data manipulations. The same features were provided in the higher resolution MIR-160 FTIR, which had a maximum resolution of $0.04 \, cm^{-1}$ (unapodized). The MIR-160, which was not evacuable, allowed a wider range of mirror scan rates to better match a range of detectors, and employed a minicomputer having 24K of memory, 16-bit words, and a 1.2-Mbyte disk. Both instruments could be used with a purpose-developed GC/IR interface.

Polytec ceased manufacture of the FIR-30 in 1975 and the MIR 20 and MIR 160 in 1976. Except for a few isolated applications, slow-scan interferometry ended with them.

11.8 IDEALAB

Idealab Inc. (Franklin, Massachusetts, USA) sold two models of commercial Fourier spectrometers, the IF-3 and IF-6. Both were continuous-drive interferometers, the IF-3 providing $0.5 \, cm^{-1}$ and the IF-6 $0.1 \, cm^{-1}$ resolution at best (2- and 10-cm maximum path differences, respectively).

The interferometers could be operated in rapid scanning mode, with scan times as short as one second, or in the more conventional step-and-integrate mode with an optional mirror stepper.

Scan range extended from 10 to $10\,000 \, cm^{-1}$, using a range of Mylar and transparent-substrate beamsplitters. Unlike the earlier Beckman RIIC and Coderg instruments, the Idealab interferometers used an He–Ne laser for position referencing and a white-light source for locating zero path difference. These two reference channels were available as bolt-on accessories to the basic cube interferometer.

The Idealab interferometers were normally sold without a data system and computer.

The IF-3 was suitable for military and space science studies because it could tolerate high ambient vibration.

11.9 GENERAL DYNAMICS

General Dynamics (Pomona, Calif, USA) manufactured a rapid-scanning FTIR intended for field use in the late 1970s. The Model PFS-201 optical head was tripod-mounted, and connected to an electronics console.

The optical head employed a conventional Michelson interferometer. The scan mirror, mounted on a lightweight carriage, was moved along machined ways by a linear motor. A linearly variable differential transformer (LVDT) and He–Ne laser were used to measure mirror position and velocity. The interferometer optics were mounted within a temperature controlled cube machined from a stress-relieved casting.

The optical alignment was maintained by a control system consisting of three-point phase measurement across the interferometer aperture and three piezoelectric positioners on the fixed mirror. The piezos were able to tilt the mirror by up to 2 minutes of arc. Various telescopes could be used to cover a field of view between 5 degrees and a fraction of a degree.

The electronics console controlled scanning, monitored voltages, and performed analogue to digital conversion of the interferogram signal. Additional electronics and a minicomputer for Fourier transformation were optional. By using the longest scan drive, resolution as good as $0.07 \, cm^{-1}$ was possible.

11.10   PRINCIPLES OF SCAN MECHANISMS

The design of early Block Engineering scan drives was discussed in Section 11.4. The main requirement of the scan mechanism is that it alter the optical path difference smoothly, without altering optical alignment. Ideally, it will have additional characteristics: insensitivity to vibration, temperature and mechanical creep; inexpensive design; straightforward maintenance; and independence from external gas supplies.

11.10.1   Sampling errors

One of the advantages of FT spectrometers is their small number of moving parts: only a single mirror need move to vary the optical path difference.

The precision of movement must be very high, however. The Fourier transform assumes that sampling points are equally spaced. Indeed, the free spectral range of the measurement is determined by the sample interval. If the scan mechanism introduces variations in sampling, the spectral scale will be smeared — each sampling interval will introduce its own scale, and the overlap of these will introduce a loss in resolution. Moreover, if the sampling varies from scan to scan, the ratio of sample to reference scans and their incoherent overlap will cause worsened measurement noise.

It might be expected that monochromatic fringe referencing would remove any problems caused by speed variations. Unfortunately, smooth scanning is still important. The detector preamplifiers used in FTIR are usually carefully filtered to cut out electrical frequencies above and below the anticipated modulation range [which is determined by scan speed and spectral range, as shown by Eqn. (11.1)]. If scan speed fluctuates, the modulation frequency will also vary, introducing distortion (phase and amplitude changes) in the interferogram waveform. Although schemes have been developed to counter this effect, it remains true that speed variations greater than a few percent are generally sufficient to degrade performance.

This discussion applies only to rapid-scanning FTIR. In slow-scan FTIR, speed is not relevant, but sampling errors are. The step increments must be accurate; if not, the same noise and resolution degradation will occur.

11.11   THE STATUS IN THE LATE 1970s

The end of the 1970s was a transitionary period for FTIR. For the first time, most new Fourier spectrometers were commercially made, rather than developed by the academic or industrial laboratory. Moreover, chemists, instead of physicists, were becoming the principal users. Tomas Hirschfeld (1978) said:

> FT-IR began its applications career as a fairly desperate last resort by astronomers to cope with extremely low signal levels and entered the laboratory as a special tool for the equally marginal signal levels of far ir spectroscopy. The advent of the minicomputer ended this specialized phase of the technique. Once FT-IR became as convenient to use as the classical techniques, its far superior performance made it the pre-eminent technique in all very high performance ir spectroscopy. In the process, the FT-IR user pattern came to resemble very much that of classical ir spectroscopists, with a vast preponderance of analytical chemists, whose interests now exert a directing influence over instrument research, development, and commercialization.

For the first time, papers on applications began to exceed publications describing instrumentation and fundamental theory. Instead of being published in journals such as *Applied Optics* and *Infrared Physics*, the new publications appeared more often in *Applied Spectroscopy* and *Analytical Chemistry*.

In a 1977 conference, Pierre Connes noted the changing face of FTIR with apparent distrust (Connes 1978):

> A major novelty is the mass intrusion of chemists upon the scene, and there is no doubt this is mainly due to the availability of commercial instruments. On the whole this is a healthy development we must applaud, a mark of maturity for the Fourier technique. It means the benefits will be made available to many groups where instrumental development cannot be achieved, and it should greatly increase the over-all scientific output .... There is little doubt that if you are an instrument builder, your viewpoint differs greatly from that of the person who buys a ready-made interferometer; the words Fourier spectroscopy are apt to mean entirely different things in both cases. I personally have some doubts about Fourier spectrometers being used properly even when producing indisputably fine results.

The new commercially available instruments generally employed dedicated minicomputers. The technology was not yet ready to be handed over in a neat package from physicists to chemists, though. The trend was toward complex, self-contained systems and dedicated operators, as described by Dunn (1978):

> The author feels quite strongly that the ideal operation of an FT-IR system should be a closed shop with one key operator. Furthermore, the key operator should be electronically oriented with a background in both machine language and high order programming. This type of key operator can easily be trained in infrared sample handling and would provide an ideal interface between the analytical chemist and the system, leaving the analytical chemist free to devise challenging experiments for FT-IR and the

operator to implement these experiments through full utilization of software and hardware capabilities.

Both Connes and Dunn thus saw the FTIR spectrometer as a complex instrument of great benefit to non-specialists, but nonetheless beyond their abilities to use effectively.

REFERENCES

Bell, R. J. (1972), *Introductory Fourier Transform Spectroscopy*, Academic Press, New York.

Chantry, G. W. (1971), *Submillimetre Spectroscopy*, Academic Press, London.

Connes, P. (1970), High Resolution Fourier Spectroscopy, in: Home-Dickson, J. (ed.) *Optical Instruments and Techniques*, Oriel Press, Newcastle upon Tyne.

Connes, P. (1978), Of Fourier, Pasteur, and sundry others, *Appl. Opt.*, **17**, 1318.

Curbelo, R. and Foskett, C. (1970), An automated interferometer spectrometer: real-time data acquisition and on-line computation to 0.5cm^{-1}, *Aspen International Conference on Fourier Spectroscopy*, eds. Vanasse, G. A., Stair, A. T. and Baker, D. J., AFCRL-71-0019, p. 221.

Dunn, S. T. (1978), Fourier transform infrared spectrometers: their recent history, current status, and commercial future, *Appl. Opt.*, **17**, 1367.

Hirschfeld, T. (1978), New trends in the application of Fourier transform infrared spectroscopy to analytical chemistry, *Appl. Opt.*, **17**, 1400.

Mertz, L. (1965), *Transformations in Optics*, Wiley, New York.

Mertz, L. (1967), Rapid Scanning Fourier Transform Spectrometry, *J. Phys.*, **28**, Suppl. 3, 88.

Mertz, L. (1969), Fourier Spectroscopy, Past, Present and Future, *Appl. Opt.*, **8**, 386.

Mertz, L. (1991), personal communications, 25 January and 19 February.

Michel, G. (1972), Real-Time Computer for Monitoring a Rapid-Scanning Fourier Spectrometer, *Appl. Opt.*, **11**, 2671.

Milward, R. C. (1972), Far Infrared Fourier Spectroscopy Made Painless, *The Spex Speaker*, **27**, 1.

Milward, R. C. (1973), A New Far-Infrared Fourier Spectrometer, *Z. Anal. Chem.*, **264**, 195.

Milward, R. C. (1974), Recent Advances in Commercial Fourier Spectrometers for the Submillimetre Wavelength Region, *IEEE Trans. on Microwave Theory and Techniques*, **MTT-12** (12), 1018.

Schindler, R. A. (1970), A Small, High Speed Interferometer for Aircraft, Balloon, and Spacecraft Applications, *Appl. Opt.*, **9**, 301.

Wyjntjes, G. (1977), A Review and Update of Certain Fourier Transform Spectroscopy Techniques, *1977 International Conference on Fourier Transform Infrared Spectroscopy, Technical Digest*, 9.

Wyjntjes, G. (1982), Advantages of Flexible Scanning, *Proc. SPIE*, **364**, 8.

Part IV
Modern Times

12

The evolution of computation

The continued growth of FTIR has been supported, in large part, by the continued development of computers. The cost of computation has steadily declined, and gives every indication of continuing for the foreseeable future.

12.1 MAINFRAMES, MINICOMPUTERS AND MICROCOMPUTERS

Through the 1950s and early 1960s, only a handful of large mainframe computers were available to Fourier spectroscopists. In 1961, about 5000 computers had been installed; by 1964, over 18000 were in place (Savitsky 1966). Most of these were used as "Business Data Processors", but those in universities and research centres, at least, were sometimes available for running physics problems.

The mainframe computers used for FTIR spectroscopy in the early sixties began to give way to minicomputers by the end of the decade. Companies such as the Data General Corporation, Hewlett–Packard, Varian Associates, and Minneapolis-Honeywell manufactured minicomputer systems and associated equipment. These computers were essentially scaled-down versions of the mainframes, but devoted to a single user. Moreover, unlike most mainframes, minicomputers were occasionally used to control equipment, not just to perform digital calculations.

Minicomputers are usually defined as single-board computers having the central processing unit (CPU) constructed from several discrete elements, whereas micro-computers incorporate all the essential functions of the central processor on a single integrated circuit (chip). These distinctions are now becoming vague, though, and will soon disappear entirely.

12.2 REAL-TIME FOURIER SPECTROSCOPY

An irritating reality during the first decade of Fourier spectroscopy was that interferograms took a considerable time to translate into spectra. The situation was exacerbated when computing facilities were located in another building or even town: many a box of punched cards was dropped and jumbled on the way to the computer centre. Even when the fast Fourier transform was used, it was common to wait many minutes after the experiment was complete before seeing any meaningful results. A number of groups developed methods to provide a rapid spectrum either during the interferogram measurement or immediately afterwards.

Yoshinaga *et al.* (1966) at Osaka University, Japan, designed an analogue computer for performing the apodization of the interferogram, and an associated digital computer to calculate the Fourier transform. Calculating the transform by summing differently than in the conventional algorithm, a complete spectrum was obtained for every path difference position of their slow-scanning interferometer. The one-thousand point spectrum could be viewed at any time by displaying the memory contents on a synchroscope (an oscilloscope synchronized with the digital transfer) through a high-speed digital-to-analogue converter. By this method, each incremental change to the spectrum calculation required 0.45 seconds; to calculate the entire spectrum from scratch took about 8 minutes.

Independently, Joseph Hoffman and George Vanasse (1966) implemented the same technique for equipment at the Air Force Cambridge Research Laboratory (AFCRL). They termed the method "spectral synthesis", because it consisted essentially of building up, or synthesizing a spectrum from an ever-increasing set of interferogram readings. As each new point of the interferogram was measured, another cosine wave was added to computer memory. The frequency of the added cosine wave was proportional to the optical path difference of the interferometer.

A similar technique was employed by the Coderg and Polytec commercial Fourier spectrometers in 1969 and 1972, respectively.

Each of these versions used a slow-scanning interferometer, in which the interferogram samples are widely spaced in time. Moreover, they calculated only the cosine Fourier transform. This requires the interferogram to be perfectly symmetrical: if not, the spectrum is distorted (see Section 10.6). The Polytec instrument incorporated a means of adjusting the position of the fixed mirror of the interferometer so that sampling occurred exactly at the zero path difference position. By making this adjustment, the interferogram was rendered symmetrical (neglecting any phase error produced by the beamsplitter) and a cosine transform was adequate.

Rapid-scanning real-time monitoring is a considerably more difficult problem. Nevertheless, Guy Michel (1972) described a special computer developed by the Laboratoire Aimé Cotton for in-flight monitoring of interferograms. The computer was hard-wired (programmed by direct electrical connections rather than by the much slower technique of software interpretation of mathematical relationships) to perform a discrete Fourier transform. The algorithm used was similar to that of the preceding instruments, but was extended to calculate both the cosine and sine transforms, as well as the power spectrum. This completely removed the need to measure symmetrical interferograms. For each interferogram sample, the appropriate sine function was looked up from a read-only memory and added to the spectrum memory. The computation time was 500 nsec to calculate a spectrum point from a new interferogram point, allowing measurement rates of more than 1 kHz.

Unlike the previous slow-scanning real-time systems which showed a spectrum of gradually increasing resolution, the Laboratoire Aimé Cotton version displayed a full-resolution spectrum with gradually improving noise. Each of its rapid-scan spectra required about 9 seconds to record; many hundreds were sometimes co-added to achieve an adequate signal-to-noise ratio. In contrast, the slow-scanning interferometers measured each point of the interferogram with adequate S/N, but took several minutes to obtain the entire interferogram.

More recent commercial instruments have not attempted real-time measurement, but calculation of the FFT is becoming so rapid that nearly the same result is obtained. The Analect fx-6200 spectrometer of the early 1980s employed a hard-wired FFT processor that was fast enough to calculate the entire spectrum between each scan. By using commercially available special-purpose processors, a 4K interferogram can now be transformed into a power spectrum in less than one second. The Lloyd Instruments FT-600+ spectrometer, for example, incorporated a TMS32010 processor to calculate a 4K spectrum during the mirror fly-back between each interferogram, allowing spectra rather than interferograms to be averaged.

12.3   THE MICROPROCESSOR

Integrated circuits were invented in the late 1950s. Within fifteen years, spurred on by the American space program, microprocessors were commercially available. These devices are essentially "computers on a chip", and consist of memory, a central processing unit (CPU) and storage registers for arithmetic operations. The microprocessor permitted simple control of instruments, calculations based on their measurements, and storage and display of the result.

The memory capacity, speed and precision of computers is determined by the length of "words" that they manipulate. Most early microprocessors employed words of 8 binary digits, or bits. An 8-bit word can represent $2^8=256$ distinct values; a 16-bit word, 65536; and, a 32-bit word, 4.29×10^9 values (if one bit is used to define the sign of the number, then only half as many values can be represented). Larger values can be represented by "double-precision arithmetic", in which the number is made up of two or more words.

The memory capacity is determined by the number of distinct "addresses" that the computer can specify. In a 16-bit computer, one word can specify 65536 addresses (usually written 64K, where K represents 1024). Computers can get over this limitation in memory size by using "paged memory", a method of switching between memory blocks, or by employing more than one word to specify the address.

The number of bits used for communication can limit speed. Many microprocessors employ more bits for internal calculations than for communication to memory or devices in the outside world. For communications, a pair of words may have to be sent, causing more complex instruction handling and slower operation.

Finally, word length determines calculating precision. By default, arithmetic calculations are performed in "single precision" by manipulating single words. With 16-bit computers, this limits numbers to the 0 to 65536 range. For more precision, pairs, triplets or quadruplets of single words must be manipulated. This takes more computer cycles and again is slower.

12.4   THE DECLINING COST OF COMPUTATION

The real cost of computation (in terms of number of calculations per unit price) has dropped continuously since the advent of commercial digital computers in the 1950s. The cost has dropped by about 30% compounded per year for four decades.

During the first decade of commercial computers, prices dropped because of increasing competition and the scale of production. By the early 1970s, computer prices were falling because of the corresponding fall in price of integrated circuits (sometimes exceeding 80% in four years), the replacement of complex inter-wiring of circuits by large scale printed circuit boards, and still larger production volumes. Today, prices are still falling because of the enormous popularity of microcomputers in business, which has led to sales of millions rather than thousands of computer units.

Peripheral devices such as tape or disc storage units have shown only slight price reductions. This arises partly because they are precision mechanical products rather than integrated circuits.

Unlike hardware, the cost of software has risen with inflation. Despite improvements in higher-level computer languages and some systematization of the coding of programs, there have been few major advances in software engineering. In fact, software design is still more of an art than an engineering discipline, with no generally reliable procedures for validating a program and verifying its operation in all circumstances of use.

12.5   MICROCOMPUTERS FOR FTIR SPECTROSCOPY

The Intel 8086 microprocessor was introduced in 1978. It quickly became a popular 16-bit processor, and benefits from a large amount of hardware and software support. The 8086 and its cousin, the 8088 microprocessor (which has similar architecture except for an 8-bit communications bus, a characteristic which, as explained above, reduces transfer rates) are the basis of the original IBM PC and XT computers and their "clones".

The 8086 design was extended in the 80286, 80386 and 80486 microprocessors. These permit increasingly large address spaces owing to the use of more bits per word and an expanded instruction set. The 80286 is the heart of the IBM AT-type computer, and the 80386 and 80486 chips are used in IBM PC-compatible computers capable of considerably faster processing and memory capacities. The IBM PC, its clones and successors are by far the most common computers available today. The original IBM forecasts had predicted sales of a couple of million; as of 1990, some forty million had been sold.

The chief competing microcomputer processor is the Motorola 68000 series. The original version, the 68000, was a 16-bit microprocessor with 32-bit internal architecture. This provided the ability to address 16 Mbytes of memory directly. The basic design has been upgraded in the 68010, 68020 and 68030 microprocessors, which are true 32-bit processors.

Each of these microprocessors is capable of performing the routine "housekeeping" tasks of spectrometer control, data acquisition and data analysis — indeed, even the 8088 microprocessor is usually available with more memory and higher process ing speed than many minicomputers of the 1970s. The newer processors are significantly faster, however, and permit more rapid data acquisition, much larger data blocks to be handled, and more rapid response to user commands.

12.6   DATA ACQUISITION WITH THE MICROCOMPUTER

The data acquisition for the FTIR system is achieved by interfacing a fast analogue-to-digital convertor (ADC) to the computer. The spectrometer electronics may include the ADC as part of the signal processing design; the resulting digital data can then be communicated to the microcomputer via a serial or parallel port (serial ports send data in sequential fashion, while parallel ports send it in simultaneous chunks, a generally faster process). This has the drawback, though, of being a relatively slow means of data communication. Rapid-scanning spectrometers therefore either store the entire interferogram (or transformed spectrum) in RAM memory in the digital electronics of the spectrometer and subsequently send the entire block to the PC, or else use Direct Memory Access (DMA) techniques to send the data to the computer memory via a quick communications route. DMA requires the installation of a card in the PC, possibly an intimidating task for users who want to use an existing computer with their new spectrometer.

Finally, commercial ADC boards are available to plug into IBM slots, and some users have designed their own versions (Lua 1984). The disadvantages of this approach are that the relatively small analogue detector signal must be brought to the computer, introducing the likelihood of noise pickup, and the necessity of the writing of software to read the data from the ADC port.

12.7   SOFTWARE — THE USER INTERFACE

Fourier spectrometers are incomplete without an associated computer. The characteristics of the computer are, in turn, determined by its software. Software therefore is an important part of any FTIR spectrometer.

Computer software, a rapidly evolving field, has more than its share of jargon. The so-called "user interface" is the term given to the way the computer communicates with its user.

A discussion of the user interface in FTIR spectroscopy would have had little meaning prior to 1975. Until then, the interferometer was typically controlled by a simple sequencer: after the data were recorded, separate programs were usually loaded from paper or magnetic tape to perform the functions of interferogram editing, averaging, transformation and examination. The computer operator, who frequently wrote the programs, kept track of the sequence of operations needed. In effect, operators programmed themselves to do the work.

When minicomputers having disk drives and more memory became available, programs could be fleshed out to perform a suite of activities. These integrated programs usually prompted the user for the information needed in sequential order. For example, to perform a Fourier transformation, the user might be asked to enter the interferogram file name, number of points to be transformed, apodization to be applied, and number of interpolated points in the output spectrum. This 'prompting' interface ensured that all necessary information was entered as needed.

When the first microcomputer-operated spectrometers were designed, the "prompted" command format was carried over. Individual operations (transformation, averaging, etc.) were frequently commanded by mnemonics. For example, the Digilab FTS-14 disk operating system was controlled through a Teletype terminal by three letter mnemonic commands. A typical measurement set-up (Cuthbert 1974) to order $4\,cm^{-1}$ resolution, 10 scans of the sample, one scan of the reference, and spectral display from 3850 to $450\,cm^{-1}$ in Absorbance units with the sample ratioed to the reference and automatic scale expansion would require the sequence:

RES=4,   NSS=10,   NSR=1,   STP=3850,
ENP=450,   ASE=Y,   PLM=A,   RSM=R.

This form of terse communication was necessary when the computer terminal printed on paper. The replacement of electromechanical Teletype terminals by cathode-ray-tube (CRT) monitors allowed more text and graphical information to be quickly presented and updated.

The introduction of personal computers, and then the IBM PC, brought personal computation to literally millions of people with no previous exposure to computers. Software developers writing programs for business, office, wordprocessing and home use quickly settled on a *de facto* standard: menu-driven operation. Menu-driven software led the user through options by presenting choices in menu form. Such schemes were adopted by FTIR spectrometers using minicomputers and microcomputers, although the minicomputers, with a tradition of FORTRAN programming and scientific users, were adapted more slowly to software advances. The presentation of operating conditions and choices gave the user a less myopic view of computer-controlled spectrometers.

In the few years since the IBM PC (1982) and Apple MacIntosh (1984) computers became widespread, the best features of both operating systems and available software packages have evolved toward a more standardized user interface for programs. The original MS-DOS operating system of the PC has been extended by a "windows environment" similar to that pioneered by Apple (which itself drew upon the minicomputer systems software developed by Xerox). This is a graphical means of displaying options, images and data in "pull down" or "pop up" menu windows on the computer screen, and employing a mouse to move the screen cursor to select displayed "icons" representing operations. This is an important simplification over remembering curt mnemonic commands for routine operations such as file copying and listing. Similar graphics-based user interfaces are available under the UNIX and OS/2 operating systems for more powerful computers.

The standardization of commercial software towards a common "look and feel" extends, to a lesser extend, to the functions the software performs. Virtually all FTIR software packages now include not only the instrument control functions (resolution, number of scans, spectral range, etc.) but versatile screen display, plotting and analysis options such as Kubelka-Munk transformation (for diffuse reflectance measurements), spectral subtraction, baseline correction, and spectral search. Software packages cover the range from easy-to-use combinations offering no difficult choices, to elaborate routines allowing customization and automation of most aspects of the system's operation.

12.8 COMMERCIAL SPECTROMETER SOFTWARE

It is incorrect to think that spectroscopic software was invented with minicomputers. Digitized spectral storage and manipulation has been around since 1950, albeit in isolated systems and locations. G. W. King *et al.* published a series of articles about digital storage and retrieval from 1951 to 1954. Rogoff and Taplin (1957) at the American Federal Telecommunications Laboratories developed a complete digital analysis system. The best known digital system through the 1960s was the library search system developed by L. E. Kuentzel in 1951 known as the ASTM IBM card system. Writing in 1960 about his digital recording system for a grating spectrometer, F. S. Brackett said:

> Older men in the field feel that the return to digital recording brings the circle full round, for it was the point-by-point tabulation of digital information which we sought to escape ... the trend has always been along analog lines successively exploiting automation in linearization through programming by cams and then through electronic devices incorporating into the recorder means of translating the data into a form more suitable for interpretation and publication.

Many of the features of mainframe computer software systems were incorporated in minicomputer and, eventually, microcomputer software. These were adapted and extended to make better use of the interactive capabilities and more versatile displays of the smaller computers.

In addition to the software packages developed by instrument manufacturers, there has been a growth of third-party software for FTIR spectrometers. These packages are often more complete than the software provided with the hardware, leading some manufacturers to offer their customers a choice. The available choices include Galactic Industries Spectra Calc, Heyden SpectraFile, Spectra-Tech Quick IR, and Sprouse Scientific Software. These generally include routines for saving and recalling spectra and interferograms on disk, viewing and plotting portions of the data, overlaying curves, converting between transmittance/absorbance and wavenumber/wavelength units, and importing/exporting data via the JCAMP-DX exchange format. The numerically and memory-intensive functions of spectral search and quantitative analysis are usually offered as optional extensions to the basic package. The commercial packages also include routines for spectrometer control, although the availability depends on the agreements reached with each manufacturer.

12.8.1 Spectral subtraction

Spectral subtraction was first popularized by Jack Koenig of Case Western University in the mid 1970s (e.g. Koenig 1975). The idea is straightforward: one spectrum, containing contributions due to background, is subtracted from a second spectrum having contributions from both the sample of interest and the background, leaving only the sample contributions. The background can be any extraneous absorption: bands due to other materials in the prepared sample, atmospheric water vapour, etc. The term "subtraction" is used because the two absorbance spectra are subtracted. The absorbance spectrum of a sample is the negative logarithm of its transmittance spectrum:

$$A(\sigma)=-\log\{T(\sigma)\} \tag{12.1}$$

Light transmitted through a material is partially absorbed by it; when passed through a second material, it is further absorbed, and the transmittance spectrum is just the product of the two individual spectra:

$$T(\sigma)=T_1(\sigma)T_2(\sigma) \tag{12.2}$$

To remove the effects of the second substance from the spectrum $T(\sigma)$, it is necessary to divide it by the pure sample 2 spectrum:

$$T_1(\sigma)=T(\sigma)/T_2(\sigma) \tag{12.3}$$

i.e. a ratio is performed.

By the properties of logarithms, if the same transmittance spectra are converted into absorbance spectra, they need only be subtracted:

$$\begin{aligned}A_1(\sigma)&=-\log\{T_1(\sigma)\}=-\log\{T(\sigma)/T_2(\sigma)\}\\ &=-\log\{T(\sigma)\}\ -(-\log\{T_2(\sigma)\})\\ &=A(\sigma)-A_2(\sigma)\end{aligned} \tag{12.4}$$

The ratioing of transmittance spectra and the subtraction of absorbance spectra are thus equivalent.

The power of spectral subtraction lies in its ability to remove the effects of different concentrations of the background from the spectrum. This is achieved by simply scaling the background spectrum by a constant k before subtraction:

$$A_1(\sigma)=A(\sigma)-kA_2(\sigma) \tag{12.5}$$

This straightforward technique was not used with much success on earlier dispersive spectrometers because the wavenumber (or wavelength) scale was not sufficiently constant. Minor shifts in the scale due to hysteresis in the scan drive of the prism or diffraction grating caused irregular slippages in the scales of spectra. When such spectra were subtracted, large anomalies would appear in any region where the absorbance changed rapidly with wavenumber.

Secondly, few dispersive spectrometers employed digital recording of spectra in the 1970s: computers were still perceived as an expensive complication to be avoided. The conventional spectral output — an analogue voltage varying with time, usually with an "event marker" to indicate increments in the wavenumber scale — did not lend itself to accurate comparison of spectra.

12.8.2 Baseline correction

In situations where scattered light is measured by the spectrometer, the spectrum is found to be "tilted". For example, if a transmissive sample has a rough surface, it may diffusely scatter some light to the sample holder, where it will reflect to the detector. The intensity of scattering is dependent on wavenumber. When the surface imperfections of the sample are much smaller than a wavelength, Rayleigh scattering dominates. This is the effect responsible for the blue colour of the sky: the molecules of air scatter light in proportion to the fourth power of wavenumber. Blue light $(25\,000\,cm^{-1}$, with nearly double the frequency of red light $(14\,000\,cm^{-1})$ is scattered about ten times more intensely.

For larger surface imperfections, Mie scattering is the dominant effect, and produces similar results. The infrared spectrum from a scattering sample thus has a stronger contribution from scattered light at high wavenumbers than at low wavenumbers, and is tilted. As the tilt is due to surface characteristics rather than to the intrinsic sample absorption, it will introduce errors when quantitative analysis is to be done. If the tilt is sufficiently severe, it may even impede identification of an unknown sample.

Baseline tilt can be removed from the spectrum by fitting a correction curve to the absorbance spectrum, and then subtracting it (the same result can be achieved by fitting a corrective 100% line to a transmittance spectrum and *dividing* it into the original spectrum). Such a correction curve in its simplest form is a straight line. As a better approximation, several straight lines may be fitted over adjacent spectral intervals. This is usually accomplished by having the operator select the starting and ending points of the line segments while viewing the spectrum on the computer screen.

More recently, baseline correction has been performed automatically by programs that take the place of the operator. The program is able to distinguish the gradual baseline tilt from more specific spectral features such as absorption peaks, and can use more points in the fit. Moreover, the simple straight-line segments can be interpolated by a smooth curve to avoid kinks in the corrected spectrum.

12.8.3 Spectral smoothing

No spectrum is entirely free of extraneous contributions. These contributions may be attributable to the measurement environment — the appearance of water vapour and carbon dioxide lines in the spectrum of a poorly purged instrument, for example. More often, the undesired components in the spectrum are due to measurement noise. This random fluctuation in the spectral intensity can obscure spectral features and limit the sensitivity of detection or identification of the sample.

Spectral smoothing is the mathematical process of reducing the intensity of noise with respect to the desired information in the spectrum. This has traditionally been done by eye: the spectroscopist observes features which she believes to be due to sample absorption, and other features which she believes are instrumental, and draws a curve that incorporates only the "true" information. This subjective method is obviously unsatisfactory, because it is both arbitrary and time-consuming.

Smoothing, either by eye or computer, involves the process of filtering. Noise can only be distinguished from the signal if it is different in some way. This difference is usually in terms of frequency: the noise fluctuations occur more closely apart, and with distinctive amplitudes, compared to true sample effects. The situation is familiar in many circumstances: the spectrum appears to consist of (true) peaks with superimposed fluctuations having a characteristic size and appearance.

Mathematical smoothing procedures typically attenuate the high-frequency "noise" with respect to the lower-frequency "signal". Smoothing is only useful if the high-frequency content of the spectrum truly is noise. In the process of filtering out the noise, the resolution of the spectrum is unavoidably degraded. This can be understood by considering how spectral smoothing is accomplished.

The spectrum is stored as a set of numbers relating intensity to wavenumber. The computer smooths the spectrum by taking a group of these numbers and manipulating them in some way to generate a new output number. In the simplest case, consider taking three adjacent numbers at a time, adding them together, and dividing by three to yield a new output number. This is simply a three-point average. If this process is carried out for all the points in the spectrum, the new spectrum will look much like the old except that noise will be somewhat reduced: any random fluctuation in intensity between the triplet of numbers is averaged out. In addition, though, spectral resolution is lost: any spectral feature that was extremely narrow (say two or three points wide) is diminished by the three-point averaging. The smoothing has reduced noise of frequencies higher than about two resolution elements in the spectrum, but has also removed true spectral information of that frequency.

More sophisticated smoothing algorithms "weight" the points in the average, and use more input points. These result in better smoothing and less severe resolution loss. A similar effect by a different process can be achieved by filtering the interferogram rather than the spectrum. As would be expected, the "filters" in the two cases are Fourier transforms of each other.

Spectral smoothing can "clean up" a spectrum and reveal previously hidden information. Filtering of the signal, whether recognized or not, occurs at several points in all measuring instruments. Nevertheless, overuse of smoothing operations can remove information and distort a measurement; they should be used with some caution.

12.8.4 Kubelka–Munk transformation

Diffuse reflectance spectra of substances such as powders or rough-surfaced specimens appear rather different from transmittance or specular reflectance spectra. They can be converted into representations that resemble absorbance spectra, and which are approximately proportional to sample concentration. For this reason,

Kubelka–Munk analysis is sometimes referred to as the "Beer's law of reflectance spectroscopy" because of its analogy to the law relating the absorbance of a sample to its concentration.

The relationship between the Kubelka–Munk spectrum $f(\sigma)$ and the measured diffuse reflectance spectrum $R(\sigma)$ is defined as:

$$f(\sigma)=\{1-R(\sigma)\}^{2}/R(\sigma) \tag{12.6}$$

where σ is wavenumber. According to theory, $f(\sigma)$ is related to the absorption coefficient and surface scattering coefficient S of an infinitely thick sample by:

$$f(\sigma)=\alpha(\boldsymbol{\sigma})/S \tag{12.7}$$

The scattering coefficient depends on the exact surface characteristics of the sample, as well as the way in which diffusely scattered radiation is collected by the sampling accessory. For similar samples, it can be treated as a proportionality constant. Thus, the Kubelka–Munk value can be considered to be proportional to absorbance.

In practice, the linear relationship holds over only a very limited concentration range (Hecht 1980).

12.8.5 Spectral search

Routine identification of spectra is possible by comparing a sample spectrum with stored spectra in libraries. Computerized databases of spectra first became available in the early 1980s from Sadtler (associated with BioRad) and are now available for most FTIR spectrometers. The databases store infrared spectra in a degraded form to reduce storage space. Normally, the spectral range, resolution, and precision of intensity measurements are reduced. This does not significantly impair identification of good "matches" but prevents library spectra from being accurately subtracted from sample spectra.

Most spectral search packages allow the user to define the spectral regions to be compared during the search, and permit editing of the spectral library to add or remove sample spectra.

Various mathematical algorithms are available to compare sample and library spectra. Sample spectra may be degraded by noise, sloping baselines, contamination by extraneous substances, and sampling effects such as interference fringes from parallel windows on sampling accessories. Various search algorithms are optimized for such conditions, permitting the undesired features to be partially filtered out or ignored.

Early search algorithms used on mainframe computers through the 1970s employed a simple peak-selection routine to locate absorbance peaks above a selectable threshold. The list of peak positions would then be compared with library values. This method was particularly fast (because few peaks were involved) but inaccurate. Modern methods generally perform a point-by-point comparison of sample and library spectra.

12.8.6 Quantitative analysis

The high wavenumber and intensity precision of FTIR spectrometers (even at low transmittance) has led to their use in quantitative analysis. Conventional dispersive instruments were hard-pressed to achieve precision to better than two decimal places, and so had never been seriously employed for demanding applications.

Quantitative analysis in its simplest form relies on Beer's law, which relates absorbance $A(\sigma)$, sample thickness b and sample concentration C:

$$A(\sigma)=\alpha(\sigma)bC \tag{12.8}$$

where $\alpha(\sigma)$ is the wavenumber-dependent absorptivity of the sample. [Actually, Beer and (independently) Bouguer discovered the relationship between absorbance and sample concentration; Lambert found the dependence on the sample thickness. It is therefore more correct to call the expression the Beer–Lambert–Bouguer law.] Thus, to measure the concentration of an unknown sample, it is usual to first measure the absorbance spectrum of a few known concentrations of the sample, note the wavenumber σ_A at which significant absorption occurred, and plot the absorbance $A(\sigma_A)$ for the known concentrations. If Beer's law holds, the result will be a straight line of slope $\alpha(\sigma_A)b$. If not, it is still possible to interpolate the curve to relate a measured absorbance $A'(\sigma_A)$ to the concentration C'.

In real life, it is more common for samples of unknown concentration to be mixed with other unknowns. This is a considerable complication, because each of these components may absorb at the wavenumber σ_A used to calculate the sample concentration. A further complicating factor is that the total absorbance of a mixture is seldom just the sum of the individual absorbances of the pure compounds, owing to chemical interactions or solvent effects.

Nevertheless, the concentrations of mixtures of compounds can be determined reasonably well by using a generalization of the Beer–Lambert–Bouguer law:

$$A(\sigma)=a_1(\sigma)bC_1+a_2(\sigma)bC_2+\ldots+a_n(\sigma)bC_n \tag{12.9}$$

That is, the absorbance seen at any wavenumber σ is the sum of the absorbances due to all the individual absorbing species at that wavenumber.

If each species absorbs most at a unique wavenumber, it is possible to solve for all the concentrations. Suppose we have a three-component mixture, with each component absorbing most at wavenumbers σ_x, σ_y, and σ_z, respectively. If the absorbance of an unknown mixture is measured at these three wavenumbers, we obtain three interrelated expressions:

$$A_x=a_{1x}bC_1+a_{2x}bC_2+a_{3x}bC_3$$
$$A_y=a_{1y}bC_1+a_{2y}bC_2+a_{3y}bC_3$$
$$A_z=a_{1z}bC_1+a_{2z}bC_2+\sigma_{3z}bC_3 \tag{12.10}$$

These simultaneous equations can be solved for the three concentrations C_1, C_2, and C_3 provided that the nine absorptivities $a_{1x} \ldots a_{3z}$ are known. These can be determined by simply measuring the three spectra of the pure compounds 1, 2, and 3. The calculation can be performed rapidly by matrix arithmetic once the requisite information is available.

There are two formal methods of solving the simultaneous equations. In each method, the equations are in matrix form:

$$A = KC \qquad\qquad (12.11)$$

where **A**, **K**, and **C** are matrices for the sets of absorbance, absorptivity, and concentration variables. In the so-called "**K**- matrix method", the concentrations **C** are solved in terms of the **K** and **A** matrices. This technique is mathematically straightforward, but suffers from two weaknesses. First, the mathematical manipulations of the **K** matrix can lead to indeterminate results for concentration in some circumstances. Secondly, the standard spectra recorded to determine the absorptivities must be entirely free of impurities. If impurities are present, their concentrations must be known and used in the calculation.

An alternative mathematical formulation is known as the "**P**-matrix method". As before, the equations are written in matrix form:

$$C = PA \qquad\qquad (12.12)$$

The **P** matrix can treat the effects of deviation from the Beer–Lambert law, and it can be solved in terms of the absorbance matrix **A** and known reference concentrations **C**. Subsequently, unknown concentrations can be calculated from Eq. (12.12). The principal drawback of the **P**-matrix method is that more reference mixtures are required to ensure that the **P** matrix is properly defined.

Single and multi-component analysis are now routinely offered as software options for most FTIR spectrometers, with 8 to 12 components being a common maximum.

12.8.7   Spectral deconvolution

Deconvolution is the process of compensating for the intrinsic linewidths of spectral features in order to resolve overlapping bands. It can thus improve the displayed resolution of a spectrum by using known information about the theoretical band-shape and the characteristics of the spectrometer (Kauppinen *et al.* 1981). With judiciously chosen parameters, deconvolution can resolve bands which had been smeared by inadequate spectrometer resolution or broadening processes. An example is shown in Fig. 12.1.

The broadening of spectral absorption lines or bands can have several causes. In gases, broadening occurs by the Doppler shift of the frequency of light emitted by

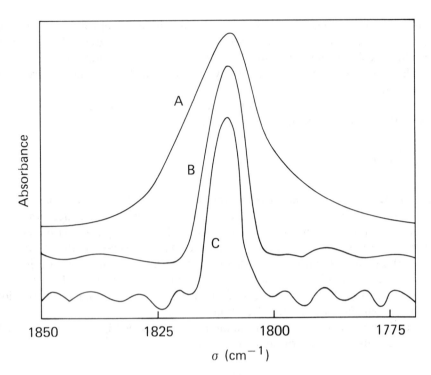

Fig. 12.1 — Deconvolution of a portion of the infrared spectrum of benzene. A: raw spectrum with instrumental resolution of $2\,cm^{-1}$; B: deconvolution spectrum with $1.2\,cm^{-1}$ resolution; C: narrow deconvolution with $0.77\,cm^{-1}$ resolution (After Kauppinen *et al.* 1981).

molecules. Those molecules travelling toward the observer have a higher wavenumber than those travelling away, causing a smearing of the observed frequency. In solids and liquids, close proximity of atoms causes frequency shifts which spread an atomic transition into a band. The interferometer itself generates an intrinsic lineshape that masks spectral features: the exact shape produced is a function of the apodizing function used.

The deconvolution technique generally involves the following steps:

(a) Computation of the interferogram of the sample by computing the inverse Fourier transform of the spectrum.

(b) Multiplication of the interferogram by a smoothing function and by a function consisting of the theoretical lineshape of the spectral line. This is normally a Lorentzian (a particular mathematical expression for the variation in intensity with wavenumber). For general deconvolution, however, it is often advisable to employ a mixture of two lineshapes: a Gaussian and Lorentzian. These line profiles represent two extremes likely to be encountered. The fraction of the Gaussian and Lorentzian components can then be adjusted by the operator to suit the circumstances of the spectrum.

(c) Fourier transformation of the resulting interferogram.

In most cases, this procedure must be performed iteratively to obtain the best results. At each iteration, the operator adjusts the lineshape function to provide narrower spectral features without excessive distortion. The amount of distortion actually produced cannot be known in advance, but is usually signalled by spectral features that have a transmittance less than zero or by "washed-out" features (i.e. only small variations in intensity).

Kauppinen and co-workers reported that typical improvements of at least three in spectral line width can be achieved, and that the procedure (even with twenty iterations) occupies ten to twenty minutes. The process can presumably be automated if proper criteria for 'distorted' lineshapes are defined.

12.9   TRENDS IN COMPUTATION

While computer hardware is a prerequisite for FTIR spectroscopy, software has only recently become important. The trend toward more sophisticated instrument control, mathematical analysis and graphical interfaces will continue.

Computers will increasingly be used to control more than one laboratory instrument, and to communicate with other processors via networks. The FTIR user will soon perceive the spectrometer solely as a sample compartment and computer screen.

REFERENCES

Brackett, F. S. (1960), Digital Recording for Spectrum Analysis, *J. Opt. Soc. Am.*, **50**, 1193.
Brown, C. W., Obremski, R. J. and Anderson, P. (1986), Infrared Quantitative Analysis in the Fourier Domain: Processing Vector Representations, *Appl. Spectrosc.*, **40**, 734.
Cuthbert, J. (1974), Fourier Transform Spectroscopy, in Carrington, R. A. G. (ed.) *Computers for Spectroscopists*, Adam Hilger, London.
Foskett, C. T. (1981), Revolution and Evolution in Fourier transform infrared (FTIR) software, *Proc. SPIE 289*, **406**.
Hecht, H. G. (1986), Quantitative Analysis of Powder Mixtures by Diffuse Reflectance, *Appl. Spectrosc.*, **34**, 161.
Hoffman, J. E. (1969) Real-Time Fourier Spectroscopy, *Appl. Opt.*, **8**, 323.
Hoffman, J. E. and Vanasse, G. A. (1966), Real-Time Spectral Synthesis in Fourier Spectroscopy, *Appl. Opt.*, **5**, 1167.
Johnston, S. F. (1986), *Michelson 100 Spectrometer User's Guide*, Bomem Inc.
Kahan, A. M. (1973), Fourier Transform Spectroscopy with a PDP-11 Computer, *Infr. Phys.*, **13**, 25.
Kauppinen, J. K., Moffat, D. J., Mantsch, H. H. and Cameron, D. G. (1981), Fourier Self-Deconvolution: A Method of Resolving Intrinsically Overlapped Bands, *Appl. Spectrosc.*, **40**, May/June.
King, G. W. and Priestly, W. (1951), Spectrometric Analysis Employing Punched Card Calculators, *Anal. Chem.*, **23**, 1418.
King, G. W., Blanton, E. H., and Frawley, J., (1954), Spectroscopy From the Point of View of Communication Theory, Part IV: Automatic Recording of Infrared Spectra on Punched Cards, *Appl. Opt.*, **44**, 397.
Koenig, J. L. (1975), Applications of Fourier transform infrared spectroscopy to chemical systems, *Appl. Spectrosc.*, **29**, 293.
Kuentzel, L. E. (1951), New Codes for Hollerith-Type Punched Cards, *Anal. Chem.*, **23**, 1413.
Levy, F., Milward, R. C., Bras, S. and Le Toullec, R. (1970), Real-time far-infrared Fourier spectroscopy using a small digital computer, *Aspen International Conference on Fourier Spectroscopy*, Vanasse, G. A., Stair, A. T., and Baker, D. J. (eds.) AFCRL-71-0019, p. 331.
Lua, K. T. (1984), Microcomputers in Fourier Transform Spectroscopy, *Infr. Phys.*, **24**, 339.

Michel, G. (1972), Real-Time Computer for Monitoring a Rapid-Scanning Fourier Spectrometer, *Appl. Opt.*, **11**, 2671.

Pritchard, J. L., Bullard, A., Sakai, H. and Vanasse, G. A. (1967), Idealab Fourier Transform Analog Computer, *J. Phys.*, **28**, Suppl. 3, 68.

Rogoff, M. (1957), Automatic Analysis of Infrared Spectra, *Ann. N. Y. Acad. Sci.*, **69**, 27.

Root, K. D. J. (1974) From Computers to Spectrometers, in Carrington, R. A. G. (ed.) *Computers for Spectroscopists*, Adam Hilger, London.

Savitsky, A. (1966), Use of Computers in Spectroscopy, in Kendall, D. N., *Applied Infrared Spectroscopy*, Reinhold, London.

Schummers, J. H. (1979), Interferometer Design and Data Handling in a High-Vibration Environment. Part II: Data Handling, *Proc. SPIE*, **191**, 92.

Yoshinaga, H., Fujita, S., Minami, S., Suemoto, Y., Inoue, M., Chiba, K., Nakano, K., Yoshida, S. and Sugimori, H. (1966), A Far Infrared Interferometric Spectrometer with a Special Electronic Computer, *Appl. Opt.*, **5**, 1159.

13

The evolution of interferometers

Although interferometers have few components, their designs continue to evolve today. Some of the designs treated in this section can be traced back to the early renaissance days of FTIR in the 1950s. Common design features will be discussed together, so that their motivation and originality can be more easily understood.

The designs of interferometers can be categorized by their approach to solving some technical problems:

(1) Maintaining optical alignment.
(2) Accurately adjusting the optical path difference.
(3) Measuring the optical path difference.
(4) Optimizing the optical characteristics.

These problems are inter-related, and interferometer designs frequently solve two or more of them with a single feature.

13.1 SCANNING DESIGNS

13.1.1 Cube-corner retroreflectors

Edson Peck (1948, 1956) originated the idea of replacing the flat mirrors of an interferometer by cube-corner mirrors. Cube-corner retroreflectors can reverse the direction of a beam of light independently of their orientation. This characteristic can compensate for a scan drive that cannot prevent tilting of the moving mirror.

A cube-corner consists of three mutually perpendicular mirrors arranged with their reflecting surfaces facing into an imaginary cube. Such an arrangement has the property of returning an incident light ray along a path exactly parallel to its input direction, independently of its angle. This is in contrast to a flat mirror, which reflects an incoming ray about the normal to the mirror surface.

The independence to tilt of cube-corner mirrors makes them advantageous for interferometry. The orientation of the assembly does not alter the return path of the light beam (as long as it does not occlude the beam at its edges). Thus, tilting the assembly has no effect on optical path difference through the interferometer. Unlike flat mirrors, displacement of the corner of the assembly does have the effect of altering the optical path, but the sensitivity to displacement is some ten times less than for an equivalent displacement of one edge of a flat mirror.

Peck wrote (1948):

> ...in spite of the seeming increased complexity of the new interferometer, it seems to retain its adjustment better than the conventional type...In such an instrument no angular adjustment whatever is needed for relative orientation of the two mirror sets.

A less obvious drawback to cube-corner mirrors is that each ray is reflected three times rather than once in order to return to the beamsplitter. Real-world mirrors are never perfectly flat; a reflection from an imperfect mirror yields an imperfect return beam, which is to say that the optical path difference will no longer be constant across the entire beam. In cube-corner mirrors, the net wavefront error is therefore somewhat worse than for flat mirrors, leading to poorer modulation efficiency.

A second problem with cube-corners is that they guarantee perfect retro-reflection only if the mutual angles between the three surfaces are exactly 90 degrees. In practice, errors of a several seconds or even minutes of arc can occur during fabrication or afterwards. This causes imperfect superposition of the two recombined beams except at one particular optical path difference. The result of the "skewing" or "shearing" of the recombined beams is a miscentred interferogram fringe pattern at the detector, and loss of modulation with increasing path difference. Such a result produces undesired apodization of the interferogram, and introduces degraded resolution.

The first cube-corner interferometer used for Fourier spectroscopy was made by Peter Fellgett (1958). The first commercial interferometer to employ cube-corner mirrors was the Mattson Sirius series in 1983. White (1985) described the stability advantages of this instrument, in agreement with Peck's expectations of nearly four decades earlier. He highlighted the potential problem of shearing of the interferometer beams, however:

> Although mirror tilt is effectively eliminated, "shear" can be a problem. In a cube-corner system, shear is caused by side-to-side or up-and-down motion of the modulating mirror during a scan. Because of shear, the interferometer beams reflecting from each of the mirrors overlap poorly at the beamsplitter. Alignment tolerances on the order of a few microns must be maintained to eliminate aberrations caused by flat-mirror tilt, because wavelengths of infrared radiation are of that magnitude. Requirements for cube-corner retroreflectors are two orders of magnitude less severe.

Cube-corner reflectors have subsequently been employed in spectrometers manufactured by Bomem (1986) and Lloyd Instruments (1988).

13.1.2   Cat's eye interferometers
The cat's eye retroreflector was first used extensively by Connes' group, and has since been employed in most high resolution interferometers. It consists of a focusing

primary mirror (usually a paraboloidal mirror) and a secondary mirror, which may be concave, convex, or flat. The cat's eye retroreflector receives an incident beam of nearly parallel light and, almost independently of angle of incidence, returns the beam in the original direction. The arrangement is thus insensitive to tilt, removing many of the constraints on a scan drive and the requirements for extreme angular stability. The replacement of the flat mirrors of an interferometer by cat's eyes reduces the need for periodic realignment and maintains fringe contrast during long scans.

The disadvantages of cat's eye retroreflectors are twofold. First, they are expensive to produce. The two curved mirrors of each assembly must have a good surface figure (i.e. must not distort the wavefront by deviating from the ideal surface shape) and maintain a precise separation to minimize distortion. Secondly, large off-axis angles will distort the wavefront and lead to reduced fringe modulation. The cat's eye cannot, therefore, compensate for gross alignment errors as effectively as cube-corner mirrors can.

Beer and Marjaniemi (1966) performed ray-trace analyses on various cat's eye retroreflector designs. They found that good retroreflection could be obtained if the separation of the primary paraboloidal and secondary spherical mirror was maintained to a tolerance of $\pm 5\ \mu m$. The combination of two spherical mirrors was much less satisfactory because of spherical aberration.

They concluded from their theoretical study that a cat's eye was superior to a cube-corner retroreflector because it was easier to produce. According to them, the only major source of misalignment was the separation between the primary and secondary mirrors. A tilt or miscentering of the elements is geometrically equivalent to a change in angle of incidence and retroreflection. Cube-corner retroreflectors, on the other hand, have six degrees of freedom: two rotational axes for each of the three flat mirrors. The optical schematic of Beer and Marjaniemi's interferometer is shown in the top half of Fig. 13.1. R. Schindler (1970) ensured that the critical distance between the primary and secondary mirrors remained constant by using a fused silica tube as spacer: this permitted operation over a wide temperature range. In addition, the primary mirror used a differential screw for fine focusing. The secondary mirror of the cat's eye was attached to a piezoelectric transducer to allow movements of a few nanometers for operation of a positioning servo-system.

Despite some excellent examples in custom-made interferometers, the practical difficulties of cat's eye mirrors are attested by the fact that only two commercial instruments have employed them (the Coderg FS4000 and the Chelsea Instruments FT500 FT-UV spectrometer).

13.1.3 High resolution interferometers using cat's eyes

The earliest high-resolution interferometers were constructed by Connes and co-workers. Describing a later version using an air bearing and linear motor for scan mirror movement, they wrote (Connes and Michel 1975):

> While the mechanical performance of the system has been adequate, the use of an air bearing in a large, lightly built interferometer, incorporating liberal use of long and thin members of light alloys, has nevertheless been a clear

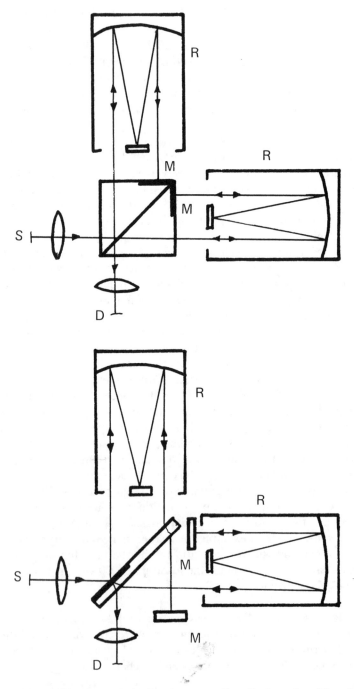

Fig. 13.1 — High-resolution compensating interferometers. Top: Configuration of Beer (1967), employing combined beamsplitter and retroreflector cube. Bottom: diagram of Balashov *et al.* (1978), employing a combined beamsplitter/compensator plate and two fixed mirrors. S: source; R: cat's eye retroreflectors; M: flat mirrors; D: detector.

mistake. Whenever the system is operated, a small thermal gradient appears after a few hours and is disturbed every time the insulating box is opened. Small interferometer misadjustments are induced, and the instrument is dismally less stable than its predecessors.

The next version replaced the air bearing by a "slave carriage". This consisted of a cat's eye mirror carriage rocking on four flexure pivots and actuated by a linear motor for fine adjustment (flexure pivots are described in Section 13.1.4). The coarser scanning movement was carried out by moving this entire assembly along five ball bearings, pulled by a small DC motor via two rubber belts. This two-stage carriage was apparently successful:

> ...routinely used with such good results that we now consider air or oil bearings obsolete for this particular purpose. A larger carriage with a 25-cm diam cat's eye and 10-m displacement has also been built and tested for interferometer VI. In this case belts are eliminated; the rotary motor is placed on the carriage and acts directly on the rollers.

A Soviet high-resolution interferometer

A non-commercial Fourier spectrometer developed at the USSR Academy of Sciences Central Construction Bureau of Unique Scientific Instruments, Moscow (Balashov *et al.* 1978) is worthy of note.

The interferometer is a high resolution (0.005 cm^{-1}) design operating between 0.6 and 100 µm, and employs compensated cat's eye optics (see Fig. 13.1, bottom). The scan mirror carriage is positioned on a catamaran floating in two oil baths. Four polished rails above the carriage stabilize the horizontal motion of the catamaran. The pressure of the catamaran on the rails can be regulated by a level-adjusting device in the oil bath. The carriage is driven directly by a precision lead screw having a diameter of 50 mm, 2-mm pitch and 1200-mm length. The local error along the screw length is said to be less than 20 µm. Maximum carriage travel is 500 mm, providing an optical path difference of 2000 mm through the double-pass interferometer. The entire unit is contained within a vacuum chamber.

The interferometer is of the slow-scanning type. A helium–neon laser is used for quadrature detection of position and direction of motion. Each laser fringe is interpolated into 16 parts, in principle allowing sampling of the interferogram in increments much smaller than the laser wavelength and permitting a spectral range into the ultraviolet. The signal is chopped at 400 Hz.

The infrared signal is detected, amplified, integrated, digitized and recorded on paper tape for subsequent transformation and analysis. The data acquisition system can operate at up to 6 measurements/second.

13.1.4 Scanning parallelogram designs

Michelson's interferometer has undergone numerous adaptations as designers sought to make it simpler, cheaper and less sensitive to problems. Much of this diversity has appeared only in the last decade; perhaps, as with living things, change evolves fastest when the environment (in this case, the spectroscopy market) is in transition.

Egevskaya (1984) described a rather different geometry based on cat's eye reflectors (Fig. 13.2). Like Connes' design, it employed a rocking carriage termed by some a "porch-swing". The porch-swing uses a parallelogram arrangement to ensure that the interferometer scan mirror keeps a constant angle with respect to the optical axis. The design was notable in moving the beamsplitter to effect the optical path difference.

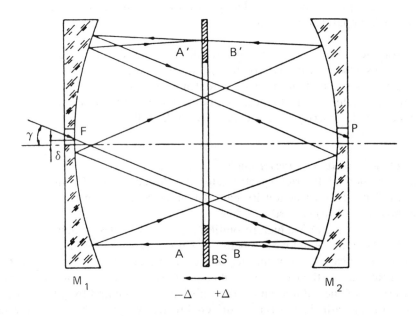

Fig. 13.2 — "Double corner cube" interferometer [reprinted from Egevskaya (1984), with permission of Pergamon Press PLC].

The origins of the parallelogram scan drive are obscure. Strong and Vanasse (1959) used three leaf-spring levers in a porch-swing arrangement in their lamellar interferometer. Gebbie *et al.* (1962) described the use of flat springs serving as the elastic elements, as shown in Fig. 13.3. The IRIS interferometers of the Nimbus, Mariner and Voyager space probes employed such an arrangement (Hanel *et al.* 1970). Walker and Rex (1979) designed a porch-swing scan mechanism that used proprietary "flexure pivots" manufactured by the Bendix corporation for AFGL aircraft-borne interferometers.

The flex-pivot version is presently the most developed parallelogram scan drive. The first AFGL prototype was constructed in 1968, and it developed through five instruments over a ten year period. A total of seven flex pivots make up the parallelogram: four in front and three behind (see Fig. 13.4). Once the parallelogram

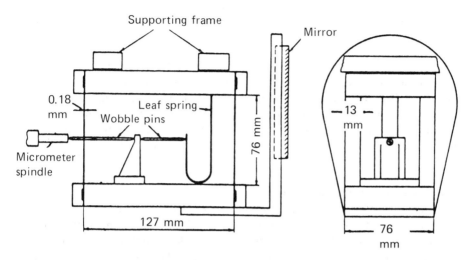

Fig. 13.3 — "Porch swing" parallel motion device (reproduced by permission of H. A. Gebbie).

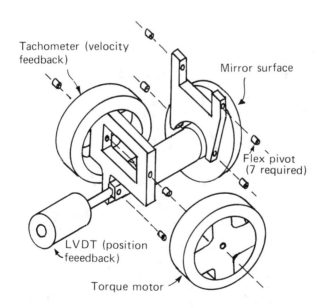

Fig. 13.4 — "Parallelogram" scan mirror design used by AFGL (adapted from Huppi, R. and Shipley, E., *SPIE*, **191**, 31 (1979)).

has been accurately assembled (which requires rotation of individual flexure pivots, for example, owing to their non-concentric centres and flex axes) it should maintain optical alignment for long periods. The reliability is such that it is claimed that a flex-pivot interferometer aligned in 1969 received continuous use for a ten year period without adjustments — surely a record in Fourier spectroscopy.

The parallelogram design is the prototype for several modern scan drives which produce movement without rolling or sliding friction. The Nicolet Corporation has used this design in commercial spectrometers since the early 1980s.

Drive mechanisms for the porch-swing are sometimes electromagnetic — voice-coil mechanisms or more sophisticated linear motors. In the version of Walker and Rex, a motor on one rotation axis was used to oscillate the assembly. The absence of friction makes this arrangement particularly effective for straightforward servo-control of the scan speed.

13.1.5 "Rotating periscope" designs

An approach used by Bomem Inc. for special applications (although not standard commercial instruments) is the rotating periscope. The scan arm of the interferometer consists of two flat mirrors mounted on a platform that can be oscillated by a torque motor, and a fixed mirror beyond (Fig. 13.5). The two rotating mirrors are

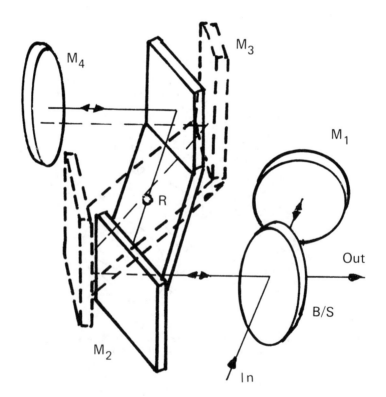

Fig. 13.5 — "Periscope" scanning optics. M_1, M_4: fixed mirrors; M_2, M_3: mirrors on frame rotating about pivot R. Dotted lines show mechanical position and ray path for a larger optical path difference.

aligned to be exactly parallel. Slight rotation of the platform then tilts this assembly, increasing the optical path.

This design is stable and allows particularly smooth scanning because optical path is altered by an easily-controlled rotation rather than linear movement. Its drawback is the relatively long optical path necessary for even a small scan distance. The long path makes the package rather bulky, and the interferometer becomes susceptible to changes in refractive index or composition of the medium in the two arms, yielding the possibility of irregular interferograms.

13.1.6   Rotating plate design

Janos Ltd have marketed an interferometer employing a rotating transparent plate to alter the optical path difference. This is the refractive analogue of the "rotating periscope" design, replacing a reflective path by a refractive path.

The characteristics of the rotating plate interferometer are rather different from the periscope, however. To produce a large enough path difference, the refractive plate must rotate through a much larger angle than the reflective arrangement. In practice, the interferometer plate simply rotates continuously. This makes for a simple drive (i.e. a slowly rotating motor) and stable scan characteristics. The optical path difference is not proportional to scan angle or time, but the use of a reference channel can ensure that the interferogram is sampled at uniform increments of path difference. Finally, the absorbance and reflectance of the refractive plate vary with angle, but the recording of a reference spectrum which is subsequently divided into the sample spectrum removes this instrumental distortion of the interferogram.

13.1.7   Rotating interferometer design

Perkin–Elmer have used a scheme proposed by Sternberg and James (1964) in their PE 1700 Series interferometers. In the Sternberg and James design, the beamsplitter and two flat mirrors are mounted on a rotating carriage. The axis of rotation is not critical, and may in fact change during scanning without problems. The authors claimed that a 20-cm diameter aperture was feasible, although this would require a beamsplitter/compensator combination having dimensions of 31×25 cm. Figure 13.6 shows the geometry as incorporated by Tittel *et al.*

13.1.8   "Rocking wishbone" designs

Kayser–Threde GmbH patented a self-compensating optical design that uses two cube-corner mirrors on a frame which rotates about an axis.

The design is an extension of an earlier scheme (patented 1980) by P. Burkert of Kayser–Threde in which a retroreflector is mounted at the end of a pendulum free to rotate about one axis (Fig. 13.7). The arrangement was intended for use in a spacecraft cryostat, where very low energy loss due to friction was desired. The idea of combining a cube-corner mirror with a flat mirror originated with M. Murty (1960). It benefits from self-compensation: if the cube-corner tilts or is displaced, the flat mirror still returns the beam along the original path. Only the position of the fixed flat mirror is important to alignment. The moving element, which is traditionally the most difficult to keep properly aligned, has only low tolerances in this design.

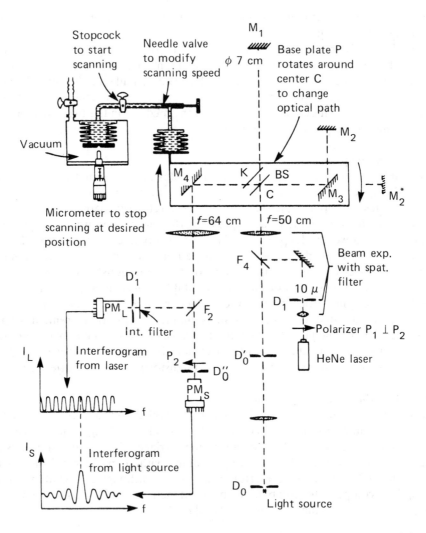

Fig. 13.6 — Rotating interferometer used by Tittel *et al.* (1984), (reprinted with permission from Pergamon Press PLC).

In the later Kayser–Threde "double pendulum" design, now being developed for commercial applications, the movement of both mirrors causes the interferometer arms to lengthen and shorten symmetrically. Light reflected from each cube-corner travels to a fixed mirror mounted on the beamsplitter assembly, from which it reverses its path (Fig. 13.8). Provided that (1) the fixed mirrors are perpendicular, (2) the cube corners are the same distance from the rotation axis and (3) the "wishbone" assembly supporting the cube corners rotates about a vertical axis, there are no further conditions for optical alignment. Because of the movement of both interferometer mirrors and the folded light path in each arm, the optical path

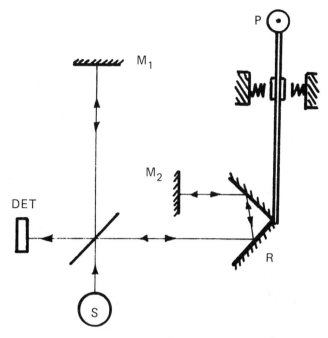

Fig. 13.7 — Pendulum interferometer of Burkert. Scanning is accomplished by pendulum rotating about pivot P, causing retroreflector R to move alternately toward and away from fixed mirror M_2. M_1: fixed mirror; S: source; DET: detector.

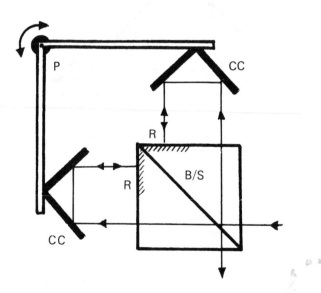

Fig. 13.8 — Compensating interferometer of Kayser–Threde. B/S: beamsplitter; CC: cube corner mirror; R: retroreflecting mirror on beamsplitter cube; P: pivot for cube corner assembly.

changes eight times more quickly than the mirror displacement, instead of by a factor of two as in conventional Michelson interferometers. The angular rotation needed is only a few degrees for resolution of better than 0.1 cm^{-1}. The design can be modified to require even less rotational movement: by replacing the cube-corner and flat mirror by two roof mirrors, the OPD changes at 16 times the mirror movement (Jaacks and Rippel 1989). This optical multiplication allows for a very compact compensated design, but has the drawbacks of accentuating any errors that might occur in scan speed, and of aggravating wavefront distortion by the multiple reflections from imperfect mirror surfaces.

Bomem Inc. have used a simplified version of this rocking wishbone for their "Michelson Series" commercial spectrometers (Baudais *et al.* 1987). In the Bomem approach, the self-compensating feature is not used: the two fixed mirrors are absent (Fig. 13.9). Instead, a single beamsplitting plate coated on opposite sides is used to act as a permanently aligned beamsplitter–compensator pair (this idea was first employed by Fellgett in his astronomical Fourier spectrometer).

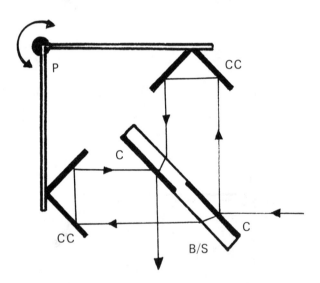

Fig. 13.9 — Schematic of Bomem Michelson 100 interferometer. B/S: beamsplitter; C: beamsplitter coating; CC: cube corner mirror; P: pivot for cube corner assembly.

The advantage of the Bomem configuration is that the input and output beams of the interferometer are displaced, allowing the option of double-beam operation. However, it requires twice the angular movement of the self-compensating wishbone configuration to attain the same optical path difference. This is still only half as much as in a conventional Michelson interferometer, because both interferometer mirrors move.

The main drawback to the rotating frame approach is that optical path difference is limited: beyond a certain angle, the input or output beams are vignetted. The design is therefore most suited to relatively low-resolution applications that demand robust operation.

13.1.9   Refractive scanning

The Janos rotating plate interferometer, already mentioned, employs refractive scanning. The refractively scanning interferometers manufactured by Analect pre-dated this instrument (Doyle and McIntosh 1980).

In the Analect TRANSEPT design, the two interferometer arms contain fixed cube-corner mirrors. The beamsplitter/compensator unit is replaced by an assembly consisting of a fixed wedge (coated on one side with the beamsplitter coating) and a moving (compensator) wedge of the same transparent material. The wedges are similar in appearance to very shallow right-angle prisms (approximately 8 degree apex angle) and are oriented with their apexes on the same side, as shown in Fig. 13.10. By sliding one prism parallel to the other, the amount of transparent material in the beam is increased.

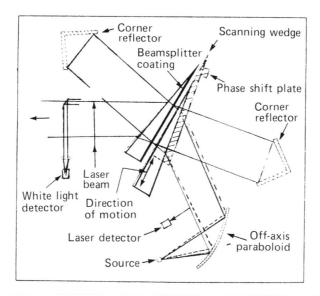

Fig. 13.10 — The Analect TRANSEPT interferometer (reprinted with permission from Laser Precision Analytical Inc.).

There are certain advantages associated with the refractive scanning Doyle interferometer. First, it is more tolerant of positional errors of the scanning mechanism. Movement of the wedge by a given distance causes a much smaller optical path shift than an equivalent movement of a standard Michelson interferometer mirror. This also means that the interferometer is less sensitive to temperature than is a conventional Michelson. Doyle and McIntosh reported that the wavenumber scale shifted by less than $0.005\,\mathrm{cm}^{-1}$ per degree C. Second, it is insensitive to either wedge or cube-corner misalignment, for the reasons described above. Third, it benefits from improved throughput.

There are certain disadvantages, however. As with the Janos design, the variation of refractive index of the wedges with wavelength causes the wavenumber scale to be non-linear. This can be corrected by software, but makes the intrinsic accuracy somewhat less than for a conventional interferometer. The other principal disadvantage is that the ultimate resolution is limited by the practical constraints on physical size of the wedge assembly.

13.1.10 Rotating cube-corner design

Tank (1989) proposed a modification of Murty's design in which a moving cube corner retroreflector and a fixed plane mirror are used in the scan mechanism. In Tank's design, the cube corner is off-centred and rotates about the optical axis. This causes a regular displacement of the optical path. The principal advantage of this scheme is that the scan motion involves no reversal of direction, allowing a constant rotational velocity to be used.

A prototype of this configuration (Haschberger *et al.* 1990) has yielded interferograms and single-beam spectra. Resolution of $2 \, \text{cm}^{-1}$ was obtained over the mid infrared band. The drawbacks of the design are that the maximum optical path difference is determined by the rotational geometry: it cannot easily be altered. Secondly, the nutation of the cube corner causes the angles of incidence on its three mirrors to vary over a wide range. This causes the mix of polarizations in the reflected beam to change throughout the scan. Finally, the optical path difference does not change at a constant rate, but is instead sinusoidal. Even with laser fringe monitoring, this requires the electrical delay in the laser and infrared channels to be well matched to avoid distortion of the frequency scale.

13.2 LAMELLAR INTERFEROMETERS

Lamellar interferometers are the only class of instruments other than Michelson interferometers that have been much used for FTIR.

The first lamellar Fourier spectrometers were those of Strong and Vanasse, as described in Section 8.2. They felt the "wave-front division" of the lamellar interferometer was superior to the "amplitude division" of a Michelson interferometer because beamsplitters covered quite a narrow spectral range in the far infrared. The dividing of the optical energy is generally more balanced in the lamellar grating because it is difficult to make a Michelson beamsplitter giving exactly 50% reflecting and 50% transmitting surfaces. In addition, the Michelson interferometer returns half the radiation to the light source, and so is half as efficient as the lamellar type. Ludwig Genzel and co-workers at the Max Planck Institute in Stuttgart, Germany, also developed lamellar interferometers (and lamellar grating dispersive spectrometers) from the late 1950s onwards.

13.2.1 Principle

The lamellar interferometer uses two sets of strip mirrors arranged to form two reflective gratings that can be separated in depth. Its resemblance to a diffraction grating is the fundamental limitation of a lamellar interferometer. In a diffraction grating, light is dispersed into several "orders". When the light diffracted and focused onto a screen is viewed, a white image of the entrance slit is seen, surrounded on either side by a series of spectra. From the slit outwards, blue light is first encountered (i.e. least diffracted), followed by green, orange and red. Past the red end of the first spectrum, a second spectrum of double the width is produced. Fainter spectra of higher order follow this spectrum, until the spectra overlap to form a faint continuous band.

In a lamellar interferometer only the "white" central image (i.e. the one corresponding to a direct reflection without dispersion) is wanted. This undispersed light is used to interfere with the similar light from the second grating to give two-beam interference. The diffracted light on either side of these direct reflections from both gratings can overlap and contaminate the undispersed component. As described above, a diffraction grating causes the highest frequencies to be least diffracted; thus, in a lamellar grating interferometer, it is the highest frequencies in the light source that cause the contamination. For a given size of lamellar grating, it can be shown that there is a maximum frequency at which the instrument can be used without overlapping of the diffracted orders.

A lamellar interferometer therefore works very efficiently until the wavelength becomes short enough for it to begin to act like a diffraction grating spectrometer. For gratings with spacing of about one centimeter and total apertures of about 30 cm, a spectral range of up to a few hundred wavenumbers can be used. The upper wavenumber limit is also affected by the quality of the lamellar mirror. Manufacturing two sets of intermeshed strip mirrors is technically more difficult than polishing two flat Michelson mirrors. As a result, surface errors introduce phase variation that reduces fringe contrast at shorter wavelengths.

At the opposite end of the spectrum, the longest wavelength that can be measured is limited by another optical effect: when the grating separation is comparable to a wavelength, the grooves formed by the two sets of facets form cavities that affect the velocity of propagation of one polarization of light. This "cavity effect" causes an apparent shift of the frequency scale of the spectrum depending on how the light is polarized. In practice, facets much narrower than 1 cm cannot be used if resolution better than 0.1 cm^{-1} is to be measured.

13.2.2 Strong and Vanasse

In the original instrument used by Strong and Vanasse, the lamellar grating was 7.5 cm in diameter; a second version used 24 mirror facets about 1.3 cm apart to give a 30 cm aperture (Fig. 13.11). They found the gratings difficult to fabricate: the set of facets could not be held rigidly during final polishing, and so tended to be tilted slightly with respect to the plane they were in. The facets were no more than 1/4 μm from a plane surface, but the tilting made the net wavefront error somewhat worse. Nevertheless, the designers were able to observe interference with wavelengths as short as 5 μm.

The moving lamellar grating was displaced smoothly by a synchronous motor driving micrometer screws. A parallelogram scan drive maintained the grating parallel to the fixed grating to within 1/2 second of arc. The interferometer reportedly gave adequate modulation to wavelengths as short as 12 μm (800 cm^{-1}), but results to about 100 cm^{-1} were published.

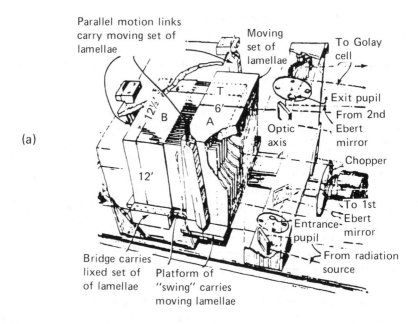

(a)

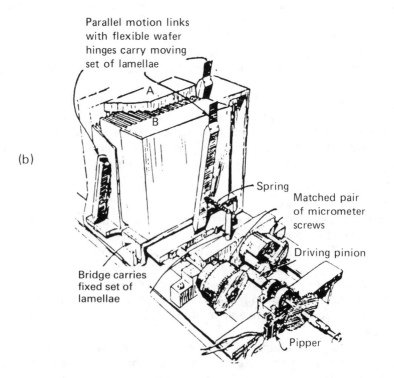

(b)

Fig. 13.11 — Lamellar interferometer of Strong and Vanasse (reproduced by permission of the Optical Society of America).

### 13.2.3	Richards

Paul Richards at Bell Telephone Laboratories directly compared diffraction grating, Michelson, and lamellar spectrometers by building one of each (Richards 1964).

His lamellar grating consisted of stress-relieved aluminium slats 1.9 cm wide, cemented together with epoxy resin and ground flat on their front faces. The front grating plate was mounted on three ball bushings and driven by a micrometer screw to produce a path difference between −0.5 cm and 10 cm.

Richards used a germanium bolometer cooled to the temperature of liquid helium. The interferogram data were recorded on punched cards, and transformed into spectra by using an IBM 7094 computer. High-resolution ($0.1 \, cm^{-1}$) spectra at frequencies as low as $2 \, cm^{-1}$ were obtained. At lower wavenumbers, the mercury source was too weak to provide a good signal-to-noise ratio, but results overlapping those of commercial microwave oscillators were still obtained. Incidentally, Richards found the lamellar interferometer to be the most efficient of the three spectrometers he tested, in accordance with theoretical predictions.

### 13.2.4	The Aerospace Corporation

The Aerospace Corporation was founded in 1960 to provide space systems integration and architectural services to the US Air Force. One of its activities has been to foster research in areas believed to be of general interest to the Air Force.

In 1962, E. B. Mayfield and Dale Vrabec of the Aerospace Corporation Laboratories began a programme of far infrared spectroscopy. They began development of a large high resolution lamellar interferometer that operated in both single- and double-beam modes. They were subsequently joined by J. M. Dowling and R. T. Hall, who completed the design and testing and used it for gas-phase spectroscopy (Randall 1991).

The construction owed much to the earlier Strong and Vanasse design. The lamellar grating consisted of two sets of interleaved plane mirrors, with each Pyrex facet about 0.6 cm wide and 31 cm long. The individual facets were flat to about two wavelengths of visible light (more than adequate for infrared use) but the assembly itself seems to have been considerably less flat: a maximum wavenumber of only $125 \, cm^{-1}$ was achieved.

The lamellar grating was scanned by mounting the upper set of facets on three flexure pivots in a porch-swing configuration. The pivots, in a parallelogram arrangement, nevertheless allowed angular errors of up to 1°. The tilt was reduced to a few seconds of arc by applying a ball bearing race against the moving facets to constrain their movement. The porch swing was scanned by a stepping motor and lead screw. Rather than Moiré fringe or laser position referencing, the investigators used an LVDT precise to $\pm 1.5 \, \mu m$ over a 2-mm cycle (position referencing is discussed in Section 13.4).

The spectrometer gave resolution as good as $0.08 \, cm^{-1}$, close to the theoretical value.

### 13.2.5	Beckman RIIC

Another well-known design of the 1960s was the sole commercial lamellar interferometer: the LR-100 of Beckman RIIC. This differed from the previous designs in several respects: it had a small aperture (8-cm diameter), was limited to very long wavelengths (125–3000 μm, or 3–80 cm^{-1}), and was designed for commercial production. A block diagram is shown in Fig. 13.12.

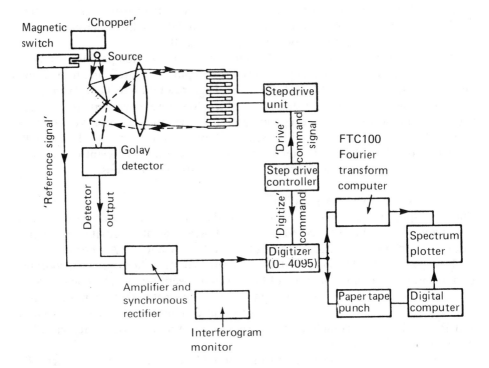

Fig. 13.12 — Layout of lamellar grating interferometer of Beckman RIIC [reprinted from Milward (1969), with permission from Pergamon Press PLC].

The lamellar gratings consisted of aluminium plates whose ends formed facets 1 cm×8 cm. The facets were lapped and polished to a dull finish so that shorter wavelengths were scattered; the facets thus acted as a short-wavelength filter. The drive kept the faces of the gratings parallel by employing an accurately honed close-fitting piston and cylinder arrangement. Parallelism of typically 2 or 3 arcseconds, and no worse than 10 arcseconds, was achieved over the 5-cm travel of the scan drive. The two gratings were not difficult to align:

> The simplified design of the stepping drive unit makes it possible for the entire drive and lamellar grating assembly to be detached from the main interferometer housing, and the lamellar grating to be aligned on the laboratory bench. The most useful method of aligning the grating surfaces under these conditions was by running a finger tip across the front surface of the grating, and adjusting the fixed plates until the entire surface of the grating felt like a perfectly smooth plane mirror when the plates were set at

the zero path position. It was found that this quick and simple method of alignment consistently allowed maximum modulation efficiency to be obtained in practice, as evidenced by the depth of modulation and degree of symmetry of the far-infrared interferogram traces recorded with the instrument. (Milward 1969)

The origins of all the lamellar interferometers so far described were in the 1950s and early 1960s. The most recent design innovation appeared around 1970, and was introduced by N. Hansen and J. Strong.

When the flat lamellar grating is replaced by a concave version, focusing and collimating mirrors are not needed. Instead, the entrance and exit apertures are placed at a distance equal to the radius of curvature of the spherical grating. The simpler construction makes the instrument less expensive and less susceptible to optical misalignment. The spherical grating can be ground almost as easily and precisely as a flat assembly, and all other aspects of the instrument are unchanged.

Apart from the smaller number of components in the spherical lamellar interferometer, it has some minor differences in performance. The use of uncollimated light causes a small, calculable shift in the wavelength scale, in the same way as an uncollimated beam through a Michelson interferometer. Shadowing of the light travelling into the recessed grating is also slightly worse in the spherical interferometer.

The further development of lamellar interferometers has been retarded with respect to Michelson types, because they are intrinsically limited to far infrared operation. Lamellar instruments nevertheless remain the best configuration for measurements in the extreme far infrared, where optical and microwave methods overlap.

13.3 BEARINGS

Linear movement always involves shifting one component with respect to another; in an interferometer, the sliding or rolling surfaces of the moving mirror bear on a fixed surface. The ideal bearing will provide frictionless support and be reliable, inexpensive and easy to manufacture.

The quality required of bearings is related to the wavelength range to be measured. The early far infrared interferometers obtained adequate results with carriages sliding on machined rails.

An early NPL near infrared instrument used a polished glass block on which slid a carriage supported on PTFE pads (Fig 13.13). More recently, the Beckman mid-infrared spectrometer used a glass bearing, correcting for deviations in mirror tilt with an automatic alignment system.

Air bearings were the most common type used in interferometers in the 1970s, and they continue to be used in some instruments such as the Nicolet 800 Series. In an air bearing, a controlled leak of gas provides a thin layer of air between the carriage and guide surface. By supporting the carriage on a cushion of gas, friction is almost completely avoided. The resistance of the air bearing to rotation in various axes

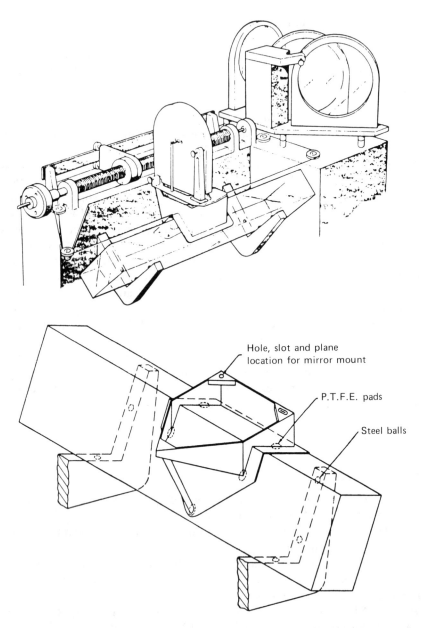

Fig. 13.13 — Glass block bearing used by NPL (reproduced by permission of H. A. Gebbie).

depends on both the bearing length and the thickness of the air cushion. For typical bearing lengths of 5–10 cm and air layer thicknesses below one micron, tilts can be kept small enough to allow moderate to high spectral resolution (better than $0.2 \, \text{cm}^{-1}$ in most cases). To reduce tilting of the carriage further, some manufacturers use either a double air bearing (e.g. two guide rails) or a guide of square cross-section (as used in the Perkin–Elmer 1800 interferometer). In either single- or double-bearing designs, the parallelism of the bearing shaft is vital to its performance.

Haycock and Baker (1974) discussed the characteristics of "gas-lubricated drive bearings" used in their instrument:

> The gas lubricated slide offers several distinct advantages compared with conventional roller element or boundary lubricated slides. Albeit, these advantages are realized only through very careful design and much patience in hand-lapping the bearing surfaces. No friction at zero velocity is achieved with gas as a lubricant, that is, stick slip friction is non-existent. Furthermore, appropriately designed and constructed, the gas bearing will perform satisfactorily even at cryogenic temperatures.
>
> The disadvantages of using gas bearings can be attributed to the compressibility of the working fluid. These surmountable drawbacks compared with contact bearings are (1) a lower load-supporting capability; (2) lower stiffness, where stiffness is defined as the displacement normal to the bearing surfaces when a unit force is applied in the normal direction; (3) stability at high stiffness; (4) auxiliary equipment necessary to maintain a steady supply of gas under pressure.

There are two practical drawbacks to the use of air bearings. First, the leak of gas in the interferometer prevents a high vacuum from being achieved, and makes complete removal of all water vapour and carbon dioxide difficult. Second, the instrument requires a gas cylinder for operation. If the cylinder is nearly exhausted, a drop in gas pressure can cause friction at the bearing and either damage or poor results.

13.4 AUTOMATIC ALIGNMENT SYSTEMS

Despite rigid (and heavy) interferometer designs and avoidance of thermal gradients, interferometers until the late 1970s were usually plagued by drifts in optical alignment. The need for operation in high-vibration or varying-temperature environments led to a new approach by several groups: active monitoring and control of interferometer alignment.

Two general variants of automatic alignment have been used: dynamic alignment only during the scan, and dynamic alignment to initially optimize and subsequently maintain correct fringe contrast.

13.4.1 Bomem

The first commercial interferometers to benefit from dynamic alignment were the Bomem DA2 series (1978). Custom designs following the same principle were supplied under government contracts prior to this. A laboratory version, the DA3 spectrometer, was marketed beginning in 1980.

In the Bomem design, the wavefront of the collimated interferometer beam is monitored at several points near the centre of the beam. Variations in phase between the fringes at each wavefront detector are used to generate a correction signal for two torque motors which tilt the fixed mirror along two orthogonal axes. A proprietary algorithm locates optimal alignment of the interferometer, and maintains this value during the scan under microprocessor control.

The use of this technique makes the interferometer insensitive to the usual problems of interferometry: temperature variation, mechanical shock, and inaccurate drive mechanics. In the DA3 and similar instruments, the scan mirror carriage runs directly along steel bar guideways up to distances of over one meter. This relatively crude system would not maintain adequate interferometer efficiency were it not for a dynamic alignment system.

The Bomem interferometers, exploiting the advantages of dynamic alignment, are well suited to both high-resolution and high-frequency (e.g. visible and ultraviolet) spectroscopy, both of which have stringent demands for accurate alignment.

13.4.2   Davis *et al.*

A non-commercial instrument produced during the same period as the original Bomem designs was a development of interferometers designed by P. Connes and colleagues at the laboratories of the Centre National de la Recherche Scientifique (CNRS, France). The Fourier spectrometer was intended for astronomical observations at the Cassegrain focus of conventional and special-purpose telescopes.

This elaborate system did not employ dynamic alignment in the sense described above. Instead, it used three interrelated servo systems to control path difference, "symmetry", and fringe phase. Like earlier Connes instruments, cat's eye retroreflectors provided the major part of compensation for mechanical errors. Two moving mirror carriages were used; these moved symmetrically about zero path difference under servo control. Such a system maintained a constant centre of gravity and reduced the effects of external shock. The fringe phase servo loop, unlike similar commercial systems, allowed fringes to be tracked and controlled over as many as 32 fringes rather than just 1/2 fringe. This feature was essential to the vibration immunity of the spectrometer.

Concerning careful environmental testing, the group reported (Davis 1980):

> Tests of this type certainly suffice to document the interferometer's tolerance of vibrations, but other demonstrations are possible. These include rapping it with a hammer during operation, kicking it (within reason, of course), stomping on the floor around it, and picking it up and walking across the room with it (requiring four people)...This performance differs markedly from other modern interferometers for which a raised voice, a telephone ring, or vibrations from the passing of a distant vehicle are sufficient perturbations to degrade instrument performance.

13.4.3   Utah State University

Development of cryogenic interferometers at Utah State required a means of maintaining optical alignment as the instrument was cooled to the temperature of liquid nitrogen. Unlike the previously described systems, the cryogenic interferometers did not require dynamic alignment, but only relatively slowly corrected static alignment after the cooling process. Cooling usually distorted the interferometer enough to completely obliterate any interferogram signal (Haycock *et al.* 1982).

Two adjustment screws of the fixed mirror of the interferometer were rotated by geared-down stepper motors under the control of a microprocessor. In the absence of an interferogram signal, the microprocessor ordered a coarse alignment search pattern, involving tilting the mirror axis through an increasingly wide spiral. Once an interferogram peak was located, a fine alignment procedure was followed: the microprocessor ordered fine mirror tilts to "map" the peak alignment in a crossed raster pattern. When the map was complete, the mirror was reset to the best alignment found. The process was relatively slow, requiring up to ten minutes to align a completely distorted interferometer. The system corrected for backlash in the motor gears, and was said to yield an interferogram having 98% of its peak intensity.

13.4.4 AFGL

Another spectrometer designed for harsh conditions and incorporating dynamic alignment was an instrument developed at the Air Force Geophysics Laboratory in Massachusetts (Walker and Rex 1979). A successor to designs stretching back to 1969, this version incorporated a dynamic alignment scheme using three piezoelectric crystal stacks to tilt the fixed mirror (Fig. 13.14). The stacks consisted of 18 piezoelectric disks mechanically stacked in series, and electrically connected in parallel to an amplifier capable of producing 300 volts. Each stack could tilt the mirror by ± 30 arc seconds.

The laser beam, modulated by the interferometer, was monitored at three points; the relative phase error of two of the signals with respect to the third (designated the reference phase) yielded a voltage which was amplified by the servo and applied to the appropriate piezoelectric stack.

The correction was continuously applied during the scan. Unlike the Bomem design, this system did not perform initial alignment before the scan itself.

13.4.5 Beckman

A commercial analogue of the AFGL system was used by Beckman Instruments in their Model 1100 and 2100 FTIR spectrometers (1982). After manual optical alignment, the dynamic alignment system maintained fringe contrast during the scan.

It should be noted that the benefits of a dynamic alignment servosystem depend on its speed of response. A system employing piezoelectric stacks can be designed to have a time constant of less than one millisecond, whereas torque motors may be limited to response times of the order of tens of milliseconds. Moreover, the rate of measurement of the error signal provides an upper limit for frequency response: a system which measures fringe error only ten times per second clearly cannot provide mirror corrections any faster than this. Filtering in the electronics of the servo may also limit rapid response.

In all interferometers employing dynamic alignment, it is important to remove external sources of vibration above the frequencies at which the servo can respond. Common methods include mounting the interferometer on a heavy frame or

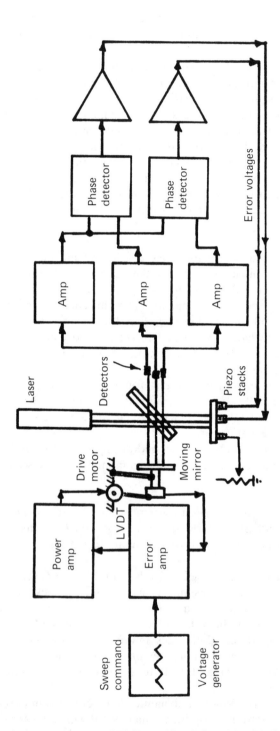

Fig. 13.14 — Servo-control system of Walker and Rex (adapted from Walker and Rex (1979)).

foundation or suspending it from elastic shock mounts to reduce the natural resonant frequency. Rubber shock mounts have the advantage of having a high degree of damping so that an external shock is rapidly absorbed.

As of 1990, several manufacturers (including Perkin–Elmer and Nicolet) have adopted automatic alignment systems for their top-of-the-line spectrometers. These incorporate one or another of the schemes described above.

13.5 POSITION REFERENCING

An important factor in the improved performance of modern FTIR spectrometers is accurate data sampling. Measuring interferogram amplitude at regularly spaced intervals and with highly repeatable scan speed is essential for undistorted spectra. To digitize the interferogram accurately, at least three quantities must be known, in practice:

(1) the position of the zero path difference maximum;
(2) the optical path difference when the sample is digitized;
(3) the speed of the scan mirror.

The ZPD position must be known if the complete phase and amplitude Fourier transform will not be calculated. By calculating only the cosine (amplitude) transform, calculation time can be reduced by a factor of two.

The optical path difference at each sampling point is essential to determining the frequency scale of the spectrum. Any uncertainty in the OPD will lead to frequency scale fluctuations and hence to distortion of the spectrum.

The scan mirror speed must be constant owing to practical limitations of the recording system. If the OPD is measured at a point which does not correspond to the instant of signal sampling, there will be a delay between the two which depends on mirror speed: any speed variations will cause a variable delay and corresponding uncertainty in the OPD position, again leading to spectral distortion.

Moiré position-measurement systems (described in Section 8.9) were used in the 1960s. Successors to these systems are described below.

13.5.1 White light monitoring

The precise position of zero path difference can be located by observing the interference fringes of a white light beam. Since white light consists of a wide range of frequencies considerably higher than the infrared frequencies being measured, the interferogram very rapidly decays to an average value away from ZPD. When viewed at precisely zero path difference, the interference pattern at the detector consists of a multicoloured bullseye fringe pattern. If the interferometer is scanned, the zero path position appears as a very sharp pulse in the detector output. This pulse is a convenient signal either to begin data acquisition or to store as a "flag" indicating the position of ZPD in a data stream.

The very existence of white light fringes was doubted in the early days of interferometry. Millikan (1938) recounts that when Michelson first demonstrated the interferometer to Cornu, a well-known French optics authority in the early 1880s, Cornu was sceptical about its ability to produce white light fringes, saying:

My dear friend, that experiment was tried fifty years ago by the celebrated Fresnel and it does not work... I admit there may be interference fringes corresponding to these fringes you have spoken of...but they were due to a different cause, namely, in this apparatus there are parallel glasses of exactly the same thickness, and where you have them you must always be careful, because you do get interference from those.

Cornu's caution was justified: there are indeed multiple opportunities to observe the wrong fringes in an interferometer. Any optically flat surface approximately parallel to the mirrors can reflect some light to generate spurious interference. Michelson, despite his familiarity with his interferometer, spent many hours in Cornu's laboratory before managing to find zero path difference and demonstrate white light fringes.

A white-light ZPD location system consists of a collimated white light source (e.g. a small bulb placed at the focal point of a lens), a path through the interferometer, and a dedicated detector at the other side. The detector is typically a photodiode. A high quality detector is seldom necessary, because the white-light source is relatively bright and the ZPD peak can be located accurately even in the presence of considerable noise. The path through the interferometer is typically chosen to be along one edge of the aperture or through its centre. Although the beamsplitter coating is usually optimized for the infrared beam, it retains sufficient efficiency for a white-light interferogram.

13.5.2 LVDTs

The LVDT — known either as a Linear Voltage-to-Displacement Transducer or Linear Variable Differential Transformer — is a compact, robust device that provides precision similar to a Moiré fringe system.

An LVDT consists of a set of hollow cylindrical transformer windings into which a ferromagnetic core passes. The core links the magnetic fields of the transformer segments in proportion to its depth in the windings, so producing a linearly proportional output voltage.

In use in an interferometer, the core piece is normally mounted rigidly on the moving mirror assembly and the hollow transformer cylinder is fixed to the interferometer frame. There is no physical contact between the halves, so friction is not introduced. Unlike laser fringe systems, no optical alignment is required to obtain an output from the LVDT.

In most cases, owing to limitations in the uniformity of the windings and parallelism of the core and coils, precision of position of about ± 2 μm is achievable, with an accuracy of 0.5%. This is adequate for far-infrared or low-resolution interferometers, but unacceptable for mid- and near-infrared use.

13.5.3 Fringe monitoring

(a) Optical path difference monitoring

A laser beam can be shone through a portion of the interferometer while the principal beam is being measured. The laser beam is separately monitored by a dedicated detector. By noting the amplitude variations of the laser fringe as the interferometer mirror scans, the optical path difference of the interferometer can be measured in terms of the laser wavelength. The laser thus provides an accurate "yardstick" by which to measure the OPD. By converting the sinusoidal laser amplitude variations into a square wave, the signal can be used to trigger data acquisition. At each transition from "high" to "low" the ADC can be triggered to sample and hold the interferogram signal. Better still is to trigger at every pulse transition (either positive or negative) to obtain two interferogram samples per laser fringe. This amounts to a measurement at every 0.316 μm when an He–Ne laser is used.

The use of a monochromatic reference to measure the wavelength of unknown sources goes back to the first experiments in interferometry by Fizeau and Michelson. Rubens and co-workers used a sodium flame to ensure accurate increments of optical path difference when they recorded interferograms. A filtered mercury lamp was used in exactly the same way by Gebbie and others in the late 1950s.

The laser is a much more convenient light source than a filtered low-pressure gas lamp because it is highly collimated: no lenses or focusing mirrors are needed to limit its divergence. Even the lowest-powered He–Ne laser has adequate intensity for the purpose, provided that the beamsplitter reflects and transmits efficiently at its wavelength.

The beamsplitter can cause problems in two circumstances. In far infrared work, the Mylar beamsplitter can flutter in air currents. The movement is insignificant in terms of far infrared wavelengths, but causes enough instability at visible wavelengths to make laser referencing difficult. The solution is either to evacuate the interferometer, or to employ a separate optical path for the laser beam. This separate path may be either a small glass beamsplitter in the same plane as the Mylar version, or a separate laser interferometer coupled to the main interferometer, usually by using opposite sides of the scan mirror. This latter approach was used in the Perkin–Elmer 1800.

The second circumstance causing difficulty is a solid beamsplitter that is insufficiently flat at the laser wavelength. This is particularly true for beamsplitters made from CsI, which is so soft and difficult to polish that a good surface figure at visible wavelengths is expensive to produce. A common solution is to mount a glass beamsplitter in the centre of the CsI plate for the laser beam.

(b) Velocity monitoring
In addition to providing fringe maxima to infer the optical path difference, the laser fringes can accurately indicate the speed of the scan mirror. The analogue output of the laser detector is a frequency proportional to scan velocity. This signal can be applied as input to a servo in order to control speed.

(c) Quadrature detection
The ability to measure not only the position and velocity of the scan mirror carriage, but its direction of motion as well, is used in most modern FTIR instruments. If the reversal of the scan mirror is noted at the end of each scan, the interferogram data can be stored as separate "forward" and "reverse" interferograms. The ability to

record in both directions maximizes the observing time, improving *S/N*. It also allows portions of the interferogram away from ZPD to be recorded, which can be useful, for example, for monitoring the linewidth or frequency of a spectral emission.

One means of monitoring scan direction is by laser fringe quadrature. In this method, the reference laser beam is divided into two parts, one of which is delayed with respect to the other by a quarter wavelength. These two beams then are modulated by the interferometer and arrive at two separate detectors. Because the two resulting signals have a 1/4-cycle relative phase difference, the direction of mirror motion can be inferred by noting which signal leads and which lags behind (Fig. 13.15).

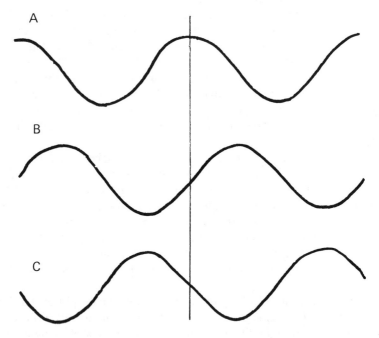

Fig. 13.15 — Principle of quadrature detection. Two fringe signals, shifted by 90° (1/4 cycle) are measured. If the interferometer mirror travels in one direction, the phase difference is positive (curves A and B). If movement is in the opposite direction, the phase difference is negative (curves A and C).

Various methods have been used to produce phase quadrature. In one, a small piece of stressed plastic serves to cause circular polarization the entire laser beam. Circularly polarized light consists of two linearly polarized components, one leading the other by 1/4 cycle. A birefringent material that circularly polarizes an incident beam is referred to as a "quarter wave plate". After the interferometer, the beam is incident on a polarizing window: this reflects one polarization to a detector, and transmits the other polarization to a second detector.

The same result can be obtained by placing a 1/8th wave plate in the laser beam through one arm of the interferometer, and subsequently separating the two polarizations as before.

(d) Heterodyne technique

In heterodyning, two frequencies are combined to yield a lower resultant frequency. Optical heterodyning can be performed by using a laser emitting two closely-spaced frequencies. A helium–neon laser line split by the Zeeman effect has been used by Beckman, for example.

The two frequencies "beat" at their difference frequency of 250 kHz. This high-frequency modulation of the laser fringe signal (modulated at about 5 kHz) is measured by the laser detector. Each fringe is divided into about 50 segments. By maintaining the oscillator and fringe phase constant some fifty times per fringe with a phase-lock loop, the mirror speed can be accurately monitored and stabilized.

(e) Alternatives to the laser

Despite their suitability for FTIR systems, lasers are not mandatory. Lasers are convenient because of their very small beam divergence, which makes collimating optics unnecessary and allows a very small area of the interferometer aperture to be devoted to the position measuring system. No other light source has this advantage. However, the laser's other distinctive feature — its extremely narrow spectral linewidth — is not important for some applications.

As described above, the pioneers of Fourier spectroscopy used other forms of nearly monochromatic light, the most popular being a filtered mercury lamp. The low-pressure mercury vapour emits a discrete spectrum consisting of a handful of visible wavelengths. One of these can be selected by a bandpass filter. The beam must then be collimated to pass through a portion of the interferometer and to its own detector. Other light sources have included neon lamps and even filtered filament lamps.

What happens if the "monochromatic" source is not truly monochromatic? Recall Michelson's measurements with yellow sodium light: the two spectral lines yield an interferogram in which the fringe intensity varies cyclically with optical path difference. As the interferometer mirror is scanned, the fringe intensity gradually falls to zero. A similar effect occurs when the light source consists of a narrow band of frequencies: the interferogram falls to zero intensity at some optical path difference. For broader-band light sources, the intensity falls sooner (indeed, for an unfiltered white light source, the interferogram is little more than a pulse at zero path difference). Clearly, the position measuring system cannot work without fringes to detect. The spectral width of the light source thus determines the maximum path difference that can be measured. The maximum path difference, in turn, is proportional to the resolution of the spectrum.

Thus, if only short optical path differences are needed (i.e. for low-resolution spectroscopy), a relatively broad-band "monochromatic" light source can be used in the position measuring system. For the case of a mid-infrared FTIR that measures at a resolution up to 4 cm^{-1}, the source bandwidth can be about 0.0015 μm (1.5 nm, or 40 cm^{-1} at the wavelength of the He–Ne laser). This is considerably broader than the emission line of a gas laser.

At the other extreme, high-resolution spectroscopy demands very stable lasers in order to measure the OPD without error. Normal He–Ne lasers vary in wavelength too much for high resolution (<0.01 cm^{-1}) spectra: variations in the length of the laser tube with temperature allow different "modes" to be amplified and emitted. Such lasers must be stabilized to emit a single mode having a constant frequency.

13.6 ASSOCIATED SPECTROMETER OPTICS

A Fourier spectrometer consists of more elements than just the interferometer itself. In addition to the beamsplitter, scan drive and fixed and moving mirrors of the interferometer, other optics are needed to, for example, supply light from the infrared source to the interferometer, to direct the light to a sample area, and to focus the result onto the detector (Fig. 13.16). These auxiliary elements depend on the measurement to be performed, but must always satisfy one condition for interferometry: acceptable beam divergence through the interferometer for the wavelength and resolution range of interest.

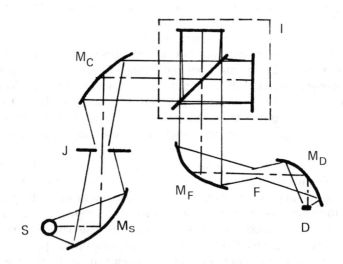

Fig. 13.16 — Optical elements of a laboratory FTIR spectrometer. S: source; M_S: source mirror; J: Jacquinot stop; M_C: collimator mirror; I: interferometer; M_F: sample focus mirror; F: sample focus; M_D: detector mirror; D: detector.

13.6.1 Jacquinot stop

The condition for beam divergence can be satisfied by what is sometimes referred to as a Jacquinot stop. This is a limiting aperture that can be placed at a beam focus to limit the extreme angles in the beam. The Jacquinot stop can be placed either before or after the interferometer; the object of preventing off-axis rays from reaching the detector is accomplished either way.

In spectrometers operating with fixed resolution and wavelength range, it is common to produce a Jacquinot stop either by a source aperture or by the detector size itself. This simplifies the optics by omitting the mirror or lens needed to create a focus at the aperture.

In any optical system, some aperture or combination of apertures limits the beam divergence. A source aperture is undesirable, because it would tend to be warmer than ambient temperature. That is, the edges of the stop radiate a spectrum of their own which becomes superimposed on the proper source spectrum.

In spectrometers employing the detector aperture as the Jacquinot stop, lower wavenumber ranges and resolutions are not optimally used. The spectrometer throughput is less than the maximum allowed for these conditions. In fact, for all Fourier spectrometers, it is actually difficult to use the maximum throughput available in these conditions: far-infrared, low resolution measurements permit a large beam divergence through the interferometer. The divergence is so large that either an unreasonably broad detector is needed, or the focusing optics are required to concentrate the infrared beam over an impossibly wide angle.

In spectrometers with an explicit Jacquinot stop, the variable aperture size is accomplished either with an iris diaphragm (sometimes actuated by a motor controlled by the spectrometer computer) or by a sliding aperture plate. The aperture diameter is usually adjustable to provide the maximum allowable beam divergence (and so energy throughput) for the selected operating conditions of resolution and maximum wavenumber.

13.6.2 Source and source optics

FTIR spectrometers can measure either emission or absorption by samples, and either local or remote sources. The requirements of the optics in each of these cases are rather different.

(a) Emission sources

For emission or remote sources, the radiation from the light source is treated by fore-optics and then admitted directly to the spectrometer. The fore-optics will consist at least of a primary lens or mirror to focus the image of the source onto a Jacquinot stop, and a subsequent collimating lens or mirror to make the light parallel for entry into the interferometer. The focal length of the primary lens or mirror and the diameter of the Jacquinot stop determine the field of view of the spectrometer: as with a photographic camera, a long focal length and small film format yield a narrow field. When an extremely narrow field of view is required (e.g. to view the emissions from a distant chimney) the simple lens or mirror may be replaced by a telescope consisting of two or more elements. The much longer focal length and compact size possible with a telescope make it more practical for mobile measurements.

(b) Throughput

For a laboratory spectrometer making absorption measurements, the light source and source optics are incorporated in the instrument.

For best sensitivity, as much energy as possible should reach the detector. An FTIR spectrometer, although having a much higher throughput than a dispersive instrument, still has a limit on how much light it can allow to enter the interferometer. This is determined by the solid-angle of light travelling through the interferometer, as discussed above. In other words, for a given spectral resolution and maximum wavenumber, the interferometer has an allowable maximum solid-angle determined by the Jacquinot stop.

While the angular acceptance of the interferometer is restricted, the area of the beam is not: in principle, the interferometer need only be made larger to allow more light to enter it. This is the same principle as used in an astronomical telescope, which is made as large as practicable to capture the greatest amount of light. As with the telescope, the size of an FTIR spectrometer is limited only by practical consider-ations. If the instrument aperture is doubled, light grasp will be four times larger, but the volume will probably be some five to ten times greater. Early interferometers had apertures of as much as 25 cm; by the 1970s, apertures had shrunk to 5 to 8 cm, and in the 1990s most new instruments have apertures of 2 or 3 cm diameter.

(c) Spectrometer sources

With the energy throughput limited by theoretical and practical considerations, there remains just one way to improve the amount of energy reaching the detector: by transmitting a brighter beam, i.e. one having a higher energy density. Here we again come up against practical limitations. A light source generating a wide range of colours or frequencies is needed for absorption spectroscopy: it is necessary to produce a background from which the sample absorbs specific frequencies. The best broad-band light sources approximate a so-called "black body" or ideal thermal source. The black body is the theoretically perfect radiator, generating the maximum amount of energy at each wavelength possible for a given temperature.

The characteristics of a black body source are similar to those of heated solids. The heated electric element of a toaster is a good example: at room temperature, it appears black, but when heated by an electric current its colour changes from dull red to orange and (if too hot) to white. Black body sources emit most light at low frequencies, and a smaller amount at high frequencies. The distribution changes with increasing temperature, shifting towards higher frequencies. The energy distribution is always unbalanced: for any temperature, a distinct peak in the emission occurs. A source at room temperature (300 K) emits most at 10 μm (1000 cm^{-1}); at 1000 K, a peak occurs at about 3 μm (3400 cm^{-1}) in the near infrared; and the sun, at a temperature of about 6000 K, emits most of its energy around 0.5 μm (19 000 cm^{-1}) in the visible spectrum.

A good infrared source for a laboratory spectrometer has changed very little since the 1920s. It must radiate approximately like a black body source, and must not have the intensity at any wavelengths reduced owing to absorption. For best energy output, it should be as hot as possible, and the heated area should be large enough for its image to overfill the spectrometer entrance aperture. An ordinary light bulb will not work: its glass envelope absorbs much of the infrared light produced. It also produces much more visible light than desired.

The practical alternatives are various types of heated filament or solid in open air. These act approximately like black bodies, but have a slightly lower output of light power.

The earliest infrared research was done with the Welsbach mantle, a gas-operated source that is now obsolete. Its successor was the globar (or "glowbar"), a silicon carbide bar heated by electric current. The current electrodes are sometimes water-cooled, because much of the input power is dissipated there: the globar has a negative temperature characteristic, causing its resistance to fall as its temperature rises. A constant-current source is necessary to maintain constant temperature and optical output.

Filaments formed from a helix of nichrome wire are an inexpensive alternative. They are sometimes wound around nonconducting solids so that a continuous heated area is produced that is less susceptible to temperature variations by air currents. Relatively cool filaments can operate for a few hundred hours in open air without the protection of an inert, constant-temperature surrounding gas. A similar approach is the use of a ceramic rod wound with a platinum filament and then coated with a refractory cement. The maximum temperature attainable is about 1000–1200°C; higher temperatures cause very drastically reduced filament life.

The Nernst glower is another strong infrared emitter used in the early days of infrared research, and that regained popularity in the 1960s. It is a hollow rod formed from a mixture of rare earth oxides. Its construction allows high-temperature operation (up to 1800°C), giving it about twice the intensity of a filament or globar source over most of the mid-infrared spectrum. Like the globar source, the Nernst source has a negative temperature coefficient: its resistance is so high at room temperature that a pre-heater is needed to start it.

With all types of heated source, operating power can be reduced by insulating it from the surrounding air. The avoidance of temperature variations is critical to obtaining stable measurements. The total output of a blackbody varies as the fourth power of temperature; a minor change in temperature will cause a much larger change in infrared output. For example, for a 1000 K infrared source, an increase to 1001 K (i.e. an increase of 1°C, or 0.1%) will cause a 1.1% increase in output. A change in signal level as large as this would noticeably distort the interferogram and lead to spectral errors.

(d) Source optics

The interferometer input optics must convert the radiation from the source into a quasi-parallel beam. For absorption spectroscopy, the broad-band source light is collimated by one or two mirrors. If an adjustable Jacquinot stop is included, the arrangement will be as in Fig. 13.16. An initial mirror or lens focuses the beam at the aperture, which passes a portion to a second element that collimates it. The ratio of aperture diameter d to collimator focal length fl determines the angle of divergence:

$$\Phi = \arctan \tfrac{1}{2}(d/fl) \qquad (13.1)$$

In the case of a remote source, a telescope can be used to provide the required field of view. The focus from the telescope can then be apertured and collimated as described above.

13.6.3 Sample optics

For routine absorption spectroscopy, the sample chamber has evolved over decades of dispersive spectrometers. The size of sampling accessories such as reflectance attachments or gas cells dictates a standard geometry for the infrared beam.

The sample beam is defined by two characteristics: the diameter at the focus, and the convergence of the beam, usually expressed as an f/number.

The f/number of any convergent or divergent beam of light is defined as the distance to the focus divided by the beam diameter (Fig. 13.17). In infrared spectrometry, sample beams typically have f/numbers between $f/3$ and $f/5$ — e.g. the beam is commonly 3-cm in diameter at a distance of 12 cm from the focus ($f/4$). The diameter of the focus is usually smaller than 10 mm.

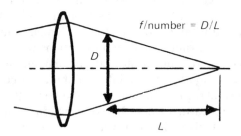

Fig. 13.17 — Definition of f/number of a convergent beam.

The f/number and focal diameter are related. The beam focus is usually an image of either the source or Jacquinot stop. The sample optics and collimator optics determine the f/number and focus size:

$$f/\text{number} = (\text{interferometer beam diameter})/(\text{sample } fl) \qquad (13.2)$$

$$\text{focal diameter} = (\text{Jacquinot stop diameter})(\text{sample } fl)/(\text{collimator } fl) \, (13.3)$$

The sample focus may be before or after the interferometer. Placement after the interferometer is usually preferable: this causes much less energy to strike the sample, resulting in less heating. More importantly, the radiation from any heating which does result is not modulated by the interferometer, and so is not added to the absorption spectrum. In this way, distortion by sample thermal emission and fluorescence is avoided.

13.6.4 Detectors
The detector, on converting the optical intensity variations produced by the interferometer into an electrical signal, can add its own characteristics. A detector that introduces distortion (i.e. that does not produce an electrical signal proportional to optical intensity) or that adds electrical noise to the signal can negate other aspects of the design.

(a) Thermal detectors
As discussed in previous chapters, the earliest detectors used for infrared spectroscopy were thermocouples and bolometers. These so-called "thermal detectors" operate by sensing temperature changes caused by absorbed light. The temperature

change can be signalled in several ways: the thermocouple creates a voltage proportional to the temperature difference between the junctions of two dissimilar metals; in the bolometer, a change in resistance of an electrical conductor is detected; in the more recent thermistor bolometer, a semiconductor changes in resistance. The Golay cell used the thermal expansion of a gas-filled sac to shift the position of a Moiré movement-detection system. In each case, the effect of the absorption of light is eventually translated into an electrical signal. The now commonly used "pyroelectric detector" is a form of bolometer based on ferroelectric materials. For example, Deuterated TriGlycine Sulphate (DTGS) produces spontaneous electrical polarization at room temperature: it has a net charge which can be measured between opposite sides of a slice of the material. At constant temperature, this charge is cancelled by ions; it reappears when the temperature of the slice rises, changing the spacing of the crystal's lattice.

Thermal detectors can respond to a broad range of optical frequencies, because they respond simply to the total power absorbed. On the other hand, the process of light absorption, thermal diffusion, and subsequent change of an electrical signal can make thermal detectors relatively slow to respond: 10–100 msec is typical. This response speed means that thermal detectors are not ideally suited for rapid-scanning FTIR. To accommodate such a slow response time, the interferometer must either be used with far-infrared radiation (which, because of its longer wavelength, modulates at a lower frequency with optical path difference) or else the scan speed must be reduced. Slower scan speed can cause irregularities of motion in some interferometers, owing to sticking and friction ("stiction") of the mirror-drive bearings or inadequate servo-control.

(b) Quantum detectors

A more direct means of converting optical energy into an electrical signal is by means of a quantum detector. To describe the operating principle, we must temporarily leave behind the wave picture of light, and instead think of it in terms of energy packets, or "photons". In a quantum detector, photons of light interact with the electrons of the solid and promote them to higher energy levels. In semiconducting materials, the affected electrons then contribute to generate a net voltage (in photovoltaic detectors) or alter the conduction properties of the material (in photoconductive detectors). When the photon carries a large amount of energy (e.g. a short-wavelength visible or ultraviolet photon) it can actually boost the electron energy sufficiently to free it from the material entirely. This "photo-emission" effect is employed in phototubes and photomultiplier detectors, which collect and detect these emitted electrons with charged grids.

The quantum detection process is inherently more efficient than secondary thermal effects, but has the drawback of being more dependent on the frequency of the light. In order to promote the electron to a higher energy level, the photon must have a minimum threshold energy; less energetic photons are not detected. Quantum detectors have a "peaked" spectral response. The spectral characteristics are altered by the composition of the detector material.

A second difficulty with quantum detectors is that the electrical characteristics of the detector material depend on temperature. Random thermal fluctuations cause electrical noise which interferes with the true signal, particularly when low-energy infrared photons are being detected. Most quantum detectors for infrared use are therefore cooled to below room temperature to reduce thermal fluctuations.

13.6.5 Detector optics

The modulated interferometer beam must be focused onto the detector element. The optics should ideally produce as small an image as possible: detector noise rises approximately with diameter, so a small detector is desirable. Producing a small focus implies having a short focal length with respect to the beam diameter. The resulting highly convergent beam may produce other problems. For example, if the focal length is too short, focusing becomes highly critical; small errors in detector position can negate any advantage. Secondly, if the beam is too convergent, the extreme rays may be reflected at the detector surface or any intervening window. Reflection losses can cancel the advantage of short focal length.

In practice, beam convergence of about $f/1$ is typical. Such a convergent beam cannot be easily obtained with spherical lenses: the surfaces are generally too curved, causing high reflection losses and severe spherical aberration. Flatter lenses can be made from materials of higher refractive index, but this again causes high reflection losses unless the lens surfaces are covered with an antireflection coating.

Spherical mirrors, too, are unsatisfactory for small f/number beams: their spherical aberration results in a relatively fuzzy focus. Furthermore, mirrors are more difficult to arrange into compact configurations than are lenses. As a result, short focal length mirrors must be used with a large angle between the incident and reflected beams. For spherical mirrors, this aggravates optical aberrations.

The standard solution is to employ aspheric mirrors for the detector optics. "Aspheric" is a vague term, simply defining a surface which deviates from a sphere. In practice, aspheric mirrors are usually conic sections, i.e. profiles having a paraboloidal, ellipsoidal or, occasionally, hyperboloidal shape. The first person to use a paraboloidal mirror in a spectrometer was Pfund (1927). A few years later, Randall (1932) used both paraboloids and ellipsoids.

A perfect paraboloid will produce a point focus from a collimated beam, and an ellipsoid will produce a point focus from an on-axis point source. With imperfect input beams (i.e. those originating from non-zero sources) the focal quality of aspherics is poorer, but still superior to spherical mirrors. Focal quality is further compromised when off-axis mirrors are used. For aspheric mirror segments not symmetrical about the axis of rotation, the effective focal length varies at different points on the mirror surface. This can cause unexpected imaging problems when aspherics are combined (Figs 13.18 and 13.19).

A final alternative is the "toroidal" mirror. Toroids are mirrors having a different spherical profile in two axes, this torus (doughnut) figure providing improved imaging in some circumstances. Perkin–Elmer, in particular, have used toroids in their FTIR instruments.

A last caution about aspheric mirrors concerns their fabrication quality. The first aspheric mirrors were produced by hand-figuring, a difficult and expensive process. In the 1970s, aspherics were often moulded from a master mirror ("replicated optics"); these had limited quality, often producing blur circle diameters of one

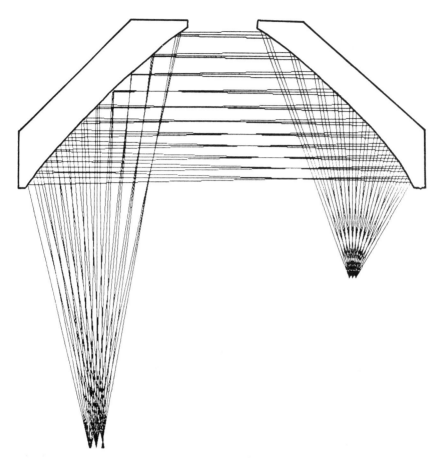

Fig. 13.18 — Optical aberration *vs.* orientation of off-axis paraboloidal mirrors. Case I: symmetric mirrors. Three source points at the right are traced to the corresponding image points at left. Off-axis points are imperfectly focused.

millimetre or more. In the 1980s, diamond-turned aspherics became available. These are metal-substrate mirrors turned on a high-precision numerically-controlled lathe. A surface coating is sometimes applied to improve reflectance or provide protection. Because the lathe is computer controlled, even complex surface profiles can be programmed. The first commercially available diamond-turned mirrors had tooling marks so coarse that they were suitable only for far-infrared use. The regular grooves generated by imperfect cutting tools effectively acted as a reflective diffraction grating, and dispersed the input beam into bright spectra on either side of the correct focus. More recent diamond-turned optics have been precise and smooth enough for use at visible wavelengths.

For applications demanding the highest possible optical efficiency, very low *f*/ number optics can be achieved with immersion lenses. An immersion lens is a highly curved spherical or aspheric front-surfaced lens having the detector directly glued to

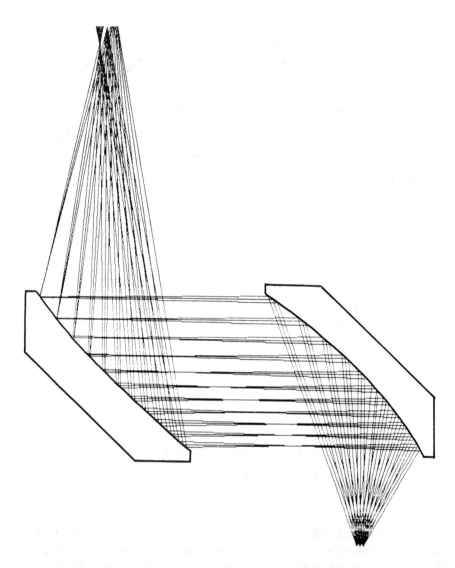

Fig. 13.19 — Optical aberration *vs*. orientation of off-axis paraboloidal mirrors. Case II: antisymmetric mirrors. Three source points at bottom are traced to the corresponding image points at top. Note larger blur circles than case I.

or otherwise "immersed" in its rear surface. By avoiding a second refracting surface, reflection losses caused by steep incident angles are avoided. *F*/numbers of 0.4 or even lower can be attained, thereby allowing wide-angle collection of light and very small detectors.

Table 13.1 — Features of interferometric spectrophotometers of the 1970s

Microprocessor control
Instruments purged with nitrogen and dry air rather than operating under a vacuum
Aspheric mirror optics
Faster, larger-memory, purpose-developed minicomputers and processors
Rapid scanning
White-light zero-path referencing
Laser position referencing
Air-bearing scan drives
Routine operation from 4000–400 cm^{-1}
Operation over as broad a range as 10 000–5 cm^{-1} with a series of beamsplitters and detectors.

REFERENCES

Balashov, A. A., Bukreev, V. S., Kultepin, N. G., Nesteruk, I. N., Perminov, E. B., Vagin, V. A. and Zhizhin, G. N. (1978), High resolution Fourier transform spectrometer (0.005 cm^{-1}) for the 0.6–100 μm spectral range, *Appl. Opt.*, **17**, 1716.

Baudais, F. L., Buijs, H., Bérubé, J.-N. and Vail, G. (1987), The Performance Criteria Imposed on FTIR Spectrometers when Used in an Industrial Environment, *Proc. Sixth Fourier Transform Conference*, Vienna.

Beer, R. and Marjaniemi, D. (1966), Wavefronts and Construction Tolerances for a Cat's-Eye Retroreflector, *Appl. Opt.*, **5**, 1191.

Burkert, P. (1980), Two-Beam Interferometer for Fourier Spectroscopy with Rigid Pendulum, *German Patent*, DE30,05,520,C2 (14 Feb. 1980).

Burton, N. J., Mok, C. L. and Parker, T. J. (1983), Laser-Controlled Sampling in a Fourier Spectrometer for the Visible and Ultraviolet Using a Phase-Locked Loop, *Opt. Comm.*, **45**, 367.

Burton, N. J. and Parker, T. J. (1984), A high precision hydraulic moving mirror drive for use in Fourier transform spectroscopy, *Int. J. Infrared Millim. Waves*, **5**, 803.

Doyle, W. M., McIntosh, B. C. and Clark, W. L. (1980), Refractively Scanned Interferometers for Fourier Transform Infrared Spectrophotometry, *Appl. Spectros.* **34**, 599.

Doyle, W. M. and McIntosh, B. C. (1981), Performance Characteristics of a Refractively Scanned Michelson Interferometer, *Proc. SPIE* **289**, 71.

Egevskaya, T. B. (1984), A Small Interferometer — A Double Cat's Eye — For Rapid-Scanning FTS, *Infr. Phys.*, **24**, 329.

Fellgett, P. B. (1958), A Multiplex Interferometric Spectrometer for Infrared Measurements on Stars, *J. Phys. Radium*, **19**, 327.

Genzel, L. and Kuhl, J. (1978), Tilt-Compensated Michelson Interferometer for Fourier Transform Spectroscopy, *Appl. Opt.*, **17**, 3304.

Hansen, N. P. and Strong, J. (1970), Performance of a Simple Spherical Lamellar Grating Beamsplitter by Wavefront Division, Vanasse, G. A. and Stair, A. T. Jr. (eds.), *Aspen International Conference on Fourier Spectroscopy*, 1970, p. 215.

Haschberger, P., Mayer, O., Tank, V. and Dietl, H. (1990), Michelson interferometer with a rotating retroreflector: a laboratory model for environmental monitoring, *Appl. Opt.*, **29**, 4216.

Haycock, R. H. and Baker, D. J. (1974), Infrared Prism Interferometer–Spectrometer Using A Gas-Lubricated Drive Bearing, *Infr. Phys.*, **14**, 259.

Haycock, R. H., Bartschi, B., and Nguyen, H. (1982), Automatic alignment technique for cryogenically cooled interferometers, *Proc. SPIE*, **364**, 30.

Jaacks, R. G. and H. Rippel (1989), Double pendulum Michelson interferometer with extended spectral resolution, *Appl. Opt.* **28**, 29.

James, J. F. and Sternberg, R. S. (1969), *The Design of Optical Spectrometers*, Chapman and Hall, London.

Jefferies, R. and Birch, J. R. (1984), An Automated Interferometer for Fourier Transform Spectroscopy at Near-Millimetre Wavelengths, *Infr. Phys.*, **24**, 333.

Hofmann, R., Katterloher, R. and Essenwanger, P. (1986), Corner cube reflector for cryogenic interferometric use, *Appl. Opt.*, **25**, 4614.

Martin, A. E. (1980), *Infrared Interferometric Spectrometers*, Elsevier Scientific Publishing, London.

Millikan, R. A. (1938), Biographical Memoir of Albert Abraham Michelson 1852–1931, in *National Academy of Sciences of the United States of America: Biographical Memoirs*, Nat. Acad. Sci. Washington, 1938, **19**, 121.

Milward, R. C. (1969), A Small Lamellar Grating Interferometer for the Very Far-Infrared, *Infr. Phys.*, **9**, 59.

Murty, M. V. R. K. (1960), Modification of Michelson Interferometer Using Only One Cube-Corner Prism, *J. Opt. Soc. Am.*, **50**, 83.

Peck, E. R. (1948), A New Principle in Interferometer Design, *J. Opt. Soc. Am.*, **38**, 66.

Peck, E. R. (1956), Uncompensated Corner-Reflector Interferometer, *J. Opt. Soc. Am.*, **47**, 250.

Pfund, A. H. (1927), Infra-Red Spectrometer, *J. Opt. Soc. Am.*, **14**, 337.

Randall, C. M. (1991), personal communication, 6 February.

Randall, H. M. (1932), An Infrared Spectrometer of Large Aperture, *Rev. Sci. Instr.*, **3**, 196.

Richards, P. L. (1964), High-Resolution Fourier Transform Spectroscopy in the Far-Infrared, *J. Opt. Soc. Am.*, **54**, 1474.

Schindler, R. A. (1970), A Small, High Speed Interferometer for Aircraft, Balloon, and Spacecraft Applications, *Appl. Opt.*, **9**, 301.

Sharov, E. M. and Arkhipov, V. V. (1978), Automatic adjustment of fast-scanning Fourier spectrometer, *Sov. J. Opt. Technol.*, **45**, 720.

Sternberg, R. S. and James, J. F. (1964), A New Type of Michelson Interference Spectrometer, *J. Sci. Instr.*, **41**, 225.

Tank, V. (1989), Pathlength Alteration in an Interferometer by Rotation of a Retroreflector, *Opt. Eng.*, **28**, 188.

Tittel, H. O., Thiel, E., Trakowski, W., Schneider, M. and Heinrich, W. (1984), A Fourier Spectrometer for Visible Light, *Infr. Phys.*, **24**, 323.

Walker, R. P. and Rex, J. D. (1979), Interferometer Design and Data Handling in a High-Vibration Environment. Part I: Interferometer Design, *Proc. SPIE*, **191**, 88.

White, R. L. (1985), Performance of an FT-IR with a Cube-Corner Interferometer, *Appl. Spectrosc.*, **39**, 320.

Zachor, A. S. (1977), Drive nonlinearities: their effects in Fourier spectroscopy, *Appl. Opt.*, **16**, 1412.

14

The optimization of FTIR

Since the origins of Fourier spectrometry, designers have analysed the performance of their instruments, in order to understand the limitations on performance and how best to improve them. Most of the attempts to optimize Fourier spectrometers date from the late 1960s, when space-borne interferometers became practical, and the 1970s, when commercial FTIR was expanding.

14.1 INTERFEROMETER EFFICIENCY

Despite the Jacquinot and Fellgett advantages which make Fourier spectroscopy far superior to dispersive techniques, the interferometer remains an inefficient instrument. A typical Fourier spectrometer makes use of less than one tenth of the energy available to it.

According to an analysis similar to that of Mattson (1978), the efficiency of a Fourier spectrometer can be factored into several terms. The optical efficiency ε_0 of a Michelson interferometer is given by:

$$\varepsilon_0 = \varepsilon_{BS} \varepsilon_T \varepsilon_R \varepsilon_A \varepsilon_S \varepsilon_N \tag{14.1}$$

These six factors are defined and estimated below.

(a) Beamsplitter efficiency ε_{BS}
The beamsplitter efficiency ε_{BS} is the factor producing the highest loss in a Fourier spectrometer. In a conventional Michelson interferometer with one input and one output, at least half the modulated radiation returns towards the source.

The efficiency of a beamsplitter depends on how equally it reflects and transmits light. A light beam entering the interferometer is divided into two components by the beamsplitter. If the reflectance is R and the transmittance is T, then the reflected light travelling down one arm is directed back to the beamsplitter and transmitted to the detector with net intensity RT. The other beam, initially transmitted, is directed back to the beamsplitter by the arm mirror and reflected to rejoin the first beam, thus also ending up with intensity RT. The total intensity of the recombined beam, if all wavelengths are in phase (i.e. at the zero path position of the mirrors) is $2RT$. Since energy is conserved, $R+T=1$ (neglecting absorbance by the beamsplitter). Thus, for any value of reflectance R, $2RT<0.5$, i.e. the interferometer directs only half the light towards the detector. The other half, generating a complementary "inverted" interferogram, leaves from the port at which it entered, i.e. back towards the source.

The efficiency of a beamsplitter can thus be described by the product of reflectance and transmittance, RT, or simply as $R(1-R)$ if the beamsplitter coating and substrate do not absorb significantly. The efficiency is maximized only when $R=0.5$; for any other values, the reflectance and transmittance are unbalanced, and energy is wasted.

A practical beamsplitter coating cannot maintain $R=0.5$ except for a narrow range of wavelengths. Better, flatter reflectance *vs.* wavelength curves can be obtained by using multilayer dielectric coatings. A typical commercial beamsplitter has between one and four layers. Such a coating is illustrated in Fig. 14.1.

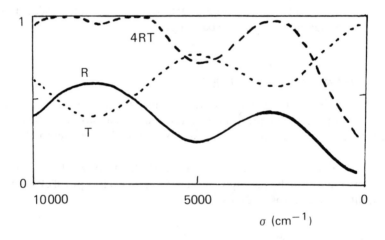

Fig. 14.1 — Example of beamsplitter transmittance, reflectance and efficiency ($\varepsilon=4RT$).

It is sometimes preferable to reduce intentionally the beamsplitter efficiency at certain wavelengths to balance other deficiencies of the interferometer. For example, beamsplitter efficiency may be reduced near the centre of the spectral range to boost the relative interferometer efficiency at the extremes.

A typical beamsplitter might have a reflectance of $R=0.4$ at a particular wavelength. T is then 0.6 and the efficiency is $\varepsilon_{BS}=0.48$.

(b)   Transmission efficiency ε_T
The transmission efficiency describes the fraction of light transmitted through optical surfaces to the detector. In most Michelson interferometers, the transmissive

elements include the beamsplitter and compensator plates and at least one window (e.g. between interferometer and sample compartments). A ray of light therefore crosses at least nine interfaces. The actual beamsplitting surface is taken into account in the beamsplitter efficiency ε_{BS}, so the number of uncoated surfaces crossed becomes 7. Transitions between air or vacuum and a medium with a higher refractive index causes some of the light to be reflected (beamsplitter reflection is shown in Fig. 14.2). If the ray of light is incident perpendicular to the interface, the reflectance is:

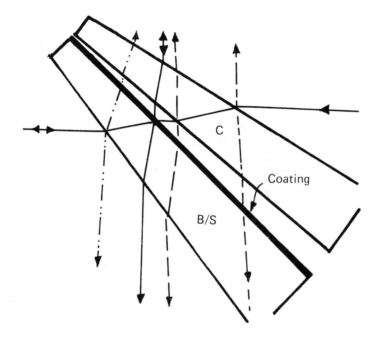

Fig. 14.2 — Principal and spurious rays through beamsplitter (beamsplitter angles exaggerated). B/S: beamsplitter plate; C: compensator plate. Note that no two plate faces are parallel.

$$R=(1-n)^2/(1+n)^2 \tag{14.2}$$

where n is the refractive index of the beamsplitter or window. The amount of light transmitted across the interface is $T=1-R$. For angles of less than 90°, such as the 45° angle at the beamsplitter and compensator plates, the reflectance is higher and depends on the polarization of the light. For simplicity, we will assume the perpendicular-incidence value. For example, the refractive index of KBr beamsplitters and windows is 1.53, yielding $T=0.956$. The net transmission efficiency is equal to the transmittance across seven such interfaces, or

$$\varepsilon_T=T^7=(0.956)^7=0.730 \tag{14.3}$$

(c)   Reflection efficiency ε_R
The mirrors of the spectrometer do not reflect perfectly, and so they reduce the intensity of the beam reaching the detector. Until the 1930s, interferometer mirrors were usually silvered. Silver tarnishes, however, and only reflects well when newly deposited. Evaporated aluminium eventually replaced silver. Aluminium quickly oxidizes to form a tough, protective skin having a high reflectance. For a typical aluminium-surfaced mirror, reflectance is generally not better than $R=0.98$. Even the simplest Fourier spectrometers for laboratory use employ five mirrors; some use as many as a dozen. The net reflectance efficiency for a five-mirror spectrometer is

$$\varepsilon_R = R^5 = (0.98)^5 = 0.904 \tag{14.4}$$

(d)   Aperture efficiency ε_A
Any Michelson interferometer channels an infrared beam that is partially obscured by apertures, small mirrors for directing the laser beam, or (in older instruments) mirrors for directing the white-light channel. The beamsplitter itself is often a limiting aperture owing to its tilted orientation in the beam. The nominal aperture is therefore larger than the actual aperture.

The aperture efficiency is simply the ratio of actual to nominal aperture. A typical interferometer obscures about 10% of the area of the beam, giving $\varepsilon_S = 0.9$.

(e)   Source efficiency ε_S
The infrared source is an imperfect radiator: instead of being a ideal blackbody source emitting the theoretical maximum amount of power for its temperature, it will have an emissivity of less than one. For example, a carborundum glower has an emissivity of about 0.95, giving $\varepsilon_S = 0.95$.

(f)   Modulation efficiency ε_M
The modulation efficiency of an interferometer is what Michelson would have termed the maximum visibility: it is the contrast of fringes generated by a perfectly monochromatic light source.

The modulation efficiency is determined by how well the interferometer keeps light waves in step as they are reflected and transmitted through it at various positions and angles. In an ideal interferometer, an incoming parallel beam of light is divided into two identical components that are phase-shifted with respect to each other and then recombined. The incoming and outgoing beams will have wavefronts that are perfectly flat, i.e. the phase across the beams will be constant.

In practice, this situation is never achieved. Neither the beamsplitter nor interferometer mirrors are perfectly flat. Instead, rays reflected at different points on their irregular surfaces are shifted with respect to neighbouring waves. When the resulting distorted wavefront is focused at the detector, the net phase will be the average over the wavefront. For any position of the scanning interferometer mirror, there will be a range of phases produced. In the most extreme case, the range of phases will approach or exceed one wavelength. If this occurs, the result will be little or no variation in intensity at the detector as the interferometer scans (Katti and Singh 1966, Birch 1990). The modulation efficiency is therefore determined by the flatness of the interferometer components. Wavefront distortion is discussed further in Section 14.5.1 below.

A second factor is optical misalignment of the interferometer. If the interferometer mirrors and beamsplitter are not correctly aligned, the optical path for rays entering at one edge of the instrument aperture will differ significantly from the path at the opposite edge. Again, the result will be a variation in phase at any position of the scan mirror, and reduced fringe contrast.

Since the optical tolerances are proportional to wavelength, it is much easier to construct and keep aligned an interferometer for far infrared use than for visible applications. For this reason, interferometers that are poorly aligned suffer most at high frequencies. Practical interferometers seldom have modulation efficiencies much better than $\varepsilon_M = 0.5$.

(g)   Net optical efficiency
From the estimates made above, a typical Michelson interferometer will have a net efficiency, due to the optical elements alone, of

$$\begin{aligned}
\varepsilon_0 &= \varepsilon_{BS}\varepsilon_T\varepsilon_R\varepsilon_A\varepsilon_S\varepsilon_M \\
&= (0.48) \times (0.730) \times (0.904) \times (0.9) \times (0.95) \times (0.5) \\
&= 0.135
\end{aligned} \tag{14.5}$$

i.e. the interferometer provides only about 13% of the sensitivity of an ideal instrument because of optical losses.

In addition to the purely optical limitations of the interferometer, there are other contributions that reduce the theoretical sensitivity.

14.2   DYNAMIC RANGE

The dynamic range is the ratio of the largest to smallest signals that can be faithfully recorded. In Fourier spectroscopy, the dynamic range of the spectrum is not simply related to that of the interferogram.

The interferogram — the raw data collected in FTIR spectroscopy — must generally have a much larger dynamic range than the spectrum that it yields. The required dynamic range depends on the spectral range covered, and on its frequency content. Consider a monochromatic light source: it will generate an interferogram consisting of a nearly constant intensity sine wave even for a large optical path difference. The intensity at various points along the interferogram can be quite accurately determined even if relatively few intensity levels can be resolved. At the other extreme, a broad-band light source yields an interferogram with a strong ZPD peak and a rapidly decaying intensity with increasing path difference: the many frequencies in the light source soon fall out of step as the path difference is increased, damping out to a nearly constant net intensity. In such a case, determining the interferogram intensity with useful accuracy demands much higher-precision measurements of intensity. A rule of thumb is that, for a dynamic range of M in a spectrum of n spectral points, the dynamic range of the interferogram must be about $M\sqrt{n}$. This means that to measure an absorption spectrum of 10 000 elements with a dynamic range of 50 (i.e. to measure with 2% precision) will demand interferogram measurements having a dynamic range of $50\times(10\,000)^{1/2}=5000$.

This need for a high dynamic range places strong demands on the data acquisition system. Fourier transform spectrometry requires the data system to have a much wider dynamic range than a dispersive spectrometer. Several methods have been used to achieve this:

(1) Employ a high-precision analogue-to-digital converter (ADC).
(2) Use gain-ranging to amplify the interferogram signal at pre-determined optical path differences to simulate the effect of a higher-precision ADC.
(3) Scan the interferometer faster, so that the observation time is shorter, the noise level higher, and the need for a high-precision ADC is reduced. The noisy interferograms can then be co-added to attain the desired measurement quality. Faster scanning thus removes the "ADC bottleneck". On the other hand, faster scanning can make some detectors less efficient, and demands faster data acquisition electronics.

All three techniques are employed, sometimes all in the same interferometer. Early interferometer data-acquisition systems used ADCs with ten or twelve bit precision (corresponding to dynamic ranges of 2^{10} and 2^{12}, or 1024 or 4096, respectively); modern low-priced interferometers usually employ 16 bits (65 536 levels), and instruments designed for state-of-the-art measurements may employ up to 22 bits. Gain ranging is less used than in the past, owing to the difficulty in applying an accurately known gain, by using analogue electronic components, that matches the software value: unless both are equal, the stored interferogram will have a discontinuity at the gain-switching point, and cause a periodic distortion of the spectrum.

14.3 AMPLIFIER LINEARITY

The linearity of the data acquisition system is particularly critical in Fourier spectrometry. Unlike dispersive instruments, FTIR spectrometers record a signal (the interferogram) that is not directly related to the final spectrum. The Fourier transformation can redistribute distortion and noise throughout the spectrum. In addition, the dynamic range of this signal must be much higher than that of a dispersive instrument for equal precision of intensity, as discussed above.

Because of this, any deviations of the detector signal from a response strictly proportional to intensity cause problems. The interferogram becomes distorted, and the ratio of two interferograms gives a final spectrum that is still distorted.

Amplifier nonlinearity usually shows up in regions in the spectrum which should have zero intensity (such as certain absorption peaks, or spectral regions that have been optically filtered). These regions frequently show a non-zero background level.

14.4   FILTERING

Filtering in Fourier spectroscopy can be either optical, electrical or digital. The range has to be limited to avoid "aliasing" of high frequencies (see Section 9.2 for a discussion of digital sampling).

Optical filtering is used to restrict the spectral range of the interferometer. It may also be used to reduce the intensity of undesired frequencies that would saturate the detector response. The filter is typically a material that absorbs the undesired radiation, or an interference filter that reflects portions of the spectrum. Interference filters can be designed with almost any desired characteristic: low-frequency pass, high-frequency pass, or bandpass. They can often be considered as fixed Fabry–Pérot interferometers, and tend to have cyclic spectral characteristics, e.g. a bandpass filter transmits a series of spectral regions differing by integer multiples of wavenumber. The combination of an interference filter (for fine-tuning a cut-off) with an absorption filter (for blocking undesired orders) can yield the desired filter response.

Electrical filtering can achieve some of the same results as optical filtering in Fourier spectrometers. The rapid-scanning interferometer converts optical frequencies into much lower electrical signal frequencies. The electrical filter acts on an analogue input voltage and yields an analogue output voltage. Like optical filters, electrical filters can be designed as high- , low-, or band-pass ("notch" or "spike") types. The steepness of the passband edge can also be tailored, for example by ganging simple filters in series.

Electrical filters have some drawbacks. First, they are difficult to design with sharp band cut-offs (attenuation slopes). Second, the magnitude (i.e. attenuation) and phase response (relationship between signal lag and frequency) cannot be independently controlled. Third, the performance of the filter depends on the values of analogue circuit components such as resistors, capacitors and inductors. The values of these components can drift with time, and may have tolerances too broad to allow sophisticated filter design.

Digital filters consist solely of software algorithms, and have advantages over analogue electrical filters. When a digital filter is used, the analogue detector signal is first converted into numeric form by an analogue-to-digital converter, producing a string of numbers that can be stored as an array or passed directly to the microprocessor for real-time calculation. As with all digital sampling schemes, the analogue signal must not contain frequencies higher than half the sampling frequency. The digital filter is an algorithm for acting on the array or incoming string of numbers to yield a new array or string.

As an example of how a digital filter works, consider a low-pass filter: a 3-point moving average filter. This works by summing three data values in the data array and dividing them by three to yield an output value. The next output value is produced by adding the next data value in the array and discarding the oldest value from the last set of three; this amounts to shifting the "averaging cell" by one value. This process is continued until the end of the array is reached. The output array will consist of data with much of the high-frequency information removed. For example, if the signal fluctuates between high and low values for alternate data points, this characteristic will be smoothed out in the output array. A more sophisticated digital filter would manipulate more than three data points at a time, and would tailor the relative weighting of the values used in the summation. By giving each point in the sum a different weight, the frequency response of the digital filter can be controlled. Even more sophisticated filtering is possible by "feeding back" output points into the input.

Digital filters are superior to both optical and electrical filters in allowing complete specification of the filtering function. Both the amplitude and phase response can be completely defined, limited only by the sampling rate and available computation time. As originally used by J. Connes, digital filtering can limit the spectrum to a sharply-defined spectral band by removing undesired frequencies from the interferogram. This has the benefit of reducing the number of points in the interferogram and the computation time for the Fourier transform.

14.5 BEAMSPLITTER DESIGN

The beamsplitter of an interferometer must perform the following functions:

(1) Cause negligible distortion of either the transmitted or reflected wavefronts.
(2) Operate over a broad spectral band.
(3) Divide incoming light into two beams of equal intensity.

In practice none of these requirements is perfectly satisfied. Factor (1) contributes to the modulation efficiency ε_M, whereas factors (2) and (3) affect the beamsplitter efficiency ε_{BS}.

14.5.1 Wavefront distortion
The beamsplitter can distort the wavefront in two ways.

First of all, the surfaces of the beamsplitter and compensator plates may not be perfectly flat, so an incoming flat wavefront will leave the assembly with superimposed irregularities proportional to the surface error. For surface irregularities of physical height h, the wave transmitted through the surface will have distortions of $(n-1)h$, where n is the index of refraction of the material (n is typically between 1.3 and 5 for beamsplitter materials). For a wave reflected from the beamsplitter surface, the resulting distortion will be $2h$. For example, if a CsI beamsplitter ($n=1.7$) has one surface with a flatness error of $h=1/4$ wavelength, then after a single transmission the wavefront error will be 0.18 wavelength, and after one reflection the error will be 0.5 wavelength. The flatness of reflecting surfaces is generally more critical than that of transparent surfaces.

For a real beamsplitter/compensator pair, all four surfaces are imperfect, and the net wavefront error will be the root-mean-square combination of these. For example, if the same CsI beamsplitter is flat to 1/4 wave on all four surfaces, the net error will be about one wavelength, owing to 1 reflection and six or eight transmissions (depending on the interferometer arm) for each beam. This wavefront error is far too large to be acceptable: when focused to a point at the detector, the variations in phase would combine and cancel to produce very little net modulation when the interferometer scans. The tiny interferogram signals would lead to very poor-quality spectra. Practical beamsplitters (and interferometer mirrors) are therefore specified to be flat to at worst 1/8 of the shortest wavelength to be measured. Interferometers designed for one spectral range may be very inefficient at shorter wavelengths for this reason.

The second way in which the beamsplitter can distort the wavefront is by variations in refractive index. The optical pathlength through a material of refractive index n and thickness t is nt. If variations having a magnitude n' occur through the beamsplitter and compensator plates, the net wavefront error will be $n't$. Thick beamsplitters are therefore more prone to cause distortion than thin beamsplitters. In practice, variations in homogeneity rarely exceed $n'=0.00001$ for common beamsplitter materials, but even this is sufficient to introduce a worst-case distortion of one wavelength of visible light for a typical beamsplitter thickness: the beam passes through a thickness of $4\sqrt{2}$ times the beamsplitter plate thickness, or typically some 5 cm of material. Beamsplitter blanks are normally selected to be homogeneous over scales larger than a few millimetres to minimize such problems. Rejection of completed beamsplitters for unsatisfactory flatness and homogeneity is common, though. Quality problems are exacerbated by the materials used for infrared beamsplitters. Unlike optical glass, infrared-transmissive materials are often soft (e.g. AgBr), hygroscopic (e.g. KBr) or both (e.g. CsI). Such materials can distort in their mountings after assembly, or develop rough surfaces by water absorption.

14.5.2 Spectral band

No infrared transmitting material has the ideal optical characteristics of transparency and low refractive index over a wide range. A low refractive index is desirable because it minimizes reflection losses at the uncoated surfaces and makes the beamsplitter less sensitive to surface flatness and homogeneity errors.

The best compromise for mid infrared interferometers is potassium bromide. KBr has a broad spectral transmittance (about 4500–450 cm^{-1} with little loss, or up to 10 000–350 cm^{-1} with usable transmittance) and low refractive index ($n=1.53$). Its mechanical properties are poor, though: it is both extremely hygroscopic and soft. The water-absorbing tendency can be reduced by the manufacturer's application of a thin coating of sealant such as parylene (a common coating for printed circuit boards). If the thickness of such a coating is appropriately chosen, the coating can also have an anti-reflection effect.

For measurements below 350 cm^{-1}, CsI is commonly used, but this is even softer and more hygroscopic than KBr. Its surface is sometimes too poor for a visible laser reference beam, necessitating the use of glass inserts or a separate reference interferometer.

Below $200\,\mathrm{cm}^{-1}$, Mylar beamsplitters are still the most commonly used type. The uncoated taut sheet needs no compensator plate: the two surfaces generate internal two-beam interference so that the reflectance varies sinusoidally with wavelength. Film thickness is chosen for the range desired, with thicker sheets used for narrower far infrared ranges. These may be as narrow as $25\,\mathrm{cm}^{-1}$ bandwidth.

Beamsplitters in the near infrared and visible commonly employ quartz. This material is hard, has a low refractive index, high homogeneity and can be polished to flatnesses better than any other optical material. Ultraviolet-transmitting grades of quartz have been used to permit interferometric measurements up to $65\,000\,\mathrm{cm}^{-1}$ (165 nm).

14.5.3 Polarization effects

The above discussion becomes slightly more complex when the effects of polarization are considered.

Light can be expressed in terms of two perpendicular components. When a ray strikes a surface at non-perpendicular incidence, one of these two components is incident at a different angle from the other. The two components have different effects on the atoms of the material they interact with: the component of light of one orientation will be capable of accelerating the material's electrons, while the other will not. This has the effect of yielding a different reflectance or transmittance for the two polarizations of light.

The beamsplitter of a Michelson interferometer normally is used at an angle of 30° or 45° with respect to incoming light; as a result, the two polarizations are affected differently.

Beamsplitter coatings generally have different efficiencies for the two polarizations, and the interferometer as a whole will also tend to favour one polarization over the other. An example is shown in Fig. 14.3.

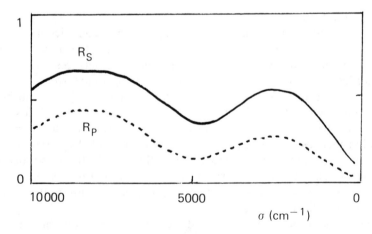

Fig. 14.3 — Reflectivity of two polarizations for a typical 45° beamsplitter.

The two polarizations of light are independent as far as interference is concerned: two perpendicularly polarized beams originating from the same source do not interfere. The interferometer can thus be analysed as a two-channel instrument, with two independent beams divided, recombined, and interfering.

Other components of the interferometer may also influence the relative intensity of the two polarizations. Any optical surfaces such as off-axis mirrors (particularly those with coatings) intercepted at other than perpendicular incidence will have a preferential effect.

REFERENCES

Birch, J. R. (1990), Imperfect Optical Figure in Fourier Transform Spectroscopy, *Infr. Phys.*, **30**, 155.

Hanel, R. A., Schlachman, B, Clark, F. D., Prokesh, C. H., Taylor, J. B., Wilson W. M. and Chaney, L. (1970), The Nimbus III Michelson Interferometer, *Appl. Opt.*, **9**, 1767.

Hirschfeld, T. (1977), Systems Analysis of the FT-IR Laboratory and Operator, 1977 International Conference on Fourier Transform Infrared Spectroscopy, *Technical Digest*, 6.

Hirschfeld, T. (1979), Digitization Noise in Fourier Transform Infrared Spectroscopy and Gain Ranging, *Appl. Spectrosc.*, **33**, 525.

Hirschfeld, T. (1986), Ideal FT-IR Spectrometers and the Efficiency of Real Instruments, *Appl. Spectrosc.*, **40**, 1239.

Kati, P. K. and Singh, K. (1966), A Note on the Surface Accuracy and Alignment of the End Mirrors in a Michelson Interferometer, *Appl. Opt.*, **5**, 1962.

Mattson, D. R. (1978), Sensitivity of a Fourier Transform Infrared Spectrometer, *Appl. Spectrosc.*, **32**, 335.

Pickett, H. M. and Strauss, H. L. (1972), Signal-to-Noise Ratio in Fourier Transform Spectrometry, *Anal. Chem.*, **44**, 265.

Pires, A. and Poultney, S. and Logan, L. (1982), Performance Models as Design Aids for Fourier Transform Spectrometers (FTS) Sensor System Developments, *Proc. SPIE*, **364**, 21.

White, R. L. and Beduhn, D. L. (1985), Dynamic range considerations in the ultimate sensitivity of FTIR spectroscopy, *Proc. SPIE*, **553**, 359.

Zachor, A. S. and Aaronson, S. M. (1979), Delay compensation: its effect in reducing sampling erorrs in Fourier spectroscopy, *Appl. Opt.*, **18**, 68.

15

FTIR since 1980

The late 1970s saw Fourier transform infrared technology pass from the hands of physicists into those of research chemists, and from laboratory-built to commercial equipment. The shift in emphasis can be seen by the topics covered in International Conferences on FTIR. At the 1970 conference in Aspen, Colorado, most of the 50 presentations were by groups that had constructed their own equipment for their own specific applications, typically far infrared research and observational astronomy. Only a few of the talks concerned analytical uses, whereas 80% dealt with special applications and 16% with commercial instruments. In contrast, at the 1977 conference at the University of South Carolina, nearly half the presentations covered analytical applications and 20% were by manufacturers.

By 1980, commercial FTIRs were being increasingly tailored to the needs of analytical chemists. Software now included such fundamental features as ratioing of spectra, spectral subtraction and (occasionally) spectral search. The beginning of the 1980s was the turning point for FTIR as a popular laboratory tool.

Manufacturers' and designers' descriptions have certain timeless features. Almost since the inception of FTIR, new interferometer designs have been claimed to be insensitive to vibration and temperature. The adjectives "fast", "robust", "automatic" and "easy to use" have been applied to each succeeding generation with some truth.

The rate of change of technology, particularly of computers, makes it difficult to keep abreast with the latest hardware. This section surveys the FTIR market of the early 1990s, looking back about fifteen years, i.e. as far as the advent of the microprocessor in commercial instruments. The coverage may not be complete, but it deals with the instruments and manufacturers that became at least briefly known in Western Europe and the Americas.

Since the early 1980s, commercial FTIR spectrometers have evolved considerably. FTIR for routine analytical chemistry has become the major application. The gradual replacement of dispersive spectrometers by FTIR alternatives in chemistry laboratories has put pressures of price, simplicity and stability on FTIR spectrometer design.

The technological trend has been toward benchtop instruments operated by general purpose microcomputers. The need for robust, stable designs has led away from the temperature- and vibration-sensitive flat-mirror interferometers of the 1970s to instruments employing various compensating optical arrangements. Today, most FTIR manufacturers produce at least one instrument satisfying these requirements.

As competition has increased for the limited number of customers, FTIR manufacturers have begun to turn away from versatile, general purpose designs to either modular versions or special purpose designs adapted for particular applications.

15.1 ANALECT INSTRUMENTS

Analect (Irvine, California, USA), or Laser Precision Analytical, was formed in 1980 as the FTIR division of Laser Precision Corp. The company sells refractively scanning spectrometers for laboratory and industrial applications.

The present range of laboratory instruments all use a common benchtop package. The RFX-30 and RFX-40 spectrometers have best resolutions of $2\,\mathrm{cm}^{-1}$ and $1\,\mathrm{cm}^{-1}$ (apodized), respectively. They employ the "Transept" interferometer design developed by founder Walter Doyle, which uses a moving transmissive wedge to scan the optical path difference (see Section 13.1.9).

The RFX-65 and RFX-75, introduced in 1986, are the most versatile models presently available from Analect. They incorporate an "Omnisept" interferometer which uses cube-corner mirrors in a compensated optical arrangement. The RFX-65 uses a rectangular bearing for precise scan motion; the RFX-75 employs a ceramic air bearing. In both, the infrared source is water-cooled. The RFX-75 has $0.13\,\mathrm{cm}^{-1}$ best resolution, and the RFX- 65, $0.25\,\mathrm{cm}^{-1}$. The instruments have modular optical and data- processing designs. Unlike other manufacturers who offer replacement beam-splitter/compensator assemblies to cover various spectral ranges, Analect designed the Omnisept cube interferometer to be factory-aligned and replaceable as an entire unit by the user.

The RFX-75 data processing system consists of a PC-compatible computer and Analect APT-827 array processor. The spectrometer and display unit each have microprocessors providing control independent of the PC itself. The single computer is capable of controlling up to 16 spectrometers and two display terminals.

The RFX-75 is available with options such as the Chromalect TLC–IR (thin-layer chromatography–infrared interface), MICRO-XAD infrared microscope, and DELTA-25 GC/IR interface system.

The "OPTIBUS" optical transfer system consists of building-block optical modules to transfer modulated light from one of the the three computer-controlled output ports to an external experiment. This scheme is convenient, since it avoids the need for custom-made interfaces between spectrometer and accessory.

Analect has specialized to some extent in industrial FTIR, and claims to have installed more units for process monitoring than any other company. The company presently sells two families of industrial FTIRs: the PCM-4000 for process monitoring, and the EVM-6400 for gas monitoring.

The PCM-4000 uses the Transept interferometer with permanently-aligned optics. The unit consists of interferometer, detector and data-collection modules. For specific applications, Optibus transfer optics are used to relay the light between interferometer, sample, and detector. Sample cells are typically designed for transmission or attenuated total reflectance (ATR) measurements, with the components mounted in an industrially rated (NEMA) enclosure to isolate both the instrument and the industrial environment from each other.

Software for the PCM-4000 stresses process control rather than spectroscopy. In most cases, multiple chemical components are monitored by specifying their characteristic infrared absorption frequencies at the initial calibration. Subsequently, information is presented as concentration *vs.* time, with upper and lower control limits indicated.

The EVM-6400 environmental monitor can continuously measure as many as 15 different gases at up to 24 sampling locations. The instrument, again incorporating a Transept interferometer, is mounted in a NEMA-type enclosure and incorporates the interferometer module, long-path gas cell, detector and control module, and gas switching valves. The software can be configured to monitor automatically a wide range of gases, industrial solvents, and pollutants, warn of dangerous levels, and provide various types of reports.

The newest laboratory instrument, the Diamond-20, employs a more compact, hermetically-sealed instrument enclosure. The associated software runs under the Microsoft Windows graphical user interface on IBM-PC compatible computers.

15.2 BECKMAN INSTRUMENTS INC.

The Beckman-RIIC slow-scan interferometer systems, manufactured in England, were sold until the late 1970s. The Beckman Corporation (Fullerton, California, USA) manufacturers of dispersive spectrometers, made a brief return to the FTIR market in 1983 with innovative benchtop FTIRs, the Models 1100 and 2100.

These systems employed a heterodyne fringe-counting position monitoring system, which permitted the scan mirror to be tracked even during reversal of direction, and an automatic alignment system actuated by piezoelectric stacks.

15.3 BLOCK ENGINEERING GROUP

Block Engineering (A Division of Contraves Goerz, Allston, Massachusetts, USA), among the first companies to design commercial FTIR spectrometers, today supplies custom instruments to government and military contract.

15.4 BOMEM HARTMANN AND BRAUN

Bomem (Quebec City, Quebec, Canada) started in 1974, initially producing a rugged FTIR spectrometer for measurements of atmospheric ozone. The company has offered commercial instruments, beginning with the DA2 transportable FTIR spectrometer for field use and special applications, since 1978. The DA3, a laboratory version, was commercially launched in 1980 and superseded by the DA8 instrument in 1989. Lower-specification benchtop instruments, the "Michelson" Series, have been marketed since 1987.

DA series

The "DA" instruments all employ dynamic alignment of the interferometer fixed mirror. This permits operation in harsh environments, to large optical differences (for high resolution) or to high spectral frequencies (up to the ultraviolet in one model). The DA2, a portable instrument, has 5-cm diameter optics; the other models in the series use 7.5-cm diameter optics.

The optical layout of the DA3 and DA8 models is along a vertical axis, providing a small "footprint" for the instrument and good access for several experimental set-ups. Three water-cooled sources, two focused sample positions and three collimated outputs are available by computer-controlled selection mirrors. Other notable features include a 30 degree incidence beamsplitter (which reduces the beamsplitter size and cost, and reduces polarization effects, but slightly narrows the usable spectral range), and separately evacuable optics and sample compartments.

A purpose-developed "vector processor", a dedicated numeric processor, is used to perform Fourier transforms and digital filtering. The digital filtering of incoming interferograms can significantly reduce the number of data points to be stored when the spectral range of interest is narrow. The system is controlled by on-board microprocessors, and commanded by a host minicomputer, typically of the DEC PDP/11 or VAX series. Most of the system software is written in Fortran and made available to users for modification.

The most recent DA8 instrument is an updated model of the DA3 having a modified scan-mirror carriage and guide-rod design to improve reproducibility, and repackaged electronics. The instrument communicates with its computer, typically a VAX 3100 workstation, via an Ethernet communications network.

Michelson series

The Bomem Michelson series is based on an interferometer design employing cube corner mirrors on a pivoting "wishbone" frame (see Section 13.1.8). It is a compact, limited-function instrument controlled by a PC-type computer. Optical alignment is permanently fixed, and beamsplitters are not removable. The basic spectrometer is sold in a variety of packages consisting of appropriate detector, beamsplitter, accessory optics and software for applications such as FT–Raman, thermogravimetric analysis, liquid quality control, and forensic spectroscopy. It is also sold in industrial form as a chemical analyser for process monitoring and control.

The Michelson series interferometer consists of aluminium castings for the scan mirror frame and baseplate. The frame is supported on two weak leaf springs which form a pivot, and is oscillated by an electromagnetic drive controlled by a servo. A quadrature detection scheme is used for the laser channel to infer position, direction and speed of scanning. Interferograms are acquired in both directions.

The heated ceramic source is contained within an insulated cavity to reduce power input, and is controlled by monitoring its near-infrared output. The instrument enclosure consists of a sealed "clamshell" supported on shock mounts, and adequate for many industrial applications.

The instrument microprocessor controls scanning, data acquisition and communication with the external computer, which is required for operation. The PC software, written mainly in the C language, provides the usual options of instrument control, data analysis and output. The original Michelson 100 model had fixed resolution of $4\,cm^{-1}$ and $5000-400\,cm^{-1}$ spectral range, but the more recent Michelson MB Series are more versatile.

15.5 BRAN+LUEBBE

Bran+Luebbe (Norderstedt, Germany) manufacture a near-infrared FTIR called the InfraProver, designed specifically for material identification and quality testing. The interferometer employs refractive wedges to generate an optical path difference (see Chapter 13). By dispensing with a beamsplitter and moving mirror assembly, the sensitivity to vibration is claimed to be much reduced. Resolution is $6\,cm^{-1}$ without the obligatory Hamming apodization over the $4000-10\,000\,cm^{-1}$ spectral range.

A single scan requires 1.1 seconds, limited by the processor speed of a 25-MHz personal computer. The total measurement time is 5.5 seconds when a reference scan and FFT calculations are included. Scans can be co-added for improved signal-to-noise ratio.

The standard sampling method is a fibre-optic cable with interchangeable termination. Liquids or solids can be measured by using reflectance or transmittance or "transreflectance". The typical area of illumination is 10 mm diameter. The fibre short-wavenumber cut-off is $4545\,cm^{-1}$ ($2.2\,\mu m$). Alternatively, the instrument can accept cuvettes for liquid samples. With the fibre optics probe, S/N is quoted as less than 0.005 Absorbance units (about 1%) for a single scan.

Communication with the PC is via an RS-232 interface. The software includes principal components analysis, spectral search, and qualitative analysis for material identification. Unlike software for most commercial FTIR instruments, the software of the InfraProver is customized for a particular application, and does not stress manipulation of spectra. The hardware is designed with few user options, emphasizing the results rather than the technology.

15.6 BRUKER ANALYTISCHE MESSTECHNIK GmbH

Bruker (Karlsruhe, Germany) entered the field of FTIR spectroscopy in 1974 with the introduction of the IFS 113v spectrometer. This instrument was based on an interferometer design by Ludwig Genzel which allowed small beamsplitters to be mounted on a wheel for easy interchange to cover a broad spectral range without breaking vacuum. The concept of a rotatable beamsplitter mount had been introduced by Polytec, also based in Karlsruhe.

The range was extended in more recent years by the 40, 60 and 80 series spectrometers.

In 1986 the research grade IFS 120 spectrometer was introduced. This versatile instrument accommodates three water-cooled sources or external sources for emission experiments. The scan drive employs a hybrid mechanical bearing and cube-corner retroreflectors. The drive precision allows measurements up to $40\,000\,cm^{-1}$ (250 nm in the ultraviolet). Up to four internal and two external detectors can be accommodated.

The IFS 120 uses an Aspect 1000 minicomputer having a 24-bit word length for wide dynamic range. An associated array processor transforms a one million point interferogram in less than 50 seconds.

This complex system is not compact: the entire system, including computer console and vacuum pump, weighs 970 kg. The Bruker IFS 120, along with the Bomem DA3 and DA8, represent state-of-the-art performance in commercial high resolution FTIR. At the other end of the range, Bruker currently manufactures the IFS 25 benchtop FTIR, controlled by a PC-type computer. Apart from the common sealed and desiccated optics, 4800–400 cm^{-1} spectral range and 2 cm^{-1} resolution, the instrument has two external ports providing modulated IR radiation for external experimental arrangements and detectors.

15.7   CHELSEA INSTRUMENTS

The FT-500 spectrometer, launched in 1988, is the first Fourier spectrometer dedicated solely to ultraviolet and visible operation. The instrument was developed by Chelsea Instruments (London, UK) in collaboration with Imperial College, London.

The spectral range is 175–700 nm (0.175–0.700 µm, or 57 000–14 000 cm^{-1}). Maximum displacement is 20 cm, leading to resolution as high as 0.025 cm^{-1} for a double-sided interferogram. A scan is performed in under 400 seconds.

The interferometer employs cat's eye mirrors, and the beamsplitter is used near normal incidence. The interferometer, in its vacuum chamber, rests on a wheeled frame, to which all associated equipment is bolted. The external dimensions of the 400 kg instrument are approximately 1.8 m×0.7 m×1.2 m. The instrument design is further discussed in Section 17.5.4.

15.8   DIGILAB

The early history and products of Digilab (Division of BioRad Laboratories Inc, Cambridge, Massachusetts, USA) have been described in Section 11.5. The company continues to be a major supplier today.

The FTS-7 Series is a low-cost range of benchtop spectrometers available in optional versions for near infrared, GC/IR or TGA-IR use.

The FTS-60 employs a high-throughput optical design, and a data system based on a Motorola 68000 microprocessor. The FTS-60A version incorporates a dynamic alignment system, giving it extended range operation into the near infrared.

15.9   HEWLETT–PACKARD

Hewlett–Packard (Palo Alto, California, USA) do not produce a stand-alone FTIR spectrometer, but sell a dedicated FTIR "detector" for their line of gas chromatographs. The GC/IR accessory attaches to an HP5890 gas chromatograph as do other types of GC detector (flame-ionization, mass spectrometer, etc.). The accessory, designed in part by Tomas Hirschfeld, is a robust mid-infrared interferometer.

15.10 HITACHI

Hitachi (Tokyo, Japan) manufactured a far infrared FTIR in the late 1970s. The company now sells a visible range FT instrument employing a detector array and coupled to a microscope, the U-6000, described in Section 18.4.1.

15.11 IBM INSTRUMENTS

IBM Instruments (Danbury, Connecticut, USA) sold instruments in the USA manufactured by Bruker GmbH from 1983 to 1987. The IBM IR/85 and IR/32 were relatively low-priced mid-infrared models. Interestingly, these were initially sold, not with the IBM PC computer, but with a Bruker data-station. The IBM IR/90 interferometer was the same as the Bruker IFS 113, and incorporated a Genzel interferometer and interchangeable beamsplitters on a rotating selection wheel. The IR/44, introduced in 1985, was mated to an IBM-AT computer.

15.12 IDEALAB

Idealab (Franklin, Massachusetts, USA) continues to manufacture custom FTIRs to special order.

15.13 JANOS TECHNOLOGY INC.

Janos (Townshend, Vermont, USA) manufactures a novel benchtop spectrometer that employs a rotating transmissive plate to modulate the optical path difference. The conventional germanium beamsplitter and compensator plates divide the incoming beam into two parts, which are directed through a rotating plate from opposite sides. The rotation of the plate causes its optical thickness to be large for one of the two beams while it is is small for the other, thereby introducing an optical path difference. The two beams are reflected back by mirrors to the beamsplitter, where they are recombined and directed as in a conventional Michelson interferometer. The design has the advantage of being compact and insensitive to vibration.

15.14 JASCO

This Japanese (Tokyo) manufacturer of spectroscopic instruments sells at least one Fourier transform instrument, the FT/IR-3, which is not generally available in most western countries.

15.15 JEOL

JEOL (Tokyo, Japan) have produced low-cost analytical FTIRs since the late 1970s, although these have not been sold in North America or Western Europe.

15.16 KAYSER–THREDE

Kayser–Threde (Munich, Germany), a company specializing in systems design since 1966, have designed interferometers under contract since 1981. Their pendulum and rotating wishbone scan designs are described in Section 13.18. The prototype "MIPAS–LM" design (Michelson Interferometer for Passive Atmospheric Sounding — Laboratory Model) was intended for measurement of trace gases in the atmosphere from spacecraft (Rippel and Jaacks 1988).

Since 1989, a commercial field model of the "double pendulum" or "rocking wishbone" design has been available. The K300 covers the $0.5\,\mu m$ to $40\,\mu m$ spectral range with a selection of detectors, providing resolution extending to $0.08\,cm^{-1}$. The instrument can scan at up to $5\,Hz$ with $1\,cm^{-1}$ resolution. With a purpose-built processor, up to one million data points can be Fourier transformed in less than 10 seconds. This allows "real-time" calculation of the FFT and co-adding at all scan speeds and resolutions.

A commercial laboratory version of the K300 instrument is scheduled for introduction in 1991.

15.17 LLOYD INSTRUMENTS PLC

Lloyd Instruments (Southampton, Hampshire, UK) introduced the FT-600 benchtop FTIR in 1985, at approximately half the price of any competing FTIR instrument. The company had previously specialized in chart recorders and tensile testing equipment. The microprocessor-controlled spectrometer plotted spectra and interferograms on an analogue pen recorder, and operated over a 4000–$600\,cm^{-1}$ spectral range. The design was notable in that it attempted to simulate the operations and features of a conventional dispersive infrared instrument.

The original FT-600, developed in conjunction with Imperial College, London, employed a 12-bit ADC for data acquisition and a 6809 microprocessor for instrument control and calculation of the Fourier transformation. The scan mechanism initially consisted of a lead screw drive acting on a towing wire, performing one scan in 40 seconds. Vibrations were partly damped by a greased piston; the piston itself was supported on four beryllium copper sheet springs. The drive voltage was tailored by analogue electronics to approximate a constant speed throughout the scan.

The optical design consisted of two spherical Cassegrain telescopes to focus the source light at the sample and detector positions, respectively; the path through the interferometer was slightly convergent. Interferograms with approximately $6\,cm^{-1}$ resolution were recorded in approximately 40 seconds; the spectrum was calculated by the microprocessor during the return stroke of the piston. The interferometer was temperature-controlled to improve reproducibility of the scan drive and to reduce optical misalignment.

A membrane keyboard allowed up to 16 spectra to be averaged. Spectra and not interferograms were averaged, because neither a white-light channel nor laser-fringe counting was employed: the zero path position was not known from scan to scan.

A second version, the FT-600+, was marketed in 1988. This model employed cube-corner mirrors and improved optics for better stability and signal quality (Johnston 1989). The interferometer drive was modified to remove the grease damping, and controlled by a simple low-frequency servosystem. Scan speed was increased to 10 interferograms per minute.

An optional microprocessor-controlled "sample shuttle" was available to alternately place the sample and a blank cell in the infrared beam. By interleaving sample and reference scans in this way, fluctuations in moisture or carbon dioxide levels are made to have little effect, so that purging or sealing of the instrument are unneccessary.

The electronic design was improved to include a lower noise preamplifier and 16-bit ADC. Fast Fourier transformation of the 4K interferogram was performed in 0.3 sec by a TMS-32010 processor, with the 6809 relegated to instrument control and communications. The spectrometer could be interfaced with an external PC for control and data analysis. The instrument firmware was written in 6809 assembly language, and PC software in compiled BASIC.

Despite their short time in the marketplace (the products were sold to Bio-Rad in 1990) the Lloyd spectrometers accelerated an industry trend towards low-cost, robust FTIR instruments as replacements for dispersive spectrometers.

15.18   MATTSON INSTRUMENTS INC.

Founded by David Mattson and Pat Coffey, both previously with Nicolet, this company (Madison, Wisconsin, USA) launched an ambitious series of instruments and associated computer systems beginning in 1983. The Sirius 100 and similar interferometers were designed as benchtop units incorporating versatile sample chambers and accessories. A novel feature of the instrument was a general-purpose sampling stage which incorporated mirrors that could be positioned for measurements of attenuated total reflectance, specular and diffuse reflectance, or to create a condensed beam for measuring the transmittance of small samples. Once the accessory had been aligned by using the inbuilt micrometers of the stage, the scale readings could be recorded for subsequent re-positioning.

The first commercial instrument to employ cube corner mirrors, the Sirius 100 was considerably less sensitive to misalignment than conventional flat-mirror interferometers. It was thus able to dispense with the air-bearing drive common to most high-quality instruments of the time, and instead used a precise cross-roller bearing. The original Sirius 100 was used with a Starlab minicomputer running the UNIX operating system. Later versions employed a standard IBM-PC compatible computer. The spectrometer used three Motorola 68000 microprocessors: one for instrument control, a second for Fourier transformation, and the third for handling the operating system.

The Sirius 100 was joined by the Cygnus, Polaris and Alpha-Centauri FTIR spectrometers, which were variants of the same basic design. The Cygnus incorporated a control panel in the instrument case, and did not require a computer for routine analyses. Output was via a hardcopy plotter.

The most recent instrument (introduced in 1989) is the Galaxy series FTIR. Incorporating many of the features of the earlier Sirius spectrometer (including the same interferometer heart), it occupies less bench space and contains a higher degree of electronic integration. Functions that would normally be performed by several circuit boards have been implemented on a single large scale integration (LSI) chip, a 4326 Applications Specific Integrated Circuit (ASIC). The ASIC electronics unit includes a two-megabyte buffer memory for holding several scans until the data are transferred to the external computer.

The Galaxy incorporates an LCD display and membrane keypad for routine operation, but can be interfaced with a variety of external computers (for example, an IBM-XT running MS-DOS, Macintosh computers or workstations running UNIX). The external computer software is mouse-driven and includes "expert system" features.

The Galaxy interferometer is available in versions having resolution between 2 and $0.09\,\mathrm{cm}^{-1}$ — an unusually high resolution for a compact benchtop unit. In common with a number of other manufacturers, Mattson offers options for GC/IR, TGA–FTIR, FT–Raman and infrared microscopy. Mattson is presently unique in offering an option for true optical null dual-beam operation (other so-called "dual-beam" commercial instruments invariably switch the modulated interferometer beam between a sample and reference position between scans, and then divide the two independent scans).

15.19 MIDAC CORPORATION

Midac (Costa Mesa, California, USA) have designed and manufactured FTIR spectrometers for aerospace and other contract work since the late 1970s. The company now sells a low-priced commercial FTIR for routine laboratory use, but capable of operation in harsher environments. The instrument has $0.5\,\mathrm{cm}^{-1}$ best resolution and an operating range of 7800–$350\,\mathrm{cm}^{-1}$, although the standard KBr beamsplitter package permits a 5000–$400\,\mathrm{cm}^{-1}$ range. The beamsplitter is protected from moisture absorption by a proprietary coating method. The scan drive employs a dual mechanical bearing.

A feature of the Midac spectrometer is a "stressed skin" construction that dispenses with a heavy optical bench and pedestal-mounted optics. This results in an unusually light (12 kg) bench weight and claimed high stability. The instrument is compact: about $70\,\mathrm{cm}\times30\mathrm{x}20\,\mathrm{cm}$. The unit is said to operate in either horizontal or vertical positions without affecting alignment.

The signal-to-noise ratio is comparable to the current best: 1400:1 at $2000\,\mathrm{cm}^{-1}$ with $4\,\mathrm{cm}^{-1}$ resolution and two second observation time.

Midac do not produce their own spectrometer control and analysis software, instead offering one of the commercially available packages. A high-speed computer interface links the spectrometer and an IBM-compatible computer.

15.20 NICOLET ANALYTICAL INSTRUMENTS

Nicolet (Madison, Wisconsin, USA), in its first incarnation as Fabri-Tek, was associated with the first Block interferometers. The company began to manufacture its own systems in the early 1970s, when it came to prominence with the NIC 7199 research spectrometer. This instrument was soon adapted via accessories for GC/IR and other special measurements. The 7199 was distinguished by an excellent "user interface" permitting, for example, spectra to be zoomed and panned rapidly on a colour computer monitor.

The scan drive of the 7199 employed dual air bearings to avoid tilt of the scan mirror. Variable scan velocities and a maximum resolution of $0.06\,\mathrm{cm}^{-1}$ were achieved. Four computer-controlled apertures limited the beam divergence for four spectral resolutions. With appropriate beamsplitters, the instrument covered a spectral range to $25\,000\,\mathrm{cm}^{-1}$ in the visible. A less sophisticated instrument, the MX-1, was introduced in the late 1970s.

Model numbers proliferated, with the Nicolet 5-MX, 5-DX, 10-MX, 10-DX, 20-MX, 20-DX and 60-SX being available by the early 1980s.

Nicolet presently offer a wide range of instruments. The Nicolet Model 205 is a low-cost benchtop unit incorporating a monochrome CRT display and limited-function membrane keypad, a geometry also used in recent Mattson and Perkin–Elmer instruments. The sample compartment uses plug-in accessories that are pre-aligned for quick exchange.

Special-purpose FTIR
The 8200 Series employs the same basic interferometer as the Model 205, but is designed for specific applications. The 8210 Liquid Analyzer includes a permanently installed attenuated total reflectance (ATR) accessory. Originally introduced specifically as an analyser of oils, it is now available programmed for quantitative analysis applications such as sugar determination of syrups and solvent quality assurance. It replaces the CRT display of the Model 205 by a two-line LED prompt and full in-built keyboard. The 8220 is a similar instrument intended for gas analysis; in it, the ATR sampler is replaced by a multipass gas cell (sampling accessories are discussed further in Section 17.9).

Another specialized FTIR available from Nicolet is the ECO-8S Semiconductor Wafer Analyzer. This automated instrument can measure the carbon and oxygen content in silicon, the thickness of epitaxial films, and make other determinations useful in semiconductor fabrication.

500 series
The Model 500 spectrometer is a higher-grade instrument that can accept accessories such as infrared microscopes, GC/IR and TGA/IR. In its original form as the 5-MX, it was the first moderate resolution FTIR instrument that did not employ an air-bearing scan drive. Instead, it used the "porch swing" parallelogram drive popularized by Walker and Rex.

The Model 500 can be controlled by three types of computer: an IBM PS/2-compatible, Macintosh II, or a Nicolet 620 Datasystem.

A version of this design is licensed to Philips Analytical, and sold as the Philips PU9800 spectrometer.

System 740
The System 740 (introduced in 1990) features pre-aligned detector modules consisting of detector and preamplifier on a pin-located mount for precise positioning. An

automated optimization routine adjusts the optical alignment and throughput for combinations of sources, beamsplitters and detectors.

The 740 employs an air bearing for frictionless movement of the scan mirror. A maximum resolution of $0.3\,cm^{-1}$ (unapodized) is possible, with up to 20 scans per second at $16\,cm^{-1}$ resolution. Rapid-scan experiments are limited only by the capacity of the hard-disk memory of the computer. Fast data transfer is achieved by using direct memory access to the computer, and high disk-transfer rate (at a sustained 10^7 bits per second). The high scan rate, some ten times faster than most competitive instruments, allows chemical reaction kinetics and other rapidly changing processes to be monitored. Once acquired, the data can be treated in batch mode for automatic processing, ratioing against a pre-stored background, co-added and displayed.

Noise performance is 0.1% peak-to-peak for a one-second scan at $4\,cm^{-1}$ resolution near $2000\,cm^{-1}$ in the infrared spectrum with a DTGS detector, and some ten times worse at 5000 and $500\,cm^{-1}$.

Six beamsplitters are available to cover the 15000–$50\,cm^{-1}$ spectral range. The beamsplitters have the useful feature of a spring-loaded cover plate which slides down to protect the two hygroscopic surfaces when the beamsplitter is removed from its mount in the spectrometer. The 650–$50\,cm^{-1}$ far infrared region is covered by a solid substrate beamsplitter instead of by a thin Mylar beamsplitter.

The computer for the System 740 spectrometer is a Nicolet 620 microcomputer. This employs a Small Computer Standard Interface (SCSI) bus for communication with peripherical devices such as streaming magnetic tape, Write Once Read Many times (WORM) disk drives, or CD laser ROMs. WORM and CD-ROM drives are very high capacity storage media useful for archiving spectra for spectral search. A communications package permits the transfer of information between the 620 computer and minicomputers such as the DEC VAX.

60SXR

Nicolet describes the 60SXR as a research spectrometer, and it is a successor to the earlier 60-SX and 60SXB systems. It incorporates automatic optimization like the System 740. The optimization adjusts interferometer alignment, microbeam focus and configuration, sample positioning, and the more routine settings of iris diameter (Jacquinot stop) and scan limits. A Nicolet 660 computer, like the above-mentioned 620, has a dual-bus architecture: one bus specifically for high-speed internal communication between spectrometer and computer, and a SCSI bus for external communications with high-density storage devices. Up to 60 individual scans per second can be accommodated. The RAM memory is 1.28 Mbytes. The system includes a dedicated 24-bit FFT coprocessor which can routinely transform arrays of up to 1.3 Mbytes in under ten seconds.

800 series

The 800 Series are versatile instruments intended specifically for research and analytical chemistry. The System 800 uses an air-bearing scan drive and a dynamic alignment system. Unlike most recent interferometer designs, the optical bench is equipped with fluid-cooled mid- and near-infrared sources and a white-light zero-path-difference locating system.

The baseplate uses a proprietary material free of thermal stresses. This is supported on a vibrationally isolated aluminium baseplate surrounded by a skirt of extruded aluminium.

The instrument housing includes a purged cavity in which spare beamsplitters can be stored. When beamsplitters are interchanged in the interferometer, the computer can adjust alignment according to stored information. With a choice of beamsplitters, the instruments can cover the $30\,000–10\,cm^{-1}$ range at better than $0.09\,cm^{-1}$ resolution.

15.21   PERKIN–ELMER

Perkin–Elmer (Norwalk, Connecticut, USA and Beaconsfield, UK), one of the first commercial manufacturers of dispersive infrared spectrometers, entered the FTIR market rather late. The company has introduced four types of FTIR optical bench, each of which has been sold with a variety of computer hardware and software as equipment has evolved. The models, known as the 1500, 1800, 1700 and 1600 series (and introduced in that order) have numbers that relate to their ranking in sophistication and price.

Model 1500
The PE-1500 was manufactured by Analect, with computer and software added by Perkin–Elmer. The optical head was a version of the Analect fx-6200 interferometer. The Analect hard-wired FFT processor was retained, but the instrument was interfaced to a Perkin–Elmer data station.

Model 1800
The 1800, Perkin–Elmer's top-of-the-line research-grade spectrometer until 1988, incorporates experience gained by P–E in fabricating various custom FTIRs under contract to the US government.

The 1800 optics are notable for the use of toroidal mirrors rather than the more commonly used off-axis paraboloids and ellipsoids (toroidal mirrors have a different radius in two perpendicular directions, like the surface of a doughnut). Whereas off-axis aspheric mirrors can give theoretically perfect imaging for point sources of radiation, they do a poorer job with actual light sources. Toroids can be tailored to produce a smaller "blur circle" at the sample position and detector, leading to better energy efficiency.

The 1800 uses "flip mirrors" to select one of two sources, sample beam positions and detectors. Flip mirrors are also used to select one of two interferometers: the first is optimized for mid-infrared operation, and the second, optional interferometer employs a mylar beamsplitter for far-infrared measurements. Opposite sides of the same moving mirror are used for the two interferometers. The mirror is mounted on a large rectangular air-bearing to minimize wobble and tilt. The instrument software automatically merges the two measurements to yield a single wide-range spectrum.

The interferometer assemblies are mounted on a stress-relieved and matched alloy base. The wire-wound source is enclosed in an insulated oven to reduce convection and thermal gradients in the instrument.

The 1800 provided the best signal-to-noise specification among commercial instruments when it was introduced: 700:1 peak-to-peak calculated at $2000\,cm^{-1}$ on a single scan at $2\,cm^{-1}$ resolution, with a DTGS detector. This figure has since been bettered by other instruments.

1700 series

The first commercial FTIR developed by Perkin–Elmer in the UK was the Model 1700 (Ford and Gee, 1985). This employs an interferometer which generates the optical path difference by rotation of a beamsplitter and mirror assembly rather than by linear movement of a single mirror as in a conventional Michelson. The principle, due to Sternberg and James (1964) is described in Section 13.1.7. The basic interferometer consists of a carriage and two fixed mirrors. Rotation of the carriage supporting a beamsplitter and parallel fixed mirror causes the fixed-mirror arm to elongate and alter the path difference. It can be shown that, if the beamsplitter and fixed mirror are parallel to better than one minute of arc, the alignment of the two beams of the interferometer is insensitive to translation and rotation about all three axes. This allows a simple scan drive to be employed; only constancy of speed is important. In the Perkin–Elmer implementation, extra mirrors are incorporated to allow for compact and rigid mounting.

Although this scheme avoids problems of dynamic alignment, i.e. changes in optical alignment due to scanning, it does nothing about static alignment: the interferometer is still subject to shifts of its mirrors due to temperature and mechanical creep. This is compensated by the provision of an automatically alignable mirror in the fixed portion of the interferometer. This mirror can be adjusted under software control when the instrument is first turned on, or occasionally afterwards. The scan carriage of the original Model 1700 was rotated on plane bearings by a belt-driven motor turning a lead screw, and oscillated about 5° on either side of zero path difference. The interferometer and "tilt table" carriage are rigid iron castings attached to the aluminium main casting of the instrument by shock mounts.

The Model 1700 can acquire data during the forward and reverse scans. The instrument employs a plane-polarized laser and an eighth-wave plate in one arm of the laser channel of the interferometer to obtain two cosine waves in quadrature (i.e. 90° out of phase). Quadrature detection of fringes is now used by most modern interferometers to monitor direction as well as absolute position and speed of the scan.

The 1700X series are an improved version of the original 1700 spectrometers. They employ an electromagnetic drive replacing the original screw-driven arrangement, and have a moderate $0.5\,cm^{-1}$ resolution.

The 1720X spectrometer is sold with a dedicated spectroscopy terminal and limited-function keypad; the 1725X version includes a PC or PS/2 compatible computer with modern mouse-driven software. Either data system, or both, can be used to run the same interferometer. In addition, up to fifteen interferometers can be controlled by a single PC. At present, P-E spectrometers provide the broadest available spectral range, 10 000–370 cm^{-1}, accomplished with a specially coated KBr beamsplitter. They also offer an unusually wide-range far-infrared option (720–30 cm^{-1}).

1600 series

Perkin–Elmer's most recent instrument, the Model 1600, was introduced in 1987 as a low-cost FTIR intended for routine applications.

Developed at Perkin–Elmer's US laboratories, the 1600 uses a rotating-carriage interferometer similar to that of the 1700 Series, but without the software-controlled realignment mechanism. The pivot bearing consists of a steel axle pin running in two Delrin V-blocks. The interfaces between dissimilar metals in the interferometer were designed to avoid misalignment introduced by temperature change.

The sensitivity to vibration of moderate to high frequencies is reduced by employing rubber shock mounts between the base and optical bench. Low frequency vibration, not attenuated by shock mounts, is compensated by the mirror drive: the scan carriage is operated by a direct electromagnetic drive and controlled by a servo. The scan servo is partly digital; the instrument microprocessor measures the laser fringe period to compute an error correction derived from both scan velocity and acceleration. As in any servo system, the immunity to external disturbances is determined by factors such as mechanical inertia, mechanical damping, and electronic time constants. The Model 1600 has adjustable compensation to reduce the effects of such influences.

The 1600 uses a 68010 microprocessor to handle the instrument control, high-level computation and user interface. The user employs a keypad which includes numeric and function keys. Results are displayed on a monochrome monitor built into the instrument case. Special functions are selected by "soft keys" whose function labels are displayed under software control at the base of the screen. In order to perform this wide range of functions with a single microprocessor, Perkin–Elmer developed a compact real-time operating system, and wrote the time-critical portions of the code in assembly language. Despite the absence of a mathematics co-processor, the software can perform an 8K cosine Fourier transform in less than three seconds. The remainder of the programming is in the C language, currently popular with most instrument manufacturers because of its ability to combine both high-level (English-like) and low-level (assembler-like) features.

At the time of the development of the Model 1600, the popularity of windows, pull-down menus, icons and the "mouse" was not universal. The company therefore opted for soft keys as the method of user interaction with the computer. The instruments are now available with an optional external computer and software package for more sophisticated analyses with interaction by mouse. The P–E 16 PC model (introduced in 1990) dispenses with the inbuilt monitor and keypad, and is controlled solely by an IBM-compatible computer.

15.22   PHILIPS SCIENTIFIC ANALYTICAL DIVISION

Like Perkin–Elmer, Philips Analytical (Cambridge, UK), (formerly Pye Unicam) was a large manufacturer of dispersive instruments in the mid 1980s. Again, the company's first FTIR product was developed elsewhere, in this case by Nicolet. The company continues to market dispersive infrared spectrophotometers. The PU9700 and PU9500, for example, are low- cost dispersive instruments that can be used with or without an external computer.

The Philips 9800 Series was the company's first FTIR product. Principally a Nicolet 500 Series clone, the PU9800 uses operating software developed by Philips and is a low-to-moderate priced instrument intended mainly for routine analytical chemistry. The interferometer scan drive employs the porch swing flexure pivot design. The instrument features a relatively wide spectral range ($7500-400\,\text{cm}^{-1}$ with a KBr beamsplitter, or $7000-200\,\text{cm}^{-1}$ with a CsI beamsplitter) and moderate resolution (2, 4, 8, or $16\,\text{cm}^{-1}$).

The interferometer bench, weighing 62 kg, is controlled solely by an IBM-AT compatible computer. The operating software incorporates a range of features now becoming standard for commercial spectrometers: baseline flattening, digital smoothing, Kubelka–Munk and absorbance conversions, and capability of automated methods. Spectral search and quantification software are available as options. The software operates in two modes: either "easy access" by menus and soft keys, or "global line entry", which commands operations by a string of mnemonic instructions.

The basic instrument is available with optional choices of two beamsplitters, three detectors, external beam and sample compartments, and a motorized sample shuttle for pseudo-double beam operation.

The newer PU9600 (introduced in 1991) has similar specifications, but is available in two versions, one with an integral keypad and the other operated by a separate PC. With the PC version, the spectrum can be observed from scan to scan and stopped when the result is acceptable.

In 1991, Philips Analytical were taken over by the parent company of Mattson Instruments Inc. The Unicam name is to be used for some instruments of both companies.

15.23 SPECAC LTD

Specac (Orpington, Kent, UK), primarily manufacturers of optical and sampling accessories for spectroscopy, also produce the RSMI (Rapid Scanning Michelson Interferometer). This is a polarizing interferometer of the Martin and Puplett type (although it can be used as a more conventional Michelson interferometer) and is intended for use in the very far infrared ($2-60\,\text{cm}^{-1}$). Polarizing interferometers are described in Section 17.4.

The instrument was developed in collaboration with NPL for measurements of Tokomak plasmas in fusion research.

The interferometer scans at up to 35 Hz (giving time resolution of 14 msec), with one rooftop mirror moving on an air bearing. The mirror position and speed are monitored by a Moiré fringe system and linear voltage displacement transducer (LVDT).

To ensure symmetrical interferograms (and thus reduce transformation time by a factor of two) a stepping motor is incorporated to move the fixed mirror to exactly zero path position.

The instrument is controlled by dedicated timing electronics, and data output is to a CAMAC computer interface.

15.24 SOVIET INSTRUMENTS

The only commercial Soviet Fourier spectrometer known to the author is the LAFS-1000 spectrometer, introduced in the Soviet Union in 1983 (Azarov *et al.* 1984). This far-infrared instrument operates between 10 and 400 cm^{-1} and has a maximum resolution of 0.1 to 0.5 cm^{-1}. The interferometer is used with a Soviet IVK-3 computer system.

15.25 EPILOGUE: COMPANIES NO LONGER MANUFACTURING FTIR INSTRUMENTS

The FTIR market has grown rapidly since the late 1970s, tempting many companies to develop and sell Fourier spectrometer systems. The competition to produce better, cheaper and more reliable instruments has led several to drop out:

Beckman Inc
Beckman RIIC Ltd
Coderg SA
General Dynamics
Grubb-Parsons Ltd
IBM Instruments Inc
Lloyd Instruments plc
Polytec GmbH
Spectrotherm Corp.

Table 15.1 — Features common to FTIR instruments in the 1980s

Rapid-scanning

Laser fringe counting to dispense with white light channel

Electromagnetic scan drives

Alignment compensation systems, either
(a) active, involving phase measurement and correction, or
(b) passive, involving self-compensating optical configurations.

Internal control by microprocessor; external control by microcomputer

Price closer to inexpensive dispersive spectrometers

REFERENCES

Azarov, I. D., Vol'kenshtein, I. A., Goroshko, V. F., Kiselev, B. A., Kovalenko, V. F., Lappo, A. P., Mavrikov, P. A., Milovanov, A. V., Pankrats, E. V. and Smirnov, A. Ya. (1984), *Sov. J. Opt. Technol.*, (USA) **51**, 533.

Balashov, A. A., Bukreev, V. S., Kultepin, N. G., Nesteruk, I. N., Perminov, E. B., Vagin, V. A. and Zhizhin, G. N. (1978), High resolution Fourier transform spectrometer (0.005 cm^{-1}) for the 0.6–100 µm spectral region, *Appl. Opt.*, **17**, 1716.

Buijs, H. (1979), Data Processing Aspects of Rapid Scanning Very High Resolution Fourier Transform Spectrometers, *Proc. SPIE*, **191**, 96.

Buijs, H., Kendall, D. J. W, Vail, G. and Bérubé, J.-N. (1981), Fourier Transform Infrared Hardware Developments, *Proc. SPIE*, **289**, 322.

Chenery, D. H. and Sheppard, N. (1978), An evaluation of the practical performance of a Digilab FTS-14 Fourier transform infrared interferometer working in the region of 4000 to 400 cm^{-1}, *Appl. Spectrosc.*, **32**, 79.

Crocombe, R. and Kuehl, D (1985), The design and performance of a moderate price, research grade FT-IR spectrometer, *Proc. SPIE*, **553**, 363.

Curbelo, R. (1977), A Real-Time Multitasking Fourier Spectrometer System, 1977 International Conference on Fourier Transform Infrared Spectroscopy, *Technical Digest*, 8.

Doyle, W. M. and McIntosh, B. C. (1981), Performance Characteristics of a Refractively Scanned Michelson Interferometer, *Proc. SPIE*, **289**, 71.

Ford, M. A. and Gee, A. R. (1985), Properties and Performance of a Rotary Scanning FTIR, *Proc. SPIE*, **553**, 365.

Griffiths, P. R. and deHaseth, J. A. (1986), *Fourier Transform Infrared Spectrometry*, Wiley, New York.

Johnston, S. F. (1989), A Low-Cost FTIR Alternative to Dispersive Spectrometers, *International Labmate*, February 25.

Martin, D. H. and Puplett, E. (1969), Polarized Interferometric Spectrometry for the Millimetre and Submillimetre Spectrum, *Infr. Phys.*, **10**, 105.

McIntosh, B. C. (1984), An Array-Mapped Display System for FTIR Spectroscopy, *Infr. Phys.*, **24**, 345.

Rein, A. J. and Morris, K. S. (1986), Design of an IBM AT-Based FTIR Spectrometer, *Am. Lab.*, **18**, 86.

Rippel, H. and Jaacks, R. (1988), Performance Data of the Double Pendulum Interferometer, *Mikrochim. Acta [Wien]*, **II**, 303.

Smith, B. T. and Gillespie, R. E. (1977), An Automated Fourier Tranform Infrared Spectrometer for Real-Time Multi-Gas Monitoring, 1977 International Conference on Fourier Transform Infrared Spectroscopy, *Technical Digest*, 8.

Thorne, A. P., Harris, C. J., Wynne-Jones, I, Learner, R. C. M. and Cox, G. (1987), A Fourier Transform Spectrometer for the Vacuum Ultraviolet: Design and Performance, *J. Phys. E. — Sci. Instr.*, **20**, 54.

White, R. L. (1985), Performance of an FT-IR With a Cube-Corner Interferometer, *Appl. Spectrosc.*, **39**, 320.

16

FTIR in Space

16.1 GROUND-BASED ASTRONOMY

The use of Fourier spectroscopy for astronomy was the original incentive for the work of Peter Fellgett and Lawrence Mertz. John Strong and H. Alistair Gebbie were interested in applying it to atmospheric physics. Even Michelson had used interference techniques to measure the diameters of stars. According to Mertz (1971) most of the progress in Fourier spectroscopy up to that time had resulted from astronomically oriented research.

As early as the 1957 Bellevue Conference, both Fellgett and Mertz showed measurements of stars (transformed spectra and interferograms, respectively). Mertz's equipment, despite his later association with rapid-scanning interferometers, initially used slow scanning.

> It is necessary to be duly cautious for astronomical applications of rapid scanning interferometric spectrometry. Two considerations reign: the first one is that the sources are extremely faint. Requisite measurement times of several hours are not uncommon. The second consideration is that the source is fluctuating due to atmospheric seeing. As a result, the direct application of rapid scanning interferometric spectrometry is not feasible. The fringe frequencies which would necessarily be encountered are far too low for detectors, tape recorders, or wave analyzers. The straightforward solution is to employ a separate chopper, so that the scan rate can be arbitrarily reduced. (Mertz 1965)

The second troubling complication for astronomy was stability of the source intensity and interferometer during the long scans. The star image could be partly degraded by clouds or tracking errors, and the interferometer typically became misaligned because of temperature changes and vibration.

Indeed, atmospheric fluctuations almost led to the second rejection of Fourier methods, as the apparent ambiguity of spectral transformation had done in Michelson's time. In spite of the theoretical advantage noted by Fellgett, the first astronomical applications of FTS were not conclusively superior to dispersive techniques. Not until the experimental demonstrations of the Connes did the astronomical and spectroscopic community thaw.

A solution to the problem of source variability was the use of a double-beam interferometer arrangement (this is described in Section 17.1). As to mechanical stability, Mertz investigated other forms of interferometer that were more compact and robust than the Michelson design.

The work of Janine and Pierre Connes and co-workers concentrated on astronomical Fourier spectrometers. These instruments were used either at a telescope focus, in the laboratory, or from aircraft.

For telescope mounting, either of two positions is normally used: either the *coudé* focus or the *Cassegrain* focus. The coudé focus has a focal point that remains fixed as the telescope moves to follow a planet or star. This allows the interferometer to be set up in relatively stable surroundings. The interferometers of the Connes and others were large and complex: the second-generation JPL model was 9 ft long by 8 ft wide (2.7 m × 2.4 m), and weighed some 3 tonnes. Even the coudé room has its problems, though. After complaining of vibration from the rotating observatory dome, Beer *et al.* (1971) note:

> As well as being a good seismometer, an interferometer is also a passable microphone, and acoustic coupling is a nontrivial problem. We endeavor to reduce the problem by working quietly but some protection is provided by an acoustic enclosure for the instrument.

The Cassegrain focus, located behind the primary mirror of the telescope, is even less protected and moves with the telescope itself. This position places constraints on interferometer size and weight, and requires it to work in different orientations and ambient temperatures.

At present (1991), the "last word" in FTS through telescopes is to be found at the Canada–France–Hawaii 3 metre telescope at the Mauna Kea Observatory in Hawaii.

16.2 AIRBORNE FOURIER SPECTROMETERS

16.2.1 JPL

The Jet Propulsion Laboratory (Pasadena, California, USA) has been involved with Fourier spectrometers since the early 1960s. In 1963, J. and P. Connes developed their cat's eye interferometer there during a 9-month stay. A second model closely following the Connes' design, referred to above, was developed by JPL researchers.

Reinhard Beer (1967) has discussed balloon-borne instrumentation developed at JPL between 1963 and 1967. Two interferometers were involved: a classical Michelson operating between 80 and 1000 cm^{-1}, and a double-pass cat's-eye interferometer intended for the 2000 to 8000 cm^{-1} range. Both instruments had design resolution of <1 cm^{-1} in order to measure the rotational structure of atmospheric gases.

The classical slow-scanning Michelson interferometer employed a 40-mm diameter aperture and maximum mirror travel of 25 mm. The zero-path position was not monitored; instead, the scan motion was reversed by microswitches. The investigators performed a power Fourier transform on the interferogram to correct for the phase errors resulting from the unknown ZPD position. A Moiré fringe system was used to determine position steps of 4.000 ± 0.001 μm during the 28 minute scan. The interferometer drive was continuous, employing a motor and lead screw, with the moving mirror constrained by a fused silica slide. The mirror tilt was said to be less than 2 sec of arc in both axes with this arrangement, and it was claimed that "as a result of the construction techniques employed, the instrument never loses alignment".

The first flight was successful except for problems with the sun-seeker servo which caused the background level to fluctuate. About one minute of good measurements was obtained from the 4.5 hr flight.

In an effort to reduce the instrument's sensitivity to alignment variations, the JPL group designed a second, optically compensated, interferometer that used cat's-eye retroreflectors in a double-pass arrangement. The optical arrangement is similar to the scheme later used by Kayser–Threde GmbH which replaced cat's-eyes by cube-corner retroreflectors, and is shown in Fig. 13.1.

16.2.2 University of Arizona

Uwe Fink (1970) with Harold Larson (1975) developed a portable Fourier spectrometer for ground-based and airborne astronomical observations. A block diagram is shown in Fig. 16.1.

The design was based on a rapid-scanning Idealab IF-3 interferometer. The instrument employed a dual-input and dual-output configuration to reduce the sensitivity to background fluctuations and to increase the total signal. The interferometer was normally used at the focus of a NASA 91.5 cm airborne telescope.

The interferometer covered a spectral range of 0.87–5.6 μm (1800–$11\,500$ cm^{-1}) in the near infrared. For use in other spectral regions, the dewars containing detectors were interchanged, and the beamsplitter was replaced.

The double-beam arrangement was used primarily to subtract the very large thermal background spectrum on which astronomical spectra are superimposed. For example, in recording the spectrum of a portion of the disk of Saturn, light from adjacent patches of sky was injected into the opposite input of the interferometer.

The interferometer was used in rapid-scan mode to ensure that the modulated signal frequencies were well above the frequencies of atmospheric scintillation. Typically several hundred interferograms were co-added to yield a spectrum. The authors recounted the difficulties they faced.

> The reliability of operation of this system concerned us greatly during its development. The rigors of frequent transportation on rough mountain roads and the low temperatures found at telescopes are among the hazards encountered by instrumentation used in observational astronomy...Many interference spectrometers used in astronomy are restricted to operation at the coudé focus, a protected, stable environment. At a Cassegrain focus, on the other hand, low temperatures and mechanical flexure and maintenance of interferometric adjustments with changing tilt are among the problems

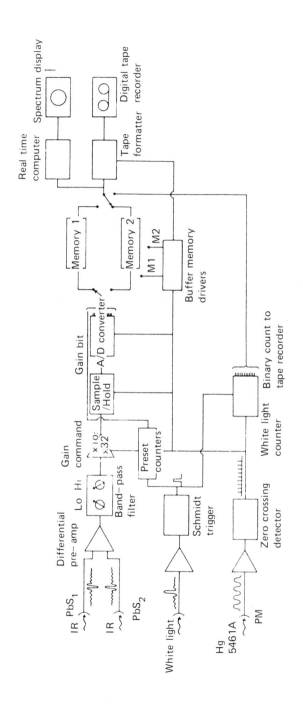

Fig. 16.1 — University of Arizona airborne Fourier spectrometer (reproduced by permission of the Optical Society of America).

that can be encountered. Aboard an aircraft, strong electromagnetic fields and mechanical vibrations become additional problems.

The instrument stored its data on magnetic tape, allowing information to be recovered even in most cases of malfunction. Electronic aids and diagnostic software were developed to check the system before and during observations. The interferogram was monitored during observations: poor quality data could be flagged and removed from further analysis by pressing a pushbutton.

16.2.3 Other airborne instruments
Larson (1978) has summarized Fourier spectroscopy experiments on NASA airborne observatories. FTIR instruments and their associated telescopes have been flown on Lear jets, converted commercial airliners and C-141 aircraft. For atmospheric studies using the sun as a source, a U-2 high-altitude aircraft has been used. This has carried a remote controlled FTIR as the space was too restricted for an onboard operator.

In Britain, J. Harries (1973) and colleagues at NPL have flown an FTIR aboard Concorde for atmospheric studies.

The one characteristic shared by most of these experiments is uniqueness. Although some employed commercially available Fourier spectrometer components, each was customized for its intended scientific program and spectral range.

16.3 SPACE-BORNE INTERFEROMETERS
16.3.1 Block Engineering
In September 1962, the newly developed Block I6-T interferometer was flown aboard an American Air Force satellite for observations of atmospheric radiance. This instrument was sensitive in the mid-infrared (1.8 to 15 μm), had a spectral resolution of $40\,cm^{-1}$, and performed one scan per second. It was particularly compact: 2.7 kg total weight, and drawing less than 8 W of power. The instrument represented the first Fourier spectrometer launched into orbit, and the first rapid-scanning type flown.

Interferograms were transmitted to earth stations by telemetry and recorded on tape. Spectral analysis was performed by the wave analyser technique, i.e. splicing together six interferograms into a continuous loop of tape and playing it into a narrow-band, variable-frequency bandpass filter which is slowly tuned over the appropriate audio frequency range.

Results were compared with those obtained by similar high altitude balloon-borne Block interferometers. The satellite observations showed errors of up to 50% (particularly at higher spectral frequencies) owing to limitations to its inflight controls and calibrations (Block 1964).

Useful data from the satellite was obtained for a period of about one week.

16.3.2 Nimbus satellites
Interest in remote sensing of the atmosphere was stimulated by the rapid evolution of satellites and associated technology. As mathematical techniques of determining

temperature profiles were developed, NASA, too, became interested in the feasibility of a space-borne Michelson interferometer for emission measurements. As Rudi Hanel (1970) reports:

> At the beginning of this project, it was not clear that a wide spectral range (approximately 5–25 μ), a relatively high spectral resolution (approximately 5 cm^{-1}), and a high precision (approximately 1%) could be combined into a small instrument which must also be capable of withstanding the launch and space environment. None of the then available instruments came close to meeting these requirements, and great doubts existed in the minds of knowledgeable people that such an instrument could be built.

Groups at the University of Michigan and the Goddard Space Flight Center (GSFC, Greenbelt, Maryland) developed a feasibility model, known as IRIS A (Infrared Interferometer Spectrometer), which was flown on a high altitude balloon in 1966. After successful results, GSFC developed a second model, IRIS B, with Texas Instruments Inc.

The first IRIS B unit was lost in an abortive rocket launch in 1968. The second unit was successfully launched in 1969 on the Nimbus III satellite.

The IRIS B interferometer was designed to rather different specifications than earth-based instruments: weight, power consumption, robustness and long-term stability were prime concerns. The optical alignment was ensured by achieving extremely high mechanical tolerances. All mating surfaces were hand-lapped; wedged spacers were fitted to provide a rigidly aligned fixed mirror mount. The instrument was repeatedly temperature-cycled between room temperature and its design operating temperature of 250 K to remove mechanical hysteresis. This 50 K operating range proved one of the more difficult aspects of the design specification.

The scan drive consisted of a linear motor acting on a porch swing supported mirror. Speed was controlled by a phase-locked loop monitoring the fringes from a monochromatic light source, a filtered neon lamp. The monochromatic fringes were generated in a separate interferometer rigidly connected to the main interferometer through the scan mirror (Fig. 16.2).

The Nimbus III interferometer provided several firsts: it operated over a broad temperature range without opportunity for realignment; it was the first generally successful space-borne Fourier spectrometer; and it benefited from a careful analysis of instrument performance. Having taken into account known optical losses, inefficiencies, spectral resolution, observing time and similar variables, the IRIS B instrument had a sensitivity (a "noise equivalent radiance", or NER) within about 3 to 5 of the theoretical value. Similar performance analyses on commercial spectrometers were not common for a further decade (see Chapter 14).

In orbit, IRIS B operated for some fourteen weeks before its bolometer detector failed. Despite suffering some misalignment which reduced its efficiency for high-frequency measurements, it provided adequate spectra.

A more advanced model, IRIS D, was flown on the Nimbus 4 meteorological research satellite in April 1970 (Hanel *et al.* 1972). This version employed a longer

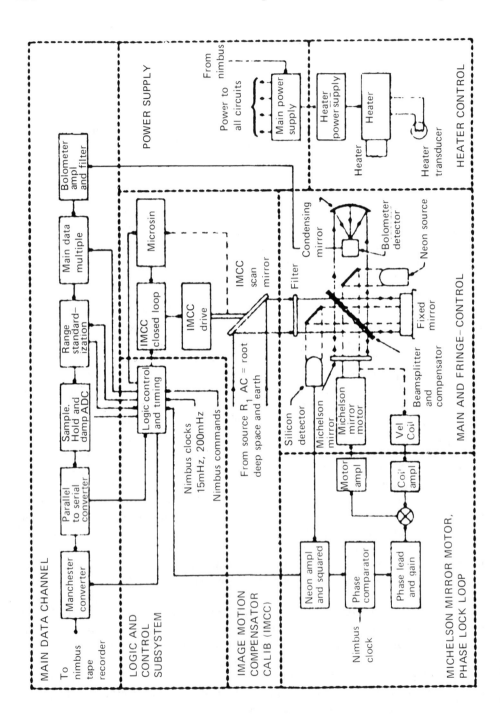

Fig. 16.2 — Iris B interferometer (reproduced by permission of the Optical Society of America).

moving mirror travel, providing higher resolution, and improved sensitivity. In order to make the instrument less sensitive to misalignment, its high-frequency spectral limit was reduced from $2000 \, cm^{-1}$ to $1600 \, cm^{-1}$.

16.3.3   EXCEDE experiment

A flex-pivot interferometer developed at Utah State University was flown aboard a non-orbiting Talos Castor rocket in October 1978 (Kemp and Huppi 1979).

The entire instrument was cooled by building it into a cryogenic dewar which contained liquid nitrogen. Cooling reduced the infrared emission of the spectrometer itself, making visible the very weak emissions from an artificial aurora created by electron accelerators carried aboard the rocket.

One of the principal design problems was maintaining optical alignment as the interferometer was cooled. This was accomplished by careful thermal design. Other challenges included shielding the detector and preamplifier from the electrically noisy environment of the rocket and its experiments, and calibrating the instrumental response. Electrical noise was minimized by running the mirror drive, calibration sources, communications and detectors from separate isolated battery sources.

In common with many space-borne payloads, the EXCEDE experiment was not a success. After launch, the instrument bay door did not eject; no data were obtained from the optical sensors. However, using the internal calibration source, the investigators at least determined that the interferometer maintained reasonable alignment (losing 20% of its original signal intensity) during and after the rocket-motor operation.

16.3.4   Mariner Mars probe

The Mariner 9 spacecraft, launched in November 1971, included an interferometer, again designed at NASA Goddard. This model, IRIS M, employed a broader spectral range. The lower limit was extended down to $200 \, cm^{-1}$, which necessitated the use of cesium iodide as a window and beamsplitter material. CsI is a particularly soft, hygroscopic material notoriously difficult to polish and mechanically support. After considerable effort, adequately flat surfaces were obtained, and the beamsplitter/compensator assembly was bonded with silicone rubber into aluminium mounting rings. This elastic mount allowed differential expansion over the wide temperature range, and provided safe support during the high launch vibration.

The operating environment was rather different from that of Nimbus:

> The motion of the scan platform with respect to the stabilized spacecraft causes acceleration along the axis of the Michelson motor drive. Even after the electrical motors that move the scan platform have stopped, the highly cantilevered platform will not come to rest immediately. Furthermore, during the planetary mapping sequence adjustments of the scan platform may occur frequently to assure near verticality at the time of camera exposure. To prevent the loss of a substantial amount of valuable data from the ir spectroscopy experiment, the interferometer had to function without

degradation even under moderate acceleration and vibration levels. (Hanel *et al.* 1980)

IRIS M proved to have almost unchanged performance between the initial vacuum tests on the ground and while in orbit around Mars.

16.3.5 Voyager space probe

The same basic interferometer design was further adapted for the Voyager 1 and Voyager 2 missions to Jupiter, Saturn and beyond. The optical layout is shown in Fig. 16.3.

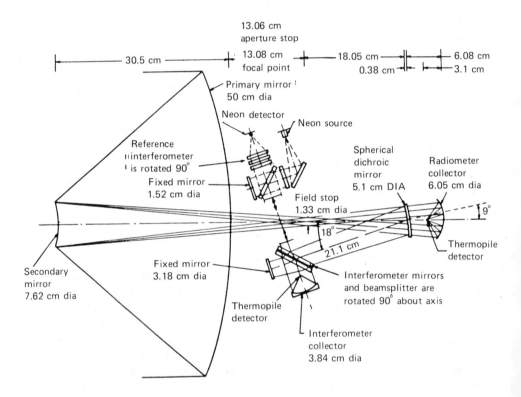

Fig. 16.3 — Optical layout of the Voyager IRIS sent to the outer planets (reproduced by permission of the Optical Society of America).

These spacecraft, launched in 1977 and reaching Jupiter in 1979, carried IRIS interferometers operating between 180 and 2500 cm^{-1} at 50 K lower temperature than their predecessors. The lower temperature caused stiffening of the silicone rubber optical and mechanical mounts: these had to be heated intermittently to prevent straining of the moving mirror motor.

A second problem was irradiation effects on optical components: the reference interferometer signal fell by several percent after Voyager passed through the

Jupiter radiation belts, probably owing to radiation-darkening of the glass envelope of the neon discharge bulb and certain compounds forming the layers of the interference filter.

Voyager 1 and 2 produced some 100 000 individual spectra of Jupiter and its satellites, covering a wide range of locations, local times and angles. Like the more widely known Voyager imager results, they have provided significant new information about the outer planets.

The same group at NASA Goddard (originally headed by Rudi Hanel, and now by Virgil Kunde) is now proposing a more advanced version of the IRIS interferometer for the planned CASSINI mission to Saturn.

16.3.6 Cosmic Background Explorer

The Cosmic Background Explorer (COBE) is a satellite designed to search for the faint remnants of the presumed Big Bang. The expansion of the present universe from an earlier singularity is signalled by the presence of a universal "bath" of far infrared light; its spectrum corresponds to a black body source having a temperature of about 2.7 K. The Smithsonian Astrophysical Observatory built the FIRAS interferometer of COBE to measure this spectrum accurately, and to detect any differences with direction. Any such temperature differences point to asymmetries in the early universe, and test theories about its evolution. COBE was launched in 1988, and continues to gather data.

16.3.7 Tropospheric emission spectrometer (TES)

The Jet Propulsion Laboratory (Pasadena, USA) is presently designing a Fourier spectrometer for observations of the troposphere by using reflected sunlight and thermal emission (Beer *et al.* 1989). The spectrometer will cover the 600–3450 cm^{-1} spectral region. The interferometer is a double-beam optical null type: the "complementary" output will view a cold reference source. Scanning is accomplished by moving two cube-corner mirrors. Building on previous JPL programs, TES will operate radiometrically (providing precise measurements of absolute intensity) and will be an imaging spectrometer. Four 1×32 element detector arrays are to be used at the focal plane of the interferometer, covering different spectral regions selected by filter wheels. Pointing mirrors ahead of the interferometer will direct the field of view. As the satellite orbits, its forward movement will trace out a swath while the linear detector arrays perpendicular to the motion resolve the other axis. This forms an image by the "pushbroom" method.

Owing to the vast quantity of data to be collected by the instrument — generating 350 000 spectra per day — data analysis will be almost entirely automated. The need for almost "real-time" observation suggests that computational rates of some 500 Mflops (500 million floating-point operations per second) will be needed. This compares with rates of well under one Mflop available with present personal computers.

The instrument, intended to operate on board a polar-orbiting satellite, is to be launched at around the turn of the century and is designed to operate at cryogenic temperatures for five years.

16.3.8 Soviet space-borne interferometers

This text has been able to give only a brief vignette of Soviet accomplishments in FTIR technology, because so few publications have been available in the West. The primary publication for reporting designs of East-European interferometers in the west is *Feingeraetetechnik*, a German-language journal. Other sources include *Kinematics. Phys. Celest. Bodies* and *Sov. J. Opt. Technol.*, both English translations of Russian journals.

The Venera 15 and 16 space probes carried the FS 1/4 Fourier spectrometer developed by the Academy of Sciences of the GDR.

The Meteor 25 probe, launched in May 1976, carried the SI-1 interferometer (Kempe *et al.*, 1977). This instrument measured the infrared signature of the earth and atmosphere, covering the 6.25 to 25 μm spectral range with a resolution of 5 cm^{-1} and accuracy of 0.5% in emittance. The opto-mechanics of the Michelson interferometer were automatically controlled to maintain alignment.

16.3.9 Manned space flight

Most NASA programs have included a Fourier spectrometer among the instrument complement. Gemini 5 carried a Fourier spectrometer to make measurements from space of the radiation signatures of earth and sky backgrounds, a Minuteman missile during launch, and a rocket motor launch on a test track.

Apollo spacecraft carried an interferometric spectrometer for the 5–20 μm region, measuring similar subjects.

Interferometers for use on the American space shuttle have rather different requirements from the previous versions. They are generally controlled by either a Mission Specialist on the shuttle, or by an operator at a ground station, instead of automatically sequenced by on-board computers.

A polymer manufacturing experiment by 3M has been monitored by a Bomem Michelson-series interferometer. The device covered the mid-infrared range, and was flown aboard the shuttle in 1989.

A Connes-type interferometer covering the 2–16 μm range was designed as a shuttle payload to measure vertical profiles of atmospheric gases down to trace level (Farmer, 1981). The experiment, known as Atmospheric Trace Molecules Spectroscopy (ATMOS), is intended to obtain measurements some one hundred times more quickly than balloon-borne spectrometers. The instrument flew on the shuttle in 1985, and is scheduled to be flown again about once a year as part of a programme to monitor the chemistry of stratospheric ozone.

An experiment to monitor the temperature and velocity of upper atmospheric winds has recently been launched. This employed an all-glass field-widened interferometer for measurement of the emission lines of the airglow and aurora (Shepperd *et al.*, 1984). The interferometer is described in Section 17.3.

REFERENCES

Beer, R. (1967), Fourier Spectrometry from Balloons, *Appl. Opt.*, **6**, 209.
Beer, R., Norton, R. H., and Seaman, C. H. (1973), Astronomical Infrared Spectroscopy with a Connes-Type Interferometer. I. Instrumental, *Rev. Sci. Instr.*, **42**, 1393.

Beer, R. and Glavich, T. A. (1989), Remote sensing of the troposphere by infrared emission spectroscopy, *Proc. SPIE*, **1129**, 42.

Block, L. C. and Zachor, A. S. (1964), Inflight Satellite Measurements of Infrared Spectral Radiance of the Earth, *Appl. Opt.*, **3**, 209.

Borman, S. A. (1981), Voyager Infrared Spectrometer, *Anal. Chem.*, **53**, 1544A.

Buijs, H. (1967), High Resolution Fourier Transform Spectroscopy, *J. Phys.*, **28**, C2-105.

Connes, P. (1970), High Resolution Fourier Spectroscopy, in *Optical Instruments and Techniques*, J. Home-Dickson, (ed.) Oriel Press.

Connes, J. and Connes, P. (1966), Near-Infrared Planetary Spectra by Fourier Spectroscopy. I. Instruments and Results, *J. Opt. Soc. Am.*, **56**, 896.

Connes, P. and Michel, G (1975), Astronomical Fourier Spectrometer, *Appl. Opt.*, **14**, 2067.

Davis, D. Scott, Lawson, H. P., Williams, M., Michel, G. and Connes, P. (1980), Infrared Fourier Spectrometer for Airborne and Ground-Based Astronomy, *Appl. Opt.*, **19**, 4138.

Farmer, C. B. (1981), High resolution spectroscopy of the Earth's upper atmosphere from space, *Proc. SPIE*, **289**, 299.

Fink, U. and Larson, H. (1970), Fourier spectroscopy at the Lunar and Planetary Laboratory of the University of Arizona, *Aspen International Conference on Fourier Spectroscopy*, Vanasse, G. A., Stair, A. T. and Baker, D. J. (eds), AFCRL-71-0019, p.452.

Hanel, R. A., Schlachman, B., Clark, F. D., Prokesh, C. H., Taylor, J. B., Wilson W. M. and Chaney, L. (1970), The Nimbus III Michelson Interferometer, *Appl. Opt.*, **9**, 1767.

Hanel, R., Schlachman, B., Breihan, E., Bywaters, R. Chapman, F., Rhodes, M., Rodgers, D. and Vanous, D. (1972), Mariner 9 Michelson Interferometer, *Appl. Opt.*, **11**, 2625.

Hanel, R., Crosby, D., Herath, L., Vanous, D., Collins, D. Creswick, H., Harris, C. and Rhodes, M. (1980), Infrared spectrometer for Voyager, *Appl. Opt.*, **19**, 1391.

Harries, J. E. (1973), Measurement of Some Hydrogen-Oxygen-Nitrogen Compounds in the Stratosphere from Concorde 002, *Nature*, **241**, 515.

Haycock, R. H. and Baker, D. J. (1974), Infrared Prism Interferometer-Spectrometer Using a Gas-Lubricated Drive Bearing, *Infr. Phys.*, **14**, 259.

Kempe, J. C. and Huppi, R. J. (1979), Rocket-borne cryogenic Michelson interferometer, *Proc. SPIE*, **191**, 135.

Kempe V., Oertel, D., Pucler, J., Roseler, A., Sakatov, D. P. and Studemutte, H. (1977), The infra-red Fourier spectrometer SI-1 in the 'Meteor-25', *Radio Fernsehen Elektron, (Germany)*, **26**, 627.

Larson, H. P. (1978), Airborne infrared astronomical observations by Fourier transform spectroscopy, *Appl. Opt.*, **17**, 1352.

Larson, H. P. and Fink, U. (1975), Infrared Fourier Spectrometer for Laboratory Use and for Astronomical Studies From Aircraft and Ground-Based Telescopes, *Appl. Opt.*, **14**, 2085.

Masleev, L. B. (1988), An Astronomical Fourier Spectrometer, *Kinematics. Phys. Celest. Bodies, (USA)*, **4**, 102.

Mertz, L. (1965), *Transformations in Optics*, Wiley, New York.

Mertz, L. (1971), Fourier Spectroscopy, Past, Present and Future, *Appl. Opt.*, **10**, 386.

Ridgway, S. T. and Capps, R. W. (1974), A Fourier transform spectrophotometer for astronomical applications, $700-10\,000$ cm^{-1}, *Rev. Sci. Instr.*, **45**, 676.

Shepherd, G. G., Gault, W. A., Miller, D. W., Pasturczyk, Z., Johnston, S. F., Kosteniuk, P. R., Haslett, J. W., Kendall, D. J. W. and Wimperis, J. R. (1985), WAMDII: wide-angle Michelson Doppler imaging interferometer for Spacelab, *Appl Opt.*, **24**, 1571.

17

Beyond FTIR

17.1 DOUBLE-BEAM FTIR

Descriptions of double-beam Fourier spectrometers have circulated since the "renaissance" in the 1950s. The principle of compensating the "sample" beam by a "reference" beam was a carry-over from dispersive instruments, as discussed in Section 6.8. The term double-beaming can, however, refer to distinctly different configurations of hardware, modes of use, and performance. Because general discussions of double-beam techniques are scarce in the literature, it will be discussed in some depth here.

The Michelson interferometer (MI) is a symmetrical instrument. A schematic diagram is shown in Fig. 17.1. The MI modulates the intensity of an incoming light beam I_A and produces two outputs O_A and O_B that are 180 degrees out of phase (one signal is of maximum intensity while the other is minimum). Two entrance "ports" are available (I_A and I_B), which are similarly out-of-phase by 180°.

The two outputs are inverted because light undergoes a 180° phase shift at every reflection and a $-90°$ phase shift at every transmission through a metallic surface. A similar result is obtained for dielectric beamsplitters. Examination of the various circuits (such as $I_A \& O_A$ and $I_A \& O_B$, or $I_A \& I_A$ and $I_B \& O_A$) will show that the two circuits have a different number of reflections and so have a relative phase shift.

In conventional single-beam FTIR spectroscopy, only one input and one output port are employed. The radiation exiting from the second output port is simply allowed to return to the source.

In interferometers employing cube-corner or cat's eye mirrors, the four ports can be spatially separated. Light can enter or exit the interferometer from any port without interfering with the others.

Owing to the complementary nature of the signals from each output port (or between the two input port signals), the combination of the output port signals will add up to a constant: a null will be produced. This is true whether the outgoing light beams are combined on a single detector, or if two detectors are used to measure the optical signals and are then combined electrically.

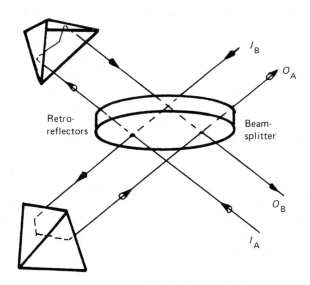

Fig. 17.1 — Generalized four-port interferometer. I_A, I_B: complementary input beams; O_A, O_B: corresponding output beams. Note that both inputs reach both outputs.

This means that any spectral variations caused by the light source or interferometer will cancel, as long as the same spectral information is available in each interferometer beam. This amounts to optical or electrical subtraction.

The detailed nature and limitations of this subtraction process determine the applications that are practical. The success of double-beam FTIR depends critically on the quality of balancing of the two beams. The quality of the subtraction, i.e. how well the two out-of-phase contributions cancel, can be expressed by a "nulling" factor:

$$N = I_d/(I_a - I_b) \qquad (17.1)$$

where I_a=single-beam intensity and $I_a - I_b$=double-beam intensity. It is convenient to use the integrated (zero-path-difference) intensity for this expression, but in general the degree of nulling will be wavenumber-dependent.

17.1.1 Double-beam configurations and applications

17.1.1.1 *Time-division double-beaming*

The simplest double-beam scheme, and that closest to its counterpart in dispersive spectrometers, is time-division measurement. In this configuration, a slow-scanning Fourier spectrometer is alternately switched between a sample and a reference position. At each optical path difference, the interferograms of the sample and reference are measured. The interferometer mirror is then moved and the process is repeated.

This scheme was used by Ballantyne (1966) for a slow-scanning interferometer. He found that the principal causes of drift in a single-beam interferometer signal were fluctuations in the mercury arc source and semiconducting bolometer detector: both were of the order of a second. He therefore switched between the sample and reference channels every 250 msec, i.e. considerably faster than the fluctuation rate.

To reduce the effects of instrumental drifts to a minimum, the beam switching can be performed rapidly and repetitively at each mirror position. Hall *et al.* (1966) of the Aerospace Corporation, constructed a far infrared slow-scanning system that used a reflective chopper rotating at 19 Hz to alternate between the reference and sample beams.

In their modification of a Beckman RIIC FS-720 interferometer, Thorpe *et al.* (1969) used a reflective chopper to alternate the two beams at a rate of 6 Hz. This caused the detector signal to be modulated, with an amplitude proportional to the difference in intensities of the two beams. The two components of the signal were electrically separated and separately recorded. The two resulting interferograms were then separately transformed and ratioed to yield the spectrum.

17.1.1.2 Pseudo-time-division double-beaming
With modern fast-scanning interferometers, time-division measurement is impractical: the beam-switching system would require very rapid alternation of the beams at a rate beyond the electrical frequency response of the detector.

An approximate analogue of the technique is to measure entire reference and sample interferograms closely spaced in time. By using a sample shuttle, the sample can be positioned in and out of the beam in alternate scans. By separately ratioing pairs of sample and reference spectra and then averaging the spectra, the effects of instrumental drifts can be reduced. This technique does nothing to compensate for more subtle instrumental problems such as scan drive errors of the interferometer. It is used chiefly to correct for variable absorption by carbon dioxide and water vapour in poorly sealed spectrometers. Motorized sample shuttles, controlled by the instrument microprocessor, have been used by Perkin–Elmer, Lloyd Instruments, and Philips Analytical.

17.1.1.3 Optical and electrical methods
The general four port arrangement for a Michelson interferometer is shown in Fig. 17.1. The interferometer employs cube-corner or cat's eye mirrors to separate the beams spatially.

The input paths are labelled I_A and I_B, respectively. The output paths are labelled O_A and O_B. Each input path directs light to both output paths, and vice versa.

Owing to the non-zero thickness of the beamsplitter, the various circuits through the interferometer are not identical, and so the practical instrument is not entirely symmetrical. In this section we will analyse various practical configurations.

(a) Two sources, one detector: optical subtraction
This arrangement uses two different sources at the two input ports and a single detector at one of the output ports, as shown in the top and middle diagrams of Fig. 17.2. The two input signals overlap at the detector. Being out of phase, they subtract

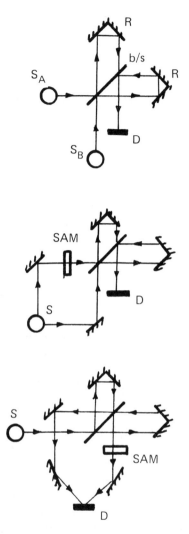

Fig. 17.2 — Three configurations for optical subtraction. Top: differential emission spectroscopy. S_A, S_B: two independent sources; R: retroreflector; b/s: beamsplitter; D: detector.
Middle: absorption spectroscopy with the sample preceding the interferometer. Bottom:
absorption spectroscopy with the sample following the interferometer.

optically. The configuration is applicable for the optical subtraction of two similar
light sources, i.e. for differential emission spectroscopy. For example, a rocket-flare
spectrum has features corresponding to both a heated body and to specific chemical
species. The heated-body spectrum, which has large intensity variations with
frequency but no significant spectral features, can be removed by optical subtraction
of a reference blackbody source. Technical advantages of this subtraction include a
significant reduction in the dynamic range of the signal. This allows more precise
signal measurement and a corresponding reduction in noise level. This geometry has

been used in Mattson spectrometers such as the Mattson Galaxy 8000 (Fig. 17.3). Although the 8000 employs cube corner mirrors, the two input beams are not spatially separated from the output beams; instead, a beamsplitter mirror reflects half of the output beam to the detector. This convenient geometry results in loss of energy, making it no more efficient in light gathering than a single-beam FTIR.

The optical circuits taken by the light here are (referring to Fig. 17.1):

Beam a of interferometer: $I_A \& O_A$
Beam b of interferometer: $I_B \& O_A$

i.e. for beam a, light enters at I_A and exits at O_A. Light travels down each arm of the interferometer, undergoing a combination of reflection R by the beamsplitter coating, transmission T through the beamsplitter coating, and transmission t through the beamsplitter material. The path followed for each arm is thus:

	Arm 1:	Arm 2:	
Beam a:	RtT	TtR	
Beam b:	t^2T^2	t^2R^2	(17.2)

where the squared factors imply two interactions. Thus the two circuits of the double beam configuration do not yield the same operations on the light beams. Note that for beam a the two arms undergo the same operations, but for beam b light through one arm undergoes two transmissions while the other undergoes two reflections. As will be shown later, this lack of symmetry has only limited importance for the performance of the double-beam system.

(b) One source, two detectors: electrical subtraction
This arrangement uses a single source at one of the two input ports and two detectors, one at each exit port as shown in Fig. 17.4. With this arrangement, the two detectors measure nominally identical signals that are 180° out of phase. The two detector signals are then summed electrically to yield a subtracted output.

If an absorbing sample is placed between the interferometer and one of the detectors, the two signals will no longer compensate each other perfectly: instead, the difference between the two signals will be measured. In this way, the dynamic range of the measurement is reduced, giving better precision. The configuration is useful principally for absorption studies. Its advantage is the reduction of dynamic range of the signal and the corresponding improvement in measurement precision.

Peter Fellgett (1958) appears to have been the first person to measure separately the two complementary outputs of an interferometer and combine them to improve signal-to-noise ratio.

Block Engineering (H. Bar-Lev 1966) developed a low-resolution (10 cm^{-1}) rapid-scanning interferometer configured for double beam operation (Fig. 17.5). Because the interferometer used flat mirrors, the input and output beams could not easily be displaced. Instead, the input beams were injected into the interferometer from small mirrors at the centre of the aperture. The uncollimated beams diverged in their passage through the interferometer and exited with a much larger diameter, at

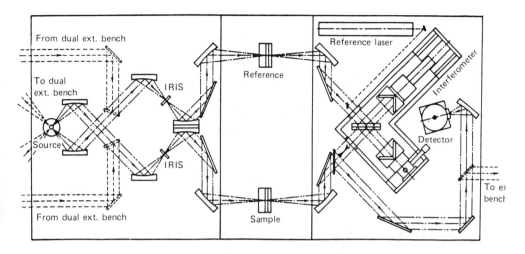

Fig. 17.3 — Mattson Galaxy 8000 double-beam layout.

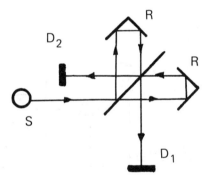

Fig. 17.4 — Configuration for electrical subtraction. S: source; R: retroreflector; D_1, D_2: complementary detectors.

which point they were focused onto two separate detectors. The two detector signals were electrically summed to yield the difference spectrum. The instrument was optimized for the 8–12μm atmospheric window, and was intended for the sensitive measurement of atmospheric gases. A nulling ratio of 40:1 was attained.

The configuration was used by Spectrotherm (Willis 1976) for one of the first GC/IR systems. As shown in Fig. 17.6, the beamsplitter was operated at near normal incidence to provide two output beams. Each of these passed through a triple-pass absorption cell. One cell served as a reference; the other received the eluent from the gas chromatograph. A separate detector was used for each channel, and signals were

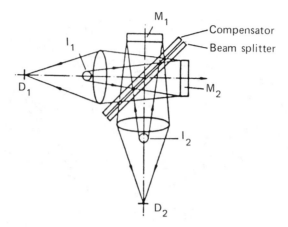

Fig. 17.5 — Block Engineering double-beam interferometer (reproduced from Bar-Lev (1967), with permission from Pergamon Press PLC).

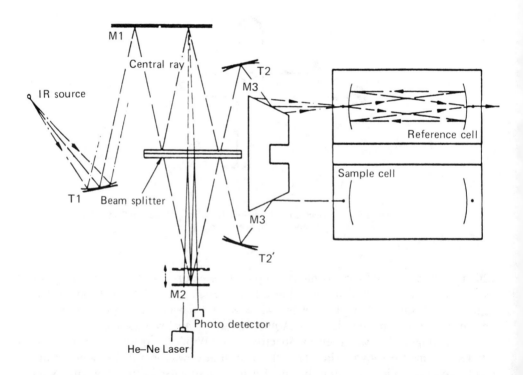

Fig. 17.6 — Spectrotherm double-beam interferometer for GC/IR measurement (reproduced from Willis (1976) with permission from Pergamon Press PLC).

subsequently combined digitally to form the ratio. Direct subtraction was not employed.

The optical circuits taken by the light here are:

Beam a of interferometer: $I_A \& O_A$
Beam b of interferometer: $I_A \& O_B$

i.e. for beam a, light enters at I_A and exits at O_A, while for beam b light enters at I_A and exits at O_B. The paths followed for each of the two arms are:

	Arm 1:	Arm 2:	
Beam a:	RtT	TtR	
Beam b:	t^2T^2	t^2R^2	(17.3)

The paths are thus identical to those of optical subtraction.

(c) Two sources, two detectors: combined optical and electrical subtraction
This arrangement amounts to a merging of the two arrangements described above, i.e. simultaneous optical and electrical subtraction. Each of the two detectors will measure a signal consisting of the superposition of two interferograms (from the two sources). Both the source interferograms and the detector signals will be out of phase, leading to a subtraction of one source from the other and one detector signal from the other.

These two techniques have distinct advantages: optical subtraction (two inputs) is suitable for differential emission spectroscopy, while electrical subtraction (two outputs) is useful for partially compensating source fluctuations. The combination is suitable for the measurement of a fluctuating source while simultaneously subtracting a stable background signal. The scheme was employed by Ridgway and Capps (1974) at Kitt Peak National Observatory (Arizona) for an astronomical interferometer. The system was built around a commercially available Idealab IF-3 Michelson interferometer. Light from the input telescope was directed to two variable apertures to define a source and adjacent sky comparison. These two beams were then separately collimated and introduced into the interferometer from opposite directions. This provided optical cancellation of the background scattered light and the thermal emission that was common to both beams. Optical nulling of 100:1 was readily achieved, a success that the experimenters attributed to the use of the variable apertures to balance the beam intensities, and to the symmetry of the optical system.

Ridgway and Capps found the use of two detectors problematical but useful. They combined the two signals, finding that it was necessary to use matched detectors and preamplifiers to observe an improvement in signal-to-noise ratio. Alternatively, they found that they could use the two outputs separately with two different types of detector, e.g. a broadband detector for one exit and a narrowband, lower-noise detector for the other. In this way, the single interferometer could simultaneously be used as a double-range instrument.

The optical circuits taken by the light here are:

Beam a of interferometer: $I_A\&O_A$ and $I_A\&O_B$
Beam b of interferometer: $I_B\&O_A$ and $I_B\&O_B$

The unavoidable mixing of the source interferograms on both detectors is apparent. The paths followed are:

	Arm 1:	Arm 2:	
Beam a:	tRt and t^2T^2	tRT and t^2R^2	
Beam b:	t^2R^2 and t^3RT	t^2T^2 and t^3RT	(17.4)

The various paths differ particularly in the number t of transmissions through the beamsplitter material.

17.1.2   Technical advantages of double-beam configurations

(a) Reduction of dynamic range
The precision of signal measurement is ultimately limited by the analogue-to-digital converter (ADC) of the instrument.

Suppose a 16-bit converter is used. By reducing the dynamic range of the detector signal by a factor of 2, one ADC bit is gained. The system is then equivalent to a single-beam instrument with a 17-bit ADC, and provides a correspondingly higher digitizing resolution. For the nulling factors of 5 to 100 realizable for practical instruments, about 2 to 6 ADC bits can be saved, leading to correspondingly better detection sensitivities compared with a single-beam instrument (if the signal-to-noise ratio and instrumental sensitivity are limited by ADC resolution).

The reduction of dynamic range has been investigated experimentally, for example, by Vanasse et al. (1977). These workers obtained a nulling factor of about 10 after extensive efforts at aligning an adapted interferometer. They concluded that their step-and-integrate instrument, which employed an external light chopper for signal modulation, was unsuitable for double-beam work because the chopper introduced a phase lag between the two beams.

(b) Background suppression
Double-beam FTIR background suppression has frequently been used for detecting a weak point-source spectrum in an intense, fluctuating background spectrum. The technique is most useful in astronomy. As Reinhold Beer and co-workers (1971) relate:

> ...the ir sky is not dark. As the wavelength increases beyond about 2.5 μ, the sky becomes increasingly bright until, around 3.5 μ, it is brighter than almost all astronomical objects. By 5 μ, the sky is totally dominant and its statistical fluctuations (sky noise) begin to play an important role in ir astronomy. Most of our activities are at shorter wavelengths but we are still faced with a serious contrast problem.

These investigators used two fields of view applied to the two complementary inputs to the interferometer. One contained the image of the star or planet of interest; the other included only a blank patch of adjacent sky. Addition of the two interferometer outputs yielded little net signal when the subject was absent, and a signal compensated for background fluctuations when the subject was present.

Another method (Zehnpfennig *et al.* 1979) employed optical subtraction with two telescopes viewing the same field of view containing a distant point-like emission source and a strong background emission. The telescopes channelled radiation to a single detector.

One of the two telescopes was defocused so that the point-like target was diffused over the field of view. The other telescope was focused to ensure good imaging onto the detector.

A defocusing lens acts as a low-pass spatial filter, tending to attenuate the high spatial frequencies in an image: i.e. the sharp features are blurred and smoothed out. The optical subtraction of the focused and defocused beams yielded a net interferogram at the detector, because the defocused optics were less efficient at transferring the source image but equally efficient at transferring the low-resolution background image. Thus the background, appearing at both interferometer input ports with near-equal intensity, was reduced with respect to the point-source intensity, which was more intense at one of the two inputs. This background suppression was equally efficient for fluctuating (time-dependent) backgrounds.

Suppression of background fluctuations by electrical subtraction was used by Forman *et al.* (1969) at NASA Goddard Space Flight Center. They found electrical matching of the two channels to be the most critical factor in obtaining good nulling.

(c) Linearization of detector response

Guelachvili (1986) described a means of linearizing detector signal by using a double-beam system with electrical subtraction. He showed that, provided that the relative gains of the two detector-plus-preamplifier combinations are appropriately selected, the first-order nonlinear terms of the detector response can be cancelled. This cancellation occurs even for two detectors having dissimilar nonlinearities. The technique is thus suitable for the accurate measurement of light sources having a wide dynamic range.

(d) Compensation for source fluctuations

A double-beam instrument can partially suppress fluctuations of source intensity. A single-beam interferogram consists of a constant portion I_c and a modulated portion $F(t)$ where t=time:

$$I_a(t) = I_c + F(t) \tag{17.5}$$

The interferogram measured at the alternate output port has the form:

$$I_b(t) = I_c - F(t) \tag{17.6}$$

i.e. out of phase with I_a.

When the a source has time-dependent fluctuations $a(t)$, the two interferograms become:

$$I_a(t) = a(t)[I_c + F(t)]$$
$$I_b(t) = a(t)[I_c - F(t)] \tag{17.7}$$

and their difference is:

$$I_a(t) - I_b(t) = 2a(t)F(t) \tag{17.8}$$

i.e. the constant terms cancel; no modulation by source fluctuations occurs for the constant intensity component of the interferogram. Thus the background term becomes much smaller if double-beam subtraction is employed.

The benefit for noise reduction occurs when the source fluctuations $a(t)$ have a time scale comparable to the interferometer modulation $F(t)$: i.e. when both the source and the interferometer modulate the signal in the same frequency range. If the source fluctuations are much slower than the scan rate, the electrical bandwidth of the instrument can be defined to exclude the source noise, i.e. a complete interferogram can be obtained before significant changes in source intensity occur.

17.1.3 Comparison with dispersive double-beam instruments

Dispersive double-beam spectrometers typically use an opto-mechanical scheme to measure alternately the reference and sample path very closely in time as described in Section 6.6. The light from the source is cyclically switched between a sample and reference position; the light is measured by a single detector. The detector measures an AC signal of which the magnitude depends on the difference between the sample and reference beams.

Dispersive instruments record the ratio I_s/I_r of the sample beam to reference beam intensities. The ratio of two intensities (i.e. of two transmittances) yields the sample-only transmittance spectrum.

Dispersive double-beam spectrometers can compensate completely for background absorbance (i.e. the "solvent subtraction" technique) and for fluctuations in the light source. Suppose that the source varies by a time-dependent factor $a(t)$. Then, since both sample and reference beams are measured at very nearly the same time t, the ratio of intensities is:

$$a(t)T_s/a(t)T_r = T_s/T_r \tag{17.9}$$

i.e. the sample-only transmittance spectrum, without any contribution from source fluctuations.

In FTIR double-beam spectroscopy, the interferogram is not related on a point-by-point basis to the sample transmittance or absorbance spectrum, because a function is not linearly related to its Fourier transform.

Optical or electrical subtraction of interferograms cannot entirely remove source fluctuations, as shown above.

For example, consider the double-beam configurations for absorption spectroscopy. For a source having time-dependent fluctuations $a(t)$, the interferogram
signal for the two beams is:

$$a(t)I_a \text{ and } a(t)I_b \qquad (17.10)$$

Optical or electrical subtraction yields a signal to the ADC of:

$$I_{ADC} = a(t)[I_a - I_b] \qquad (17.11)$$

i.e. the source fluctuations still contribute to the modulated component of the signal.
The source fluctuations $a(t)$ could be entirely removed from the interferogram signal
by dividing I_a by I_b, but this would only be possible for the two-detector configuration, in which the two electrical signals could be ratioed.

17.1.4 Factors affecting performance

The nulling produced by double-beam subtraction is directly related to the dynamic
range of the signal: a nulling factor of 10, for example, implies that the double-beam
interferogram modulation is 10 times less intense than a single-beam interferogram,
but that the actual signal content of interest has the same variation. The large
background excursions are therefore removed, allowing the signal to be measured
with ten times better precision. This, in turn, allows weaker signal variations to be
measured.

The degree of "nulling" or compensation of one beam by the other is influenced
by several factors, which are analysed below.

(a) Intrinsic MI geometry

The optical and electrical subtraction schemes described above yield the same optical
paths. They can therefore be analysed together.

The intensity of each beam can be considered the intensity I_0 of the incoming
beam multiplied by the R, T and t factors listed in expressions (17.2) and (17.3). This
gives intensities:

	Arm 1:	Arm 2:	
Beam a:	$I_0 R t T$	$I_0 R T t$	
Beam b:	$I_0 T^2 t^2$	$I_0 R^2 t^2$	(17.12)

The intensity of the output beams is:

Beam a:	$I_{12} = I_0[2RtT(1\cos(4\pi\sigma d))]$	(17.13)
Beam b:	$I_{12} = I_0[t^2(R^2 + T^2) - 2t^2 RT\cos(4\pi\sigma d)]$	(17.14)

As the interferometer scans, d changes and so the output intensity I_{12} is modulated.
The AC-coupled preamplifier removes the first (constant) term of this expression,
leaving the time-varying part. The two beams are thus imbalanced by the factor t, the

transmittance for a single passage through the beamsplitter at 45° incidence. Except for this factor, the interferogram modulation is equal for the two beams.

The imbalance by the factor t can be important because t generally varies with wavenumber. Even if the two beams can be balanced at a particular wavenumber, they will be imbalanced at another. The degree of nulling N will therefore be limited.

This imbalance can be easily compensated, though. Beam a, which has one beamsplitter transmittance fewer than Beam b, should include a compensator plate of thickness equal to the beamsplitter and oriented at 45° to the beam axis. This plate must be placed outside the interferometer so that Beam b does not pass through it. With this compensated double-beam system, there are no nulling problems caused by the interferometer itself.

(b)   Beam apertures

The two beams of the double-beam interferometer must have identical size and divergence because:
(1) The energy reaching the detector(s) from the two beams should be as similar as possible (requiring equal aperture area).
(2) The divergence of the interferometer beam determines the effective frequency scale according to:

$$\sigma_{observation} = \sigma_0(1 - \Omega^2/2) \tag{17.15}$$

where $\sigma_{observation}$=measured wavenumber, σ_0=true wavenumber, and Ω=maximum angle of divergence through the interferometer.

Thus any difference between the two beams will lead to a difference in the wavenumber scales of the corresponding spectra. The optical or electrical subtraction of the interferograms will then be imperfect because the effective "scales" of the interferograms will differ by the factor $(1-\Omega^2/2)$.

Divergence through the interferometer is determined either by the diameter of the Jacquinot stop or by the detector itself. Any occultation or limitation of the beam divergence anywhere else in the interferometer may imbalance the two beams and reduce the nulling.

(c) Interference at detector

Optical subtraction requires that two interferograms be superimposed on the detector. Two cases are possible:

(1) Two independent light sources are applied to the two inputs I_A and I_B, respectively, and subsequently recombined onto a single detector. These two sources will have no mutual coherence, and so will not interfere; the net intensity will simply be the sum of the individual intensities:

$$I_{ab} = I_a + I_b \tag{17.16}$$

(2) A single light source is divided into two beams and applied to the two inputs I_A and I_B. The output beams O_A and O_B are then recombined onto a single detector.

If the path lengths between the source and detector for beams a and b are of similar length, there will be mutual interference. This interference will appear as undesired interference fringes, the scale of which will depend critically on the stability of the entire system from beamsplitter to detector. When the two output beams are colinear (as in the Mattson 8000 spectrometer) this is not a problem. However, for the configuration shown in Fig. 17.2, bottom, it can be.

The interference between the two beams could cause the measured interferogram intensity to fluctuate because of dimensional changes of the order of a wavelength. The quality of nulling could thus be unreliable. In practice, this spurious interference can be removed by techniques such as:

— Imaging the two interferogram patterns onto separate portions of the same detector to avoid overlap and therefore mutual interference. This has the disadvantage of requiring a larger detector, and leads to greater electrical noise.
— Preventing mutual interference by orthogonal polarization of the two beams (perpendicularly polarized beams of light do not interfere). This would cause a loss of at least half the available energy.

(d) Detector matching

For the electrical subtraction technique, the matching of the response of the two detector chains is directly related to the nulling factor N by:

$$N(\sigma) = S_a(\sigma)/(S_a(\sigma) - S_b(\sigma)) \qquad (17.17)$$

where S_a and S_b are the two detector signals that depend on wavenumber σ. Two detector elements generally have slightly different wavenumber-dependent responsivity, detectivity and time constant, owing to minor differences in chemical and physical composition. The preamplifiers for the two detectors may have different frequency-dependent gains and phase shifts. The optical filters used to restrict the detector passband, if used, will usually be matched to no better than several percent. The use of optical filters in double-beam instruments can therefore lead to poor nulling.

(e) Noise

A double-beam FTIR instrument can be superior to a single beam FTIR with respect to noise. A double-beam instrument can collect twice the intensity of a single-beam interferometer, since two exit ports are used. It thus has a twofold energy advantage.

The doubled signal will, even without the additional advantage of reduction of dynamic range that is possible with a double-beam FTIR, produce an improvement in signal-to-noise ratio (S/N) of as much as $2^{1/2}$.

Another advantage of the double-beam configuration is related to measurement stability, i.e. to very low-frequency noise. An interferometer signal often has gradual variations owing to dimensional and temperature changes. In single-beam FTIR, the sample and reference interferograms are acquired at different times. Any differences in measurement conditions are thus reflected in the final spectrum.

In double-beam FTIR, the sample and reference are measured simultaneously. Any gradual instrumental drifts cannot thus contribute to the measurement precision. In practice, though, this advantage probably does not exist. Practical double-beam interferometers have imperfect nulling. It is therefore necessary to measure a separate interferogram that records the response of the instrument to perfectly balanced input beams — i.e. to measure the instrument nulling directly. The final spectrum is then the combination of two separate measurements:

$$S_{\text{corrected}} = F[I_{\text{sam}} - I_{\text{ref}}]/F[I_{\text{ref a}} - I_{\text{ref b}}] \qquad (17.18)$$

where $S_{\text{corrected}}$ = corrected final spectrum, $F[I_{\text{sam}} - I_{\text{ref}}]$ = Fourier transform of the double-beam subtractive measurement of a sample and reference (e.g. two emission sources, or an absorption spectroscopy configuration), and $F[I_{\text{ref a}} - I_{\text{ref b}}]$ = Fourier transform of the double-beam subtractive measurement of two nominally identical beams (a and b).

Since the corrected spectrum is the combination of two separate measurements made at different times, the problems of instrumental drift are again present, and the double-beam advantage disappears.

17.1.5 Summary

The two general types of double-beam configuration have specific applications:

(1) Optical subtraction is most applicable for differential emission spectroscopy; it can also be used for differential absorption spectroscopy either (a) if the absorbing sample is placed between the light source and the interferometer or (b) if the two output beams are merged onto the detector either at an angle or with the aid of a beamsplitter. Case (a) has the disadvantage that any emission from the sample will be modulated by the interferometer and therefore will appear in the Fourier-transformed spectrum. Case (b) has the disadvantage that either the beams are not colinear (limiting nulling) or else half the light is lost by the use of a beamsplitter.

(2) Electrical subtraction is most applicable for differential absorption spectroscopy.

Optical subtraction is therefore the most versatile configuration, but electrical subtraction is less critical to implement.

The quality of double-beam subtraction depends on good optical symmetry and alignment. Electrical subtraction requires well-matched detectors. Owing to the number of factors that can affect the nulling ratio, double-beam FTIR is generally more problematic than single-beam FTIR, but has clear advantages for specific studies. The advantages include a reduced interferogram dynamic range for greater sensitivity, the suppression of extraneous background and source fluctuations, and/ or the linearization of detector response.

The practical difficulties of double-beam FTIR, and its limited range of applications, is attested by the few instruments produced; at the time of writing, only Spectrotherm and Mattson have marketed double-beam instruments.

17.2 ASYMMETRIC FTIR

What happens to a Michelson interferometer that is not perfectly symmetrical? For example, what if one of the two Michelson mirrors is dirty, or if the beamsplitter and compensator plates are not of equal thickness?

Such an interferometer, intentionally or not, is being operated in asymmetric mode. When the two arms of an interferometer do not have identical optical properties, the resulting interferogram will not be symmetrical about the zero path difference position. Instead of appearing to be a mirror image on either side of ZPD, the interferogram is skewed and offset.

The asymmetry of the interferogram is caused by materials in either of the two beams of the interferometer that alter not only the *intensity* of light transmitted, but also its *phase*. The phase of a light wave is not normally detectable: the human eye (or light detectors, for that matter) cannot distinguish when or where the peaks and troughs of a light wave occur. For this reason, light travelling straight through a transparent sheet looks the same as light travelling in open air. The phase character-istics are nevertheless as fundamental to the transparent sheet as its absorption properties. As with light absorption, the phase shift of a material can vary with wavelength, temperature, molecular composition and so on.

The absorption and phase spectra are in fact aspects of the same quantity. The relationship can be expressed in various forms, but the most common is in terms of the *complex refractive index, $\hat{n}$*. This can be written:

$$\hat{n}(\sigma) = n(\sigma) - i\alpha(\sigma)/4\pi\sigma \qquad\qquad (17.19)$$

where $n(\sigma)$ is the conventional refractive index of the material, i is the square root of minus one, α is the absorption coefficient, and σ is the wavenumber. The absorption coefficient is related to the transmittance T of the material by:

$$T(\sigma) = \exp\{-\alpha(\sigma)d\} \qquad\qquad (17.20)$$

where d is the thickness of the sample.

The real part of the complex number $\hat{n}$ corresponds to the phase characteristics of the sample, while the imaginary part coincides with its absorption properties. Although this representation may be unfamiliar, it is a compact mathematical notation that shows the relationship between two more commonplace quantities: the refractive index n and the absorption coefficient α. Other quantities sometimes used to describe the relationship are amplitude and phase, power and phase, or real and imaginary dielectric constants.

The interferometer can measure both the absorption and phase characteristics of a sample. Consider the transparent sheet mentioned above. If the sheet is placed either in front of or after the interferometer to intercept the light entering or leaving it, there will be no net effect: the light is shifted in phase, but not absorbed, so the interferometer modulates each wavelength with respect to its original phase. As with the human eye, any phase variations caused by the material are invisible to the interferometer.

If, though, the transparent sheet is placed in one of the two interferometer arms, the situation becomes unbalanced. The phase shift of the plate is added to the regularly varying phase shift produced by the interferometer. Suppose that a very thin transparent sheet introduces a phase shift of 50.2 wavelengths (phase is actually denoted in terms of a single cycle, one wavelength, between 0 and 360 degrees, or 0 and 2π radians). In one arm of the interferometer, it intercepts the beam both travelling to and from the mirror, resulting in a total shift of 100.4 wavelengths, or a net shift of 0.4. When the beam is recombined with the other at the beamsplitter, the two interfere to produce a new net intensity. As the interferometer scans, the optical path difference is modulated as usual.

The resulting interferogram will be shifted from the usual ZPD position. However, it does not appear simply as a displaced symmetrical interferogram. The transparent plate may shift the phase by 100.4 wavelengths at a particular wavelength, but appears thicker or thinner at adjacent wavelengths: the material is said to be "dispersive", i.e. has a refractive index that varies with wavelength. The interferogram is therefore shifted a different amount for each component wavelength. The resulting spread-out appearance is called "chirping" after a similar effect in the dispersion of sound waves in communications.

All but the most carefully manufactured and aligned interferometers have some degree of asymmetry. In conventional FTIR spectroscopy, this is unimportant: by calculating both the sine and cosine Fourier transforms of the skewed interferogram, the desired symmetrical component (the cosine FT) can be corrected by the antisymmetric component (the sine FT). In the simplest procedure, this requires the calculation of the magnitude $M(\sigma)=(C^2(\sigma)+S^2(\sigma))^{1/2}$. Other phase correction methods are discussed in Section 10.6.

However, asymmetric interferograms can, in fact, yield useful information. The possibilities of asymmetric Fourier spectroscopy (or, using its more accepted designation, Dispersive Fourier Transform Spectroscopy, or DFTS) were first investigated independently by John Chamberlain and co-workers at the National Physical Laboratory in Teddington, England (Chamberlain *et al.* 1963) and by Ely Bell and E. E. Russell at Ohio State University.

Until the mid-1960s, most work in Fourier spectroscopy had been concerned with the measurement of the positions of spectral absorption lines or bands; little effort was devoted to quantitative measurements of transmittance or reflectance. Russell and Bell (1965) designed their interferometer for quantitative measurements of both spectral power and spectral phase.

Their design was a Michelson interferometer for far infrared use. It employed a metal-mesh beamsplitter, which has a higher efficiency in the far infrared than the more conventional Mylar film. To make best use of the beamsplitter, the angle of incidence was just 10° instead of 45°. The beam through the interferometer was slightly convergent so that small interferometer mirrors could be used while capturing a reasonably large solid angle of light. The sample to be measured was mounted in front of the fixed mirror of the interferometer. If a reflectance measurement was to be made, the reflective sample was mounted on three posts to orient it correctly with respect to the moving mirror. The resolution of the instrument was limited to about 5 cm^{-1} by the short travel of the moving mirror, which was mounted in a parallelogram arrangement and moved by a stepping motor rotating a micro-meter screw.

The power and phase spectra were obtained from the measured interferogram as follows.

(1) Calculate the cosine C and sine S Fourier transforms of the interferogram.
(2) Calculate the power spectrum:

$$I(\sigma)=\{C^2(\sigma)+S^2(\sigma)\}^{1/2} \tag{17.21}$$

The power spectrum can be either reflectance $R(\sigma)$ or transmittance $T(\sigma)$, depending on how the sample is arranged.

(3) Calculate the phase spectrum:

$$\Phi(\sigma)=\arctan\{C(\sigma)/S(\sigma)\} \tag{17.22}$$

Russell and Bell used their instrument to measure the power and phase spectra of materials such as alkali halide crystals and metal mesh screens. Even the dispersion characteristics of gases could be measured by placing a transmission cell in the sample arm of the interferometer. By repeating measurements over a three-month period, they were able to demonstrate that reproducible spectra could be measured with precise intensity information.

Chamberlain *et al.* (1969), using similar experimental methods, expressed their results as a complex refractive index $\hat{n}$ as defined above. The real and imaginary parts of the refractive index are calculated from the power and phase measurements as follows:

(1) Calculate the power reflectance $R(\sigma)$ as described above.
(2) Calculate the phase spectrum $\Phi(\sigma)$ as described above.
(3) Calculate the complex refractive index:

$$n(\sigma)=(1-R(\sigma)-2iR^{1/2}\sin\Phi)/(1+R(\sigma)+2R^{1/2}\cos\Phi)$$

$$\tag{17.23}$$

Work on asymmetric Fourier spectroscopy has continued at NPL with J. Birch and colleagues (Birch 1972).

J. Gast and L. Genzel (1973) at the Max Planck Institute in Stuttgart, Germany, constructed the first interferometer for dispersive spectroscopy in the mid-infrared at high resolution. With cube-corner mirrors, the instrument had a theoretical resolu-tion of $0.04\ \mathrm{cm}^{-1}$ and worked up to $1000\ \mathrm{cm}^{-1}$. For reflective measurements, one interferometer mirror was replaced by the flat sample. In a later version (Zwick *et al.* 1975) a practical problem with dispersive FTIR was solved: how can the sample phase information be separated from phase errors due to the interferometer itself? To do this, three interferograms were measured: a background (with no sample in the interferometer), an interferogram with the sample in one arm, and a third interferogram with the sample in the opposite arm. From the background interfero-gram, the severity of any asymmetry could be determined. The subsequent two interferograms obtained with the sample in opposite arms could be used to cancel any instrumental effects that were observed.

Despite the increased mathematical complexity of dispersive FTIR compared to conventional FTIR, the computer bears the brunt of the extra work. There are further practical problems with the method, however. Unless the interferometer mirrors are very small, it can be difficult to prepare a sufficiently large sample. The sample should be as large and as flat as the mirror it replaces, and must be positioned with its reflecting face in precisely the same plane. Very small alignment errors can lead to extremely large errors of phase. For these reasons, dispersive spectroscopy is more demanding than conventional FTIR. No commercial instruments have been produced.

17.3 FIELD-WIDENED INTERFEROMETERS

Despite the large throughput advantage of Michelson interferometers compared with prism and diffraction grating spectrometers, there are applications that demand even more "light-grasp". Examples include measurements of the aurora borealis and airglow, both of which are weak sources of radiation that extend over a large angular field.

In discussing field-widening it is useful to begin by defining terms. The words throughput, light-grasp, light-gathering power, flux acceptance and radiance response are interchangeable and all refer to the amount of energy that can be channelled through an optical instrument. This can be expressed as the area of the optical element that limits the throughput, multiplied by the solid angle accepted through this area, and has units of cm^2steradians. Throughput is sometimes more precisely called "solid angle area product". The accepted term for this quantity today is étendue.

Two types of instrument have been used for such studies. The first, popularized by P. Jacquinot, was the scanning Fabry–Pérot spectrometer. Fabry–Pérot interferometers have the drawback of having a restricted spectral range: different spectral orders overlap, and must be filtered out.

The second instrument used for weak-source studies was the Michelson interferometer. The standard Michelson interferometer has the same throughput as the Fabry–Pérot, and so offers no advantage in sensitivity. It does not suffer from overlapping spectral orders, but does require Fourier transformation to yield the spectrum.

A method for increasing the throughput of a Michelson interferometer was first described by G. Hansen (1955). The scheme was later discussed by P. Connes (1956) and L. Mertz (1965).

17.3.1 Principle of field-widening

In a conventional Michelson interferometer, the optical path difference is different for rays travelling through it at various angles (see Fig.17.7, top and middle). Consider two positions of the moving mirror: the first position is zero path difference (ZPD), at which it is the same distance from the beamsplitter as the fixed mirror. The second position is farther away, giving an unequal path. In position 1, a ray entering

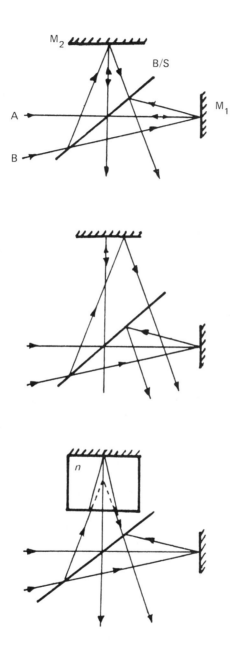

Fig. 17.7 — Illustration of field-widening. Top: conventional Michelson interferometer with zero path difference. M_1, M_2: mirrors; B/S: beamsplitter; A: on-axis ray; B: off-axis ray. All rays are in phase. Middle: conventional Michelson interferometer with a non-zero path difference. The optical path difference depends on the angle of the ray from the axis. Bottom: Field-widened Michelson interferometer. The transparent block having refractive index n refracts off-axis rays to follow nearly the same trajectory as on-axis rays.

the instrument travels the same distance along either arm of the interferometer. The optical path difference (which is zero) does not depend on the angle of incidence.

For position 2 of the mirror, though, the extra distance travelled by the ray in the moving-mirror arm depends on its angle of entry. This means that the optical path difference of the interferometer varies with angle. The situation gets progressively worse as the mirror moves farther from ZPD. If the interference pattern is viewed at the detector focus, it appears as concentric rings as shown in Fig. 9.4. The angular acceptance of the interferometer can be visualized as the size of the central fringe. As path difference is increased, the pattern becomes smaller, indicating that the central portion viewed by the detector has a smaller angular extent. On the other hand, as the path difference approaches zero, the angular field gets larger until it becomes infinite at ZPD. The conventional Michelson thus trades throughput for resolution. A high-resolution spectrum is obtained at the expense of smaller energy acceptance.

A field-widened interferometer works by producing the zero-path condition at other path differences. This is shown schematically in the bottom diagram of Fig. 17.7. The moving mirror is augmented by a block of transparent material having refractive index n. For an interferometer used with visible light, the block could be an accurately polished glass piece having its rear surface coated with aluminium.

A ray of light entering the interferometer at any angle will now be refracted in the transparent block. The path of the ray outside the block is the same as before, but the higher refractive index inside the block causes it to travel a longer optical path. The same effect occurs when you look into an aquarium tank or a swimming pool: the bottom appears to be closer than it actually is. On travelling a distance d through the transparent medium, the ray will undergo an optical path equal to nd. It can be shown that the block makes the interferometer output almost independent of angle for a particular optical path difference. At other values (i.e. other positions of the moving mirror) the angular field diminishes, just as it does away from ZPD in a conventional interferometer. Even at the designed path difference, though, the optical path is not perfectly independent of angle; the glass block introduces optical aberration. This effect, too, can be seen by looking into an aquarium tank: movement of one's head to change the angle of view causes the apparent distance to vary disconcertingly. Despite aberration, field-widening can produce usable angular acceptance as large as several degrees, providing an étendue larger by several orders of magnitude than that of a conventional Michelson interferometer.

17.3.2 Practical instruments

P. Connes originally proposed a scanning field-widened interferometer consisting of two wedges. The two wedges were adjusted to produce a rectangular block of adjustable thickness; for any optical path difference, the wedges could be arranged to yield the optimum throughput. In a later design in the early 1960s, he employed two prisms having reflective rear surfaces (known as Littrow prisms after the originator of their use in dispersive spectrometers). The scanning of one of the two wedges caused optical path difference to vary while maintaining the field-widened condition was maintained at all times.

Schofield and Ring (1970) elaborated on the Connes design by incorporating up to six glass blocks of two types of glass. Two versions are shown in Fig.17.8. In the

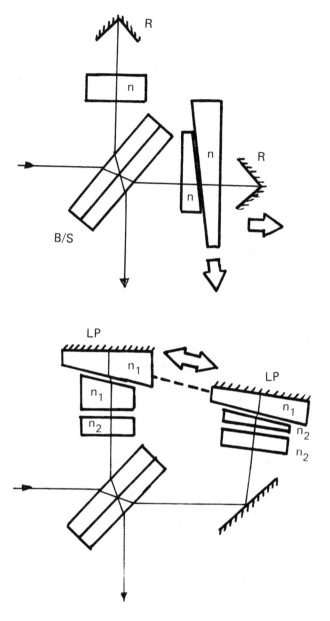

Fig. 17.8 — Field-widened interferometers of Schofield and Ring. Top: large wedge and retroreflector R move to adjust the path difference and field-widening condition.
Bottom: Littrow prisms LP move as a unit perpendicular to the ray axis. Two transparent materials having refractive index n_1 and n_2 are used.

first, the path difference is obtained by moving a retroreflector along the optical axis, and the field-widened condition is maintained by shifting a moving wedge perpendicularly. The need to co-ordinate the precise movement of two separate elements

made the arrangement complex and easily misaligned. Adequate fabrication tolerances were said to be 25 μm for the thickness of each glass block and 30 seconds of arc
for parallelism of surfaces. The throughput was equivalent to that of a conventional
interferometer having a 1-m aperture, despite having an actual aperture of 0.1 m.

In their second instrument, Schofield and Ring employed three prisms in each
arm of the interferometer. Two of the prisms are oppositely wedged to form a plane
parallel block (as in the original Connes design); the third prism provides the correct
zero path difference field-widening condition. Two types of material are used to
provide improved compensation. The outermost prisms are mounted on a common
carriage, which moves them along the prisms' hypotenuse to change the optical path
difference. This version is considerably easier to keep aligned. But, in a refractive
interferometer such as this, the prism movement is typically four or five times larger
than the corresponding movement of a plane mirror producing the same optical path
difference. This forces the scanning prisms to be large, and places stringent demands
on glass uniformity and fabrication tolerances.

Hilliard and Shepherd (1966) and co-workers have designed field-widened
instruments in which the OPD was varied only over a small value. By observing the
interferogram over a narrow region far from ZPD, they could measure the fringe
contrast and phase, which were sufficient to infer the temperature and velocity of
monochromatic sources. This approach has been extended by interferometers
incorporating further corrections for aberrations. By using more than one type of,
refractive block in one or both arms of the interferometer, the instrument can be
compensated much as a camera lens is corrected by combining different glasses. The
variations of glass properties such as the refractive index and expansion coefficient
with temperature and wavelength can be "played off" to make the interferometer
almost completely independent of temperature variations, angle of incidence, or
wavelength (Gault, Johnston and Kendall 1985).

Doran Baker and associates at Utah State University have designed field-
widened interferometers for night sky observations for several years (e.g. Despain *et
al.* 1970, Haycock and Baker 1974, Steed 1979). The Haycock and Baker design
consisted of a glass cube beamsplitter and two glass wedge interferometer mirrors.
One mirror was motionless, and the other moved perpendicularly to the ray axis on a
gas bearing. Haycock and Baker analysed the tolerances for movement of the glass
wedge mirror of their instrument as follows.

1. The prism must not displace from a straight-line path more than 1×10^{-5} cm.
2. The movable prism must not rotate by more than 2×10^{-5} rads about any [axis]
   through the centre of gravity as it travels a distance of 4.2 cm.
3. The velocity of the prism must be maintained within 1%.
4. The position of the prism must be known to within 0.1 μm.

The carriage was actuated by an electromagnetic drive. The position of the mirror
carriage was measured coarsely by a linear voltage differential transformer (LVDT)
for speed control, and more precisely by a separate conventional Michelson
interferometer and He–Ne laser source for accurate sampling of the interferogram.

17.3.3 Imaging interferometers

Field-widened interferometers can be designed with fields of view of several degrees. Instead of using the wide field to gather more light onto a single detector, it can instead be used for imaging an extended source of light. The WAMDII (Wide Angle Michelson Doppler Imaging Interferometer) was designed as an imaging interferometer to measure interferogram visibility and phase over an 85×105 grid (Shepherd *et al.* 1985).

The interferometer is a solid unit consisting of a hexagonal beamsplitter block to which are cemented arms of two types of optical glass (Fig. 17.9). A hexagonal form was used to reduce the angle of incidence on the beamsplitter, which allowed a more efficient beamsplitter coating design. One arm has a reflective end face to serve as the fixed mirror. The other arm is anti-reflection coated and carries a scanning mirror. The quartz mirror assembly is supported on piezoelectric transducers controlled by a servomechanism (Hicks *et al.* 1974): the servo monitors the output of three small capacitative sensors to measure position and maintain alignment. The mirror scans through only a few wavelengths of visible light, but with an accuracy and parallelism better than 1/200th wavelength.

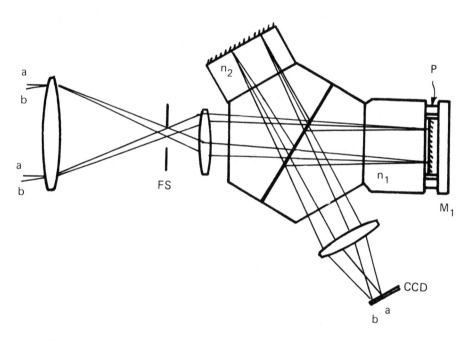

Fig. 17.9 — Schematic of the WAMDII interferometer. On-axis ray "a" and off-axis ray "b" travel through the interferometer to CCD array detector. The interferometer consists of a hexagonal beamsplitter block and two glass arms. The larger arm supports capacitative position sensors and a mirror M_1 on piezoelectric transducers.

The visibility of the prototype WAMDII is better than 0.9 in monochromatic light, indicating good glass homogeneity, surface flatnesses and mirror alignment.

The variation in phase across each pixel (imaging element) is less than 1/400th wavelength.

In use, the interferometer observes monochromatic light produced by the aurora. This generates nearly sinusoidal fringes as the moving mirror is scanned. Each pixel measures fringe intensity at three or four mirror positions. From the 8925 individual data sets, the fringe contrast (visibility) and phase (i.e. displacement of the fringe peak from a reference position of each pixel) is calculated. Fringe visibility is related to the temperature of the source, whereas fringe phase indicates the source velocity by the Doppler effect. Thus, images of the temperature and velocity of upper atmospheric winds can be produced by observing the emissions of their molecules.

Although the Schofield and Ring and later designs can theoretically provide interferometers having excellent characteristics, they can be limited in practice. The use of too many optical parts places stringent requirements on the quality of polishing, the homogeneity of the materials, their positioning and mechanical stability. Also, the correction of properties such as wavelength- or temperature-dependence depends on the exact matching of opposing characteristics in different materials. Despite the high quality of modern glass manufacture and evaluation, few tests are as stringent as interferometry (Wimperis and Johnston 1984). Often, the physical properties of optical glasses are not known with sufficient accuracy to make the best use of the theoretical options. The success of a particular field-widened design frequently owes as much to the optician's skill and luck of glass selection as to the optimum calculation of glass types and dimensions.

Field-widened interferometers have not been sold commercially because they offer no advantages for most applications. Their use has been restricted almost entirely to extremely weak sources of large angular extent, a domain in which they are presently unrivaled. The Analect "Transept" interferometer, used in several of their laboratory models, benefits from a certain amount of field-widening. It uses fixed interferometer mirrors but a beamsplitter consisting of two prisms in contact. The smaller prism supports the beamsplitting coating; a larger prism is shifted parallel to this surface to alter the optical path difference in one of the two arms. This 2.5-cm aperture instrument, through field-widening, achieves signal-to-noise performance comparable to conventional Michelson interferometers of 5-cm aperture.

17.4   POLARIZING INTERFEROMETERS

Polarizing interferometers allow polarized light to be spectrally analysed, and can be more efficient than conventional Michelson interferometers. The first polarizing interferometer for Fourier spectroscopy was designed and used by Mertz in 1954. Mertz (1965) ascribed his incentive to develop a polarizing interferometer to the dearth of transmitting materials in the far infrared; suitable beamsplitter materials are hard to find.

17.4.1   Wire-grid polarizers

All far infrared polarizing interferometers employ polarizing elements formed from wire grids. These appear superficially like coarse diffraction gratings formed from thin wires wound on posts. Unlike diffraction gratings, though, polarizing grids have wire spacing considerably larger than the wavelength of interest. Opposite to intuition, a vertical wire grid will transmit the horizontal polarization of light: the conducting wires allow electrons excited by the vertical component of the electromagnetic wave to oscillate, leading to reinforcement of a reflected vertical component. The horizontal component has no gross effect, and passes through the grid unscathed. This characteristic is different from visible-wavelength polarizers, which usually absorb one of the two components.

The polarizing effect is strong only at far-infrared wavelengths. At shorter wavelengths, the grid can, like any object, shadow or scatter light.

In Mertz's interferometer, the wire grids consisted of about 40 wires per millimetre supported by a dielectric (nonconducting transparent) substrate. More recent polarizers, developed by NPL and manufactured by Specac Ltd in the UK, are also available as free-standing wire gratings.

17.4.2 Mertz's polarizing interferometer

The interferometer made by Mertz employs three wire-grid polarizers (Fig. 17.10). Unpolarized radiation from the light source to be analysed falls on a wire grid beamsplitter at 45° incidence. The grating is oriented to transmit the vertical polarization (which is not used) and reflect the horizontal component.

The reflected beam is incident on a retardation system consisting of two more wire grid polarizers. The grid axes are oriented at plus and minus 45° to the horizontal. The first grid reflects one 45° component of the horizontal beam, and the second grid does the same with the other 45° component.

One of the two grids is mounted on a movable piston. As it is moved away from the other grid, the path difference between the pair increases twice as fast as the grid separation. If the path difference is a full wavelength or multiple of full wavelengths, the reflected beams recombine to recreate a horizontally polarized beam. This beam, identical to the input beam, therefore retraces its path to the source and does not reach the detector. But if the path difference is exactly a half wavelength (or a multiple of half wavelengths), the beam reflected by the second polarizer returns to the first out of step by 180°. When the two polarization vectors add, a net vertical polarization is produced. This vertically polarized output beam is transmitted by the beamsplitter to the detector.

In practice, the light source consists of a spectrum of wavelengths, and the detector receives the superposition of sine waves as the retardation system scans. The interferogram is identical in form to more conventional Michelson interferometer measurements.

It should be noted that Mertz's polarizing interferometer is twice as efficient as a nonpolarizing Michelson: the beamsplitter initially wastes half the incoming radiation to obtain a single polarization, but afterwards loses no light at each reflection. If polarized incident light is used, there is no loss. On the other hand, the ideal properties of perfect separation of the two polarizations cannot be achieved in practice. The wire grids polarize efficiently up to frequencies at which the wavelength is comparable to the wire grid spacing.

The Mertz interferometer employed few components. A rotating pre-polarizer served to chop the radiation reaching the Golay cell detector. This pre-polarizer

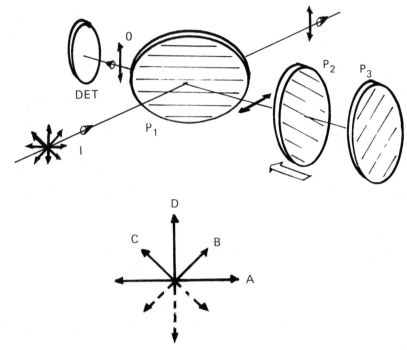

Fig. 17.10 — Top: schematic diagram of Mertz polarizing interferometer. *I*: unpolarized input beam; P_1: polarizing beamsplitter; P_2: moving polarizer; P_3: fixed polarizer; *O*: output beam; DET: detector. Bottom: polarization direction for beams through interferometer. A: reflected by b/s; B:reflected by moving polarizer; C: reflected by fixed polarizer; D: resultant output beam, returned to b/s when the optical path difference equals $(n+\frac{1}{2})$ wavelengths; A: resultant returned to beamsplitter when optical path difference equals *n* wavelengths.

acted as both a chopper and optical filter, because it was effective at polarizing only far-infrared light. The retardation system had an aperture of about 4.5 cm diameter.

The system was used successfully to record interferograms of a mercury arc and other sources. Transformation of the interferograms into spectra some ten years later showed that interference between reflections from the two parallel faces of the Golay cell detector obscured spectral information.

17.4.3   The Martin and Puplett design
An alternative to the Mertz geometry was originated by D. Martin and E. Puplett (1969). The arrangement is shown schematically in Fig. 17.11.

A pre-polarizer P_1 polarizes the input beam of light. A polarizing beamsplitter P_2 with its grid oriented at 45° with respect to the pre-polarizer grid transmits one component,to the scan mirror and the other component, with 90° rotated polarization axis, to the fixed mirror of the interferometer. The interferometer mirrors reflect back the beams without altering their polarizations. As in a conventional Michelson interferometer, the scan mirror introduces an optical path difference between the two beams.

At the polarizing beamsplitter, the two beams recombine. The originally transmitted beam is completely transmitted and the reflected beam completely reflected

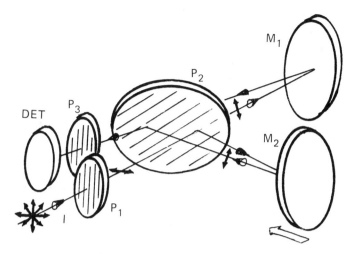

Fig. 17.11 — Schematic diagram of Martin and Puplett polarizing interferometer. I: unpolarized input beam; P_1: pre-polarizer; P_2: polarizing beamsplitter; M_1, M_2: interferometer mirrors; P_3: output polarizer; DET: detector.

back in the direction of the source. In practice, the input beam can be tilted slightly with respect to the interferometer axis so that the input and output beams are separated by a small angle.

Depending on the optical path difference, the relative phase of the two components leads to a new polarization state for the output beam, as shown in Fig. 17.12. A final polarizer P_3 placed in front of the detector (and oriented either parallel or perpendicular to the pre-polarizer grid P_1) selects one component of this beam, yielding the same result as the Mertz interferometer.

Polarization state

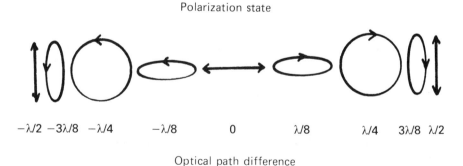

$-\lambda/2$ $-3\lambda/8$ $-\lambda/4$ $-\lambda/8$ 0 $\lambda/8$ $\lambda/4$ $3\lambda/8$ $\lambda/2$

Optical path difference

Fig. 17.12 — Polarization state *vs.* optical path difference for Martin and Puplett polarizing interferometer without an output polarizer.

The Martin and Puplett design is commercially available from Specac Ltd in the UK. This is a slow-scan far infrared interferometer that employs a rotating pre-polarizer (as in the Mertz configuration) for chopping the signal.

17.4.4   Polarization interferometry for dichroism measurements

The Martin and Puplett interferometer can be adapted to measure linear and circular dichroism, i.e. the spectrum of the difference in absorption for two perpendicular linear polarizations, or between right- and left-handed circular polarized light.

A conventional Michelson interferometer can be converted into a polarizing interferometer by replacing the usual intensity-dividing beamsplitter by a polarizing grid, and by adding a pre-polarizer between the source and the interferometer. The arrangement is schematically identical to the Martin and Puplett design except that the output polarizer P_3 is omitted. As shown in Fig. 17.12, motion of the scan mirror modulates the polarization of the output beam between linear, elliptical and circular polarization states. In the absence of a sample, and with ideal conditions, the detector will receive a constant amplitude signal for all optical path differences. But, if a sample is introduced that preferentially absorbs one polarization state, the output beam intensity will be modulated. The resulting spectrum is the dichroism spectrum of the sample.

Examination of Fig. 17.12 shows that the linear polarization states of the output beam are symmetrical about zero path difference: e.g. with horizontal polarization at ZPD, vertical polarization is produced for an optical path difference of $\pm 1/2$ wavelength. On the other hand, circular polarization states are antisymmetrical about ZPD: right-circularly polarized light is produced at OPD$=1/4$ wavelength, but left-circularly polarized light occurs at OPD$=-1/4$ wavelength. Because of this, the cosine (symmetric) Fourier transform of the interferogram results in the linear dichroism spectrum, while the sine (antisymmetric) Fourier transform gives the circular dichroism spectrum.

This experimental arrangement is thus able to provide, from a single interferogram, two dichroism spectra. To obtain the same results with a conventional, non-polarizing Michelson interferometer would require four interferograms: one each using a horizontal, vertical, right-circular and left-circular polarizer, respectively (i.e. two linear polarizers, a quarter-wave and three-quarter-wave plate). As these interferograms would have to be measured separately, transformed and subtracted to yield two dichroism spectra, instrumental effects such as alignment drift and restricted dynamic range could yield poorer spectra than would the direct method.

In practice, several factors limit the usefulness of the polarized dichroism interferometer. The beamsplitter is difficult to fabricate in the 5–9 cm diameter typical of commercial spectrometers. The purity of polarization is then compromised, and so modulation efficiency is reduced. Also, as both the cosine and sine transforms provide information about the sample, there is no independent means of removing instrumental phase errors from the results: instrument symmetry and stability become considerably more critical than in conventional FTIR. The polarizing interferometer must be carefully adjusted to ensure that the pre-polarizer and beamsplitter are oriented to balance the intensity of the two polarization components. Despite these drawbacks, polarizing interferometry for dichroism measurements still is more straightforward than conventional methods, at least for the far-infrared region over which wire-grid polarizers are efficient. Bomem Inc. have sold an adaptor kit for their DA3 Series spectrometers for dichroism spectroscopy.

17.5 FT SPECTROMETRY IN THE ULTRAVIOLET (FT/UV)

Fourier spectrometers operating in the ultraviolet are similar to infrared technology, except that the shorter wavelengths force several practical modifications. The advantages of Fourier spectrometry over dispersive techniques are also considerably reduced at higher frequencies.

17.5.1 Optical quality

The same constraints as for infrared mirrors apply: namely, surfaces must be flat to a fraction (at most 1/8) of the shortest wavelength to be measured. Interferometers working up to 200 nm thus need mirrors and beamsplitters flat to about 25 nm or better across their entire aperture, or about ten times flatter than the requirement for infrared measurements. Surfaces of this flatness approach the state of the art in optical fabrication: quartz surfaces can be polished to better than 1/100 wavelength in the visible (about 1/40 wavelength at a wavelength of 200 nm), but other materials are more recalcitrant, seldom being homogeneous enough to allow better than 1/30 wavelength in the visible. Fortunately, quartz is the most suitable transmitting material for visible and ultraviolet work.

17.5.2 Scanning accuracy

The required accuracy of interferogram sampling is also proportional to wavenumber. The tenfold increase in maximum wavenumber thus demands a tenfold increase in scanning accuracy.

The position of the moving mirror carriage is determined by observing fringes generated by a monochromatic laser source. Available lasers all emit in the visible, with Helium–Neon at 633 nm being the most common. According to Nyquist's sampling rule, to measure frequencies up to m wavenumbers, the interferogram must be sampled at twice this frequency. By taking an interferogram measurement each time the He–Ne laser fringe reaches an intensity peak, sampling occurs at $15\,803\,\text{cm}^{-1}$, permitting measurements up to $7901\,\text{cm}^{-1}$. To measure higher frequencies, it is necessary to interpolate the laser reference frequency.

By measuring zero crossings of the laser fringes (two of which occur per wavelength), measurements can be extended to $15\,803\,\text{cm}^{-1}$; by interpolating these into 2 or 4 segments and sampling at each, frequency can be extended to $31\,600$ or $63\,200\,\text{cm}^{-1}$ into the visible or ultraviolet regions. This interpolation procedure is dangerous, though, if the scan speed is not perfectly constant: any variation in speed between pulses will lead to sampling error. Such sampling error has the effect of smearing the spectral scale and leading to increased noise when two spectra are ratioed.

17.5.3 Alignment

Optical alignment is considerably more critical than for infrared interferometers. Angular and displacement tolerances are about ten times smaller, making the instruments more susceptible to perturbations from temperature changes, mechanical creep and external vibration.

17.5.4 Practical instruments

Luc and Gerstenkorn (1978) of the Laboratoire Aimé Cotton in France first showed conclusively the advantage of FT-UV spectrometers over dispersive types. P. Jacquinot had encouraged them to build a Fourier spectrometer specialized for near-infrared to ultraviolet use, and P. Connes had proposed the "slave carriage" scan drive described in Section 13.1.3. The instrument was completed in 1975.

The first ultraviolet results were spectra of a neptunium emission lamp. The interferograms contained up to one million points. Even for very weak emission lines having a signal-to-noise ratio of only 15, line positions were determined with a precision of ± 0.001 cm^{-1}. On an iodine absorption spectrum, the noise level was 2.5% and the recorded line positions agreed with theoretical values with a standard deviation of 0.0007 cm^{-1}.

There are presently at least two commercially available FT-UV systems (although several manufacturers sell ultraviolet "expansion kits", their spectrometers are not primarily designed for this spectral range). The first was the Bomem DA3, first available with UV optics in 1982. This uses dynamic alignment to maintain tight optical alignment. The standard optics are replaced with higher-quality components for ultraviolet measurements. In addition, surfaces normally coated with an SiO protective overcoating are replaced by MgF$_2$ coating, which absorbs less in the ultraviolet. The Bomem system uses the same scan drive as for infrared measurements. Despite speed fluctuations, useful results were obtained first to 35 000 cm^{-1} and eventually to 55 000 cm^{-1}.

The second commercial instrument is the Chelsea Instruments FT-500 FT-UV spectrometer, introduced in 1988. Designed by Anne Thorne and a team at Imperial College, it operates specifically over the visible and ultraviolet range (160–700 nm, 0.16–0.70 μm or 64 500–14 300 cm^{-1}) (Thorne *et al.* 1986). The instrument aperture is 20 mm, considerably less than the 75 mm diameter of the Bomem instrument. An optical schematic diagram is shown in Fig. 17.13. Instead of a dynamically aligned

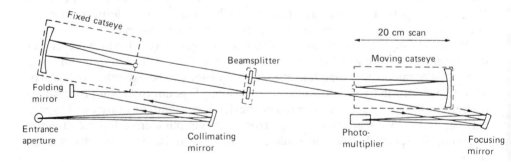

Fig. 17.13 — Optical layout of the Chelsea Instruments FT500 UV spectrometer (reproduced with permission of Chelsea Instruments Ltd).

flat scan mirror, the Chelsea Instruments interferometer employs a 60-mm diameter cat's eye retroreflector moving on a kinematic slide, and driven by an air-pressurized oil-driven piston, connected to the mirror carriage by a wobble-pin and two retaining springs (a wobble-pin moves the carriage without applying any sideways force). The preliminary alignment of the V-block slide is highly critical, but once it is adjusted, it requires only slight day-to-day corrections for shear (sideways movement of the beam). The prototype guidance systems, which employed lapped edges and various bearing pads and loadings, were eventually abandoned owing to unresolved problems of residual stick and slip.

A single thickness of beamsplitter/combiner plate is employed, with a coating on opposite sides.

The beamsplitter is used at 5° incidence to make the instrument narrow (for more compact entry into its vacuum chamber, and to pass easily through doorways). This has the secondary advantage of removing polarization effects. The original beam-splitter design incorporated an adjustment mechanism, but later versions were permanently aligned with epoxy.

A high-resolution 0.025 cm^{-1} scan can be obtained in approximately six minutes. With the PDP 11/34 computer originally available with the instrument, a one-million point FFT required over four hours; with the purpose-developed array processor and less powerful general computer, the same result is achieved in a few minutes.

17.5.5   Types of noise and their effect on the multiplex advantage

Ultraviolet Fourier spectrometers do not benefit from all the advantages of their infrared counterparts. Besides the practical problems of much tighter manufacturing tolerances, FT/UV spectrometers also suffer from theoretical constraints. Among these is the nature of noise sources in ultraviolet and visible spectroscopy.

Noise can be defined as an irregular or spurious variation in a measured quantity. We can consider any quantity to consist of a stable signal superimposed on a fluctuating source of noise. Because noise varies randomly with time, it is as likely to fluctuate downwards as upwards; it can be shown that averaging the noise for a time period t results in a value that gradually increases according to the square root of the observation time, $t^{1/2}$.

If the stable signal alone is observed for a time period t, it increases in proportion to the observation time. The ratio of the steady signal to the random noise is therefore proportional to $t/t^{1/2} = t^{1/2}$. Thus the S/N ratio can be improved by a factor of two by averaging a noisy signal for four times longer. This relationship holds for any source of noise, if it is random. But, different types of noise can have very different effects in Fourier and dispersive spectrometers.

(a) Detector-limited noise: the best case

In infrared spectroscopy, the major source of noise is usually the detector. Detector noise is independent of the intensity of radiation falling upon it (provided, of course, that the radiation does not heat or damage the detector and change its characteristics).

As Fellgett first showed, in Fourier spectroscopy each spectral element is measured for the entire duration t_e of the interferogram, because all frequencies from the source contribute to the signal at all times. So, at any particular wave-number, the observation time is $t_0 = t_e$. With a dispersive spectrometer, on the other hand, the observation time for each frequency depends on how many increments the spectrum is divided into. To observe twice as many spectral elements, for example, the slit width must be halved, and each wavelength viewed for half as long. Assuming a fixed experiment time t_e, each of the N spectral elements is viewed for a time $t_0 = te/N$.

So, in the case of detector-limited noise, the FTIR spectrometer observes N times longer than a dispersive spectrometer to measure an N-point spectrum in a given time, and so has an S/N advantage of $t^{1/2}_0 = N^{1/2}$.

(b) Photon noise: breaking even

In the visible and ultraviolet portion of the spectrum, sensitive detectors ensure that the dominant source of noise is not the detector, but photon noise. Photon noise, or shot noise, is caused by the statistical variation in arrival of high-energy photons at the detector. Here, the noise is proportional to the square root of the number of photons, or equivalently to $S^{1/2}$ where S is the total signal level.

In a "flat" spectrum, where all the spectral elements have the same intensity, the total intensity S is proportional to the number of spectral elements N. The shot noise is then proportional to $N^{1/2}$. As a result, the signal-to-noise ratio will be proportional to the Fellgett advantage divided by the shot noise, i.e. to $N^{1/2}/N^{1/2}$. The multiplex advantage is exactly cancelled by the noise statistics. A sequentially scanned spectrometer would seem to perform as well as a Fourier spectrometer in the visible and ultraviolet regions.

In practice, though, a real spectrum is not entirely uniform. Some spectral elements will be much more, or less, intense than others. The total intensity S will then not be quite proportional to the number of elements N, and some multiplex advantage will remain. Kahn (1959) showed that the multiplex advantage depends on the square root of the ratio of the intensity of a peak to the average intensity of the entire spectrum. The best case is in either emission spectra or sparse absorbance spectra where the number of peaks is small, as illustrated in Fig. 17.14. The multiplex advantage is therefore different for each spectral peak, and depends on the structure of the entire spectrum.

Moreover, Fourier spectroscopy, even in the ultraviolet, retains the Jacquinot throughput advantage, which typically provides at least a tenfold improvement in S/N over dispersive instruments. As a result, there is always a net advantage over dispersive spectrometers when high resolution measurements are to be made.

(c) Source noise: the multiplex disadvantage

The worst situation for a Fourier spectrometer is when the measurement noise is dominated by fluctuations of the light source. This happens, for example, with scintillating starlight, with the flickering output from an inductively coupled plasma light source, or even with a vibrating sample in the sample chamber. In these situations, a Fourier spectrometer actually suffers a multiplex *disadvantage* compared with a dispersive instrument.

Unlike noise originating in the detector itself, which is additive, fluctuation noise is multiplicative. That is, the noise is directly proportional to the total signal.

Consider a uniform spectrum of constant intensity. If there are N spectral elements, the total intensity will be proportional to N. In this worst-case situation,

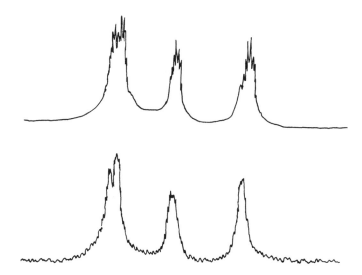

Fig. 17.14 — Photon-limited measurement noise. Top: dispersive spectrometer; bottom: Fourier spectrometer.

the noise level is therefore proportional to N, but the Fellgett "advantage" is proportional to $N^{1/2}$: the net effect is an S/N disadvantage of $N/N^{1/2} = N^{1/2}$, i.e. proportional to the square root of the number of spectral elements.

This suggests that a monochromator will measure a cleaner signal than an FT spectrometer if source noise predominates. The situation is not quite this discouraging, though. First, source noise is only of concern to a Fourier spectrometer if the fluctuations are faster than the period of scanning one interferogram; the system is immune to slower fluctuations. Secondly, because of the conversion of the interferogram by the Fourier transformation, the noise in the spectrum is distributed quite uniformly over all spectral intervals. In a dispersive spectrometer, the source noise appears exactly where it was measured: strong spectral emission peaks are noisiest, and the blank featureless areas of the spectrum are essentially noise-free. If, then, instead of a "flat" uniform spectrum we have an emission or absorption spectrum with a few strong lines, the noise measured at those important peaks will be considerably smaller than that measured in a dispersive spectrometer in the same observing time (and having the same throughput).

17.5.6   The Jacquinot advantage in FT/UV

The throughput advantage, unlike the multiplex advantage, survives unscathed in the ultraviolet. However, the practical benefits are considerably smaller than for infrared measurements.

The interferometer detector diameter is chosen to be always contained within the central fringe of the bull's-eye interference pattern. This pattern contracts as either the optical path difference or spectral frequency increases. The scale of this pattern depends on beam divergence and scan distance according to

$$\Omega = 2(\delta\sigma/\sigma_{max})^{1/2} \tag{17.24}$$

where Ω is the full angle field of view at the detector, $\delta\sigma$ is the spectral resolution, and σ_{max} is the maximum wavenumber thus measured. The measurement of ultraviolet wavelengths thus restricts the acceptable angular divergence by about a factor of 3 compared with infrared spectrometers. This leads to a tenfold reduction in throughput, which is proportional to solid angle. The optical acceptance at 200 nm in the ultraviolet, for example, is an order of magnitude smaller than the allowable maximum at 2 μm in the near infrared.

The net result of a smaller throughput advantage and small or even negative multiplex advantage, coupled with much more severe operating conditions, make FT/UV spectroscopy a technique of marginal usefulness. There are strong benefits to Fourier spectroscopy in the ultraviolet for certain applications, but the choice between Fourier and dispersive methods is considerably less clear-cut than in the infrared.

17.6   GAS CHROMATOGRAPHY AND IR (GC/IR)

Gas chromatography became one of the most popular techniques of analytical chemistry in the 1960s. In chromatographic separation, a liquid or gaseous sample is injected into a long and narrow heated column or tube, through which it is transported by a carrier gas and separated into its component molecular species. Different chemical species travel at different rates through the column owing to their interactions with the packing or wall material. Differences in molecular weight and polarity (electrical asymmetry) of the molecules affect the time for which they are retained in the column. At the column exit, a detector senses the presence of molecules and displays a peak on a chart recorder. The principal measurement of a gas chromatographic record is the retention time (the time taken for the species to travel through the column) and the area under peaks of the curve, which corresponds to the amount of the species.

The GC trace cannot uniquely identify a chemical species: different substances can have nearly identical retention times. To discriminate between components, GC columns can be packed with different materials, and chemical detectors can be used that respond to specific types of molecule.

Tomas Hirschfeld coined the term "hyphenated technique" in the late 1970s to describe the combination of two analytical methods. The hyphenated technique of GC/FTIR unites the advantages of gas chromatographic separation and infrared identification. The primary problem to solve in this union is one of sample volume: in a typical gas chromatograph, each eluent (individual sample peak) appears at the column exit over a period of seconds or tens of seconds, and in amounts ranging from tens of micrograms to nanograms. It is necessary to measure such samples in an optical thickness that gives adequate measurement sensitivity in a period of no longer than a few seconds or so.

There are clearly compromises in the measurement configuration: ideally, the infrared spectrometer would measure a sample in a large-volume cell, because the infrared sample beam should not be vignetted by a narrow aperture, and requires a reasonable depth (a few centimetres to tens of centimetres) to obtain adequate absorption from the vaporized sample. This arrangement would yield the best infrared sensitivity, but poor time resolution. The various peaks from the GC effluent would be inextricably mixed in the infrared sample cell, negating most of the advantages of GC separation. Alternatively, a short, wide cell could be used: this would retain the infrared signal quality and reduce the cell volume, so improving the time resolution. It would, however, lead to unacceptably weak sample absorption. At the other extreme, a long, narrow bore sample cell (or "light pipe") could be used. This would have low volume and adequate sample absorption length, but very high attenuation of the infrared beam. Even with condensing optics to reduce the diameter of the beam focus, it would reflect many times down the walls of the light pipe. Unless the walls were highly reflective, most of this channelled light would be absorbed before leaving the cell.

From the time of the invention of the gas chromatograph in 1954, researchers have devised methods of trapping and measuring the separated species with infrared spectrometers. The idea of using a Fourier spectrometer to analyse the components in each gas chromatographic peak originated in the mid 1960s. Low and Freeman (1967) combined a commercial GC with a rapid-scanning interferometer (a Block Engineering Model 200) for their first GC/IR experiments. By using a 4-mm diameter×5-cm long light pipe, they measured the eluents flowing directly from the gas chromatograph. For better detection sensitivity, they also tried trapping the effluent in the sample cell while interferograms were signal-averaged. Clancy and Low continued to use early FTIR spectrometers for the on-line measurement of the eluted materials. By 1968 Clancy was typically obtaining sensitivities down to 1 µg quantities.

Digilab marketed the first GC/IR accessory from 1970 to 1974 for use with their rapid-scanning Fourier spectrometers. They used a light pipe of about 6-mm diameter×5-cm long, and obtained sensitivities of a few micrograms for samples that had strong infrared absorption. To reduce the amount of data collection (which Low and Freeman had accommodated by using a tape recorder), the Digilab version used a conventional GC detector to detect when a peak was eluting. This detector triggered infrared data acquisition. The accessory, based on the first efforts of Low and co-workers, was apparently a commercial failure (Dunn 1978).

Non-commercial designs also appeared. Leo Azzaraga of the American Environmental Protection Agency (EPA) developed his own system owing to lack of good commercial alternatives. Azzaraga influenced light-pipe design by originating a method for applying a highly reflective gold coating on the interior surface of a glass tube. Both Digilab and Nicolet introduced new GC/IR accessories in 1975 that owed much to his design. These achieved measurement sensitivities down to 100 ng.

By the end of the decade, gas chromatograph design was changing. The previously used wide-bore columns packed with various materials were beginning to be replaced by narrow-bore silica columns. The use of these support-coated open tubular (SCOT) capillary columns had first been demonstrated by Azzaraga and A. C. McCall in 1974. These columns had considerably smaller internal diameter and led to faster elution times with more accurate time resolution, and the ability to use smaller sample volumes. The smaller sample volume was bad news for GC/IR designs. As described above, the infrared absorption depends on optical thickness, not on sample volume. To maintain the same optical thickness as had been used with packed-column GCs, it was necessary to reduce the diameter of the infrared light pipe. This smaller bore sample cell accepted less light from the spectrometer, and caused higher attenuation by reflection losses on its walls.

Peter Griffiths (e.g. 1977) did much to promote the acceptance of GC/IR methods. To get around the limited data-storage capacity of GC/IR systems, he established the conditions for when GC peaks should be recorded for optimal signal-to-noise ratio. He also investigated design parameters such as the dead volume of the light pipe, best compromise dimensions, and practical factors such as light-pipe reflectivity.

By the early 1980s, several commercial GC/IR systems were available, based on capillary GC columns. The Wall Coated Open Tubular (WCOT) fused-silica columns have internal diameters of only 0.25 mm or 0.32 mm, and can easily be overloaded by large sample volumes. The light-pipe diameter is always considerably larger, so there is a volume mismatch. A new GC peak must fill the light pipe volume, causing an unavoidable loss of time resolution. To combat this, the light pipes in most accessories today have volumes in the 100 μl range.

One final technical problem with GC/IR systems is that the hot light pipe itself gives out a large amount of infrared radiation. Although this light is not modulated by the interferometer (and so does not appear as an offset to the interferogram) it still affects the detector signal. If the detector is flooded with a large constant signal in this way, it can be driven into a regime of operation that is less linear: that is, the detector signal is no longer proportional to the intensity of light reaching it. This signal distortion will cause interferogram and spectrum distortion. The problem can be reduced by shielding the detector as much as possible from the light pipe emission, by use of baffles or cool plates that pass only the optical energy from the light-pipe exit aperture.

In the early 1980s most FTIR manufacturers developed GC/IR accessories. These consist of more than just a light pipe: the elements of the accessory include the following:

(1) A mechanical interface to the gas chromatograph.
(2) A heated transfer line from GC to light pipe, capable of various controlled temperatures.
(3) A heated light pipe, again capable of temperature control.
(4) Transfer optics between the spectrometer sample focus, light pipe, and detector.
(5) Software capable of rapid interferogram acquisition and storage. Storage must either be "on the fly" (i.e. in individual recoverable scans) or averaged. Data acquisition should be triggered by the operator or automatically by another detector associated with the GC.
(6) Software for post-experiment analysis. This typically requires routines for quickly recalling sets of interferograms, deciding on their grouping, averaging the grouped sets, and transforming the result. In addition, some convenient means of displaying both the raw "on the fly" data and grouped data is needed.

Such systems were expensive. Most interferometer sample chambers had not been designed to accommodate the insulated light pipe and transfer optics. Also, the need for external control of scanning and the expanded requirements for data manipulation placed large demands on the available computers and the efficiency of their programming.

Later commercial GC/IR systems have been simplified in several ways. Manufacturers have dispensed with the valves used for trapping or splitting the effluent flow or redirecting it to other detectors, which were common on earlier systems. Modern fused-silica columns and small-volume light cells introduce little mixing, and allow GC detectors to follow the light pipe. Light pipe and transfer optics designs have been simplified. Indeed, the light pipe manufactured by Aabspec (Dublin, Ireland), available as an accessory for several FTIR instruments, can be mounted in a conventional sample compartment with no change to the optics at all. Faster computers with larger memories have eased the strain on data transfer and manipulation.

A unique approach adopted by the Hewlett–Packard Corporation (manufacturers of gas chromatographs as well as a variety of other laboratory and engineering equipment) is to make the infrared spectrometer an accessory of the GC, instead of vice versa. HP sells an "IR detector" (IRD) which attaches to its most popular gas chromatograph. The company also sells other types of detector, such as the more conventional flame-ionization detector (FID) or thermal conductivity detector (TCD), and, having a complexity at least equal to that of the FTIR detector, a mass spectrometer detector (MSD). These can be combined on the same GC, yielding such double-hyphenated techniques as GC/IR/MS. The Hewlett–Packard IRD is a compact Michelson interferometer having fixed resolution and scan-time. By making the spectrometer an adjunct to the GC, problems with transfer lines and temperature control are avoided.

A completely different GC/IR technology introduced commercially by Mattson Instruments is based on a cryogenic approach. Originated in 1977 by Gerald Reedy of Argonne National Laboratory, the technique, sometimes called matrix isolation GC/IR, involves diluting the effluent with a gas and freezing the mixture onto a cold surface for subsequent examination. The sample molecules are each held individually in a matrix of infrared-inactive atoms. In the Mattson Cryolect accessory, the effluent from the GC is deposited directly on a cryogenically cooled, slowly rotating disk. The 10-cm diameter copper disk is gold-plated to act as an infrared mirror. Once deposited, the condensed line of effluent can be analysed at leisure by the FTIR spectrometer via integral beam-condensing optics. In the Mattson accessory, the effluent can be deposited for up to five hours, with spatial resolution on the disk corresponding to six seconds of elution time. Samples below 1 ng in weight can be determined in this way.

The matrix isolation technique has the advantage of storing the GC separation for as long as desired, with no mixing of components, and the ability to average as many interferograms as required for good signal-to-noise ratio. By saving and subsequently analysing the GC run in this way, most of the constraints imposed by limited measurement time are relaxed; the specifications of the data acquisition system and software are considerably eased. After the measurement, the cryogenic disk can be heated to release the volatile sample components and prepare the system for another run, a process that requires about two hours. This recovery time is probably the main weakness of the system.

Although hardware cost has generally been reduced, there is little reduction in the complexity of software. As summarized above, the software must both record a large amount of data in limited time, and subsequently present it in a form that does not take much of the operator's time. At present, the time needed to process and analyse GC/IR data is the major bottleneck in the technique.

Some of the best schemes for presenting GC/IR data were developed in the early days of the technique, and are still used today. In 1977, Pat Coffey and David Mattson (then at Nicolet Instruments) reported a method of constructing an artificial gas chromatogram from the infrared data of a GC/IR system. By presenting the measurements in a format already familiar to GC operators, they simplified the identification of samples for further processing. The method relied on identifying up to five specific spectral regions, or "windows". The software performed a low-resolution Fourier transform on each interferogram, calculated the absorbance in the specified bands, and plotted the result as a function of time. The spectral absorbance in each of these windows yielded a series of chromatograms sensitive to specific functional groups. The operator was able to decide, based on this information, which interferograms should be recorded on disk for further analysis. Other manufacturers soon incorporated similar software in their GC/IR packages.

The other general technique for constructing a pseudo-chromatogram from infrared data is known as the Gram–Schmidt method. The name derives from the originators of a mathematical procedure long established for manipulating vectors, or sets of ordered numbers. An interferogram or spectrum can be considered as a vector: both consist of a string of numbers, each of which represents intensity for a specific optical path difference or wavenumber. The Gram–Schmidt method works on pairs of vectors — e.g. a reference and sample interferogram — and generates a number indicating to what degree they are mutually independent.

For example, suppose that a spectrum is obtained from a GC/IR system, and that it consists of a mixture of chemical components. By performing a Gram–Schmidt calculation of this interferogram with a pre-recorded interferogram of one of the pure substances, a number is obtained. The size of the number is determined by how closely the two interferograms coincide; if they are a perfect match, the number will be maximized, but if there is no commonality the number will be a minimum.

In practice, the Gram–Schmidt method is employed by initially storing reference interferograms of pure components expected to appear in the GC/IR separation. When the GC/IR experiment is run, each measured interferogram is manipulated with the reference interferograms, and the output number is plotted *vs.* time for each pure component. Correlations between any of the pure components and the GC effluent will generate a peak in the respective curve.

The principal advantage of the Gram–Schmidt method is speed: vector manipulations on short portions of interferograms are relatively fast compared with even low-resolution Fourier transforms, and produce a similar result. Equivalent results can be obtained from another mathematical technique, factor analysis (e.g. Brown *et al.* 1986). All these methods indicate that both the interferogram and spectrum contain the same information, albeit in reorganized forms, and that the information can be extracted by an appropriate mathematical algorithm.

17.7   THERMOGRAVIMETRIC ANALYSIS AND IR (TGA/IR)

Like GC/IR, TGA/IR is the combination of two complementary techniques. In thermogravimetric analysis, a solid sample is heated in a purged sample cell and simultaneously weighed on an accurate balance. The weight loss is recorded as a function of time and temperature, and the information is used to infer the volatile species present. In common with gas chromatography, the TGA measurement must be calibrated with known pure components to determine the evaporation character-istics of a particular instrument. Also as in GC, the evolved gases cannot be unambiguously identified by the time record of mass change alone.

In TGA/IR accessories, the gases evolved by heating the sample are passed to an infrared cell by a flow of purge gas. The purge gas is chosen to be infrared inactive and free of interaction with the sample components. The infrared spectrum of the gases is measured periodically during the experiment and recorded with the TGA output.

The combination of TGA and IR yields quantitative information about the constituents of samples that would otherwise be difficult to analyse by FTIR: nearly opaque tars, for example.

TGA/IR accessories have been produced by several FTIR manufacturers. Most (e.g. Digilab and Nicolet) employ a commercial TGA unit with a heated transfer line leading the evolved gases to a light pipe similar to those used for GC/IR. The small-volume light pipe ensures good time resolution. A few manufacturers (e.g. Bomem) instead use a larger multipass cell to measure gas spectra. This provides improved sensitivity but slower response and less sensitivity for species evolved in small volumes. As for GC/IR experiments, there is an optimal trade-off between light-pipe volume, light-pipe length, sample flow-rate, sample volume and optical attenuation.

Associated software packages usually permit the periodic plotting of absorbance for selected infrared "windows" associated with particular functional groups, very much like GC/IR.

17.8   RAMAN SPECTROSCOPY (FT/RAMAN)

The Raman effect gains its name from C. V. Raman, the Indian physicist who discovered it in 1928. He found that light scattered by a sample can be re-emitted as a spectrum of closely-spaced wavelengths. The frequency shift is towards lower energies for molecules in the ground-state, while a shift to higher energies is associated with molecules in excited vibrational states. The shift is the result of inelastic scattering of light by molecules — absorption and re-emission of a photon, with some of the original energy redistributed to the molecule.

This Raman spectrum provides information similar to, but complementary to, conventional infrared spectroscopy. Molecular vibrational modes that produce no infrared spectral features can be active in the Raman spectrum, and vice-versa. For example, diatomic molecules such as O_2 and N_2 do not absorb in the infrared, but have distinct Raman spectra.

In conventional Raman spectroscopy, a bright monochromatic light source is used to excite the sample. This was originally a filtered mercury lamp, and later a variety of visible lasers. The Raman output from the sample is then analysed by a high-resolution monochromator, typically a double- or triple-passed grating spectrometer. Originally, the spectrum was recorded on a photographic plate, but this method has been replaced by sensitive photomultiplier detectors or photodiode arrays. The Raman spectrum is scaled by the wavenumber shift from the excitation line.

The conventional technique is often hampered by sample fluorescence. Many optical transitions are active at the frequencies of visible-wavelength lasers, and the resulting re-emitted light can be many times stronger than the weak Raman scattering: fluorescence can prevent Raman spectra of many types of sample from being measured at all. Also, since the effect itself is so weak, Raman spectra are time-consuming to record. Overnight spectral scans were common before laser sources became available.

The fluorescence problem can be avoided by using laser wavelengths in the near infrared. Near-infrared wavelengths are not absorbed or fluoresced by most samples. Unfortunately, the intensity of Raman scattering is proportional to the fourth power of the excitation frequency. A doubling of the laser wavelength therefore leads to a sixteen-fold loss in signal intensity. Nevertheless, the absence of significant fluorescence provides an opportunity for Fourier spectrometers.

The possibility of Raman spectroscopy by Fourier spectrometers was first discussed in the 1970s. The first theoretical analyses of the method were discouraging:

> ...Raman is almost a contrived worst case for Fourier transform spectroscopy. Because Raman is shot noise limited, Fellgett's advantage does not apply. Because it is dominated by the Raleigh [*sic*] line due to the unchanged laser wavelength, the distributive effect is a disadvantage. Because its effective source is a small focused laser spot, there is no room for Jacquinot's advantage. Various attempts to cope with these difficulties have taken FT-Raman from the ranks of the impossible to the merely undesirable. (Hirschfeld 1978).

Despite this dissuading opinion by Tomas Hirschfeld, renowned for his careful analyses of FTIR performance, various investigators (including Hirschfeld himself) persevered and discovered that the results were considerably better than expected.

The throughput advantage of a Fourier spectrometer provides a significant improvement in signal quality at near-infrared wavelengths. The Connes advantage of a highly precise frequency scale is also valuable: many hundreds of interferograms can be co-added to improve the signal-to-noise ratio. Unfortunately, at near infrared wavelengths, the multiplex character of Fourier spectroscopy can actually be a hindrance: the very intense laser source dominates the signal, and its intensity fluctuations become distributed over the entire spectrum when the interferogram is transformed into a spectrum (this effect is discussed further in Section 17.5). To combat this disadvantage, the frequency of the laser must be very well filtered to prevent its light from contributing to the interferogram. Attenuation by about a factor of 10^8 is required.

All presently available commercial FT–Raman systems employ an Nd:YAG near-infrared laser emitting around a watt of optical power. The scattered light is captured over a large solid angle by either lens or mirror collecting optics. The laser wavelength is removed from the resulting beam by a narrow-band filter; the laser output itself must occasionally be filtered to remove all but the primary excitation wavelength. Owing to the weakness of Raman scattering, there is a compromise between the laser beam intensity and the amount of acceptable sample heating.

The light captured from the sample is subsequently passed into the interferometer and treated as for any other emission spectrum. The only special conditions are that the emission is in the near infrared, demanding good-quality optics and interferometer drive. Also, the resulting emission spectrum is normally scaled in frequency so that the Raman spectrum is displayed as a frequency shift from the excitation wavelength, to allow more straightforward comparison with the mid-infrared spectrum of the sample that can be obtained with the same spectrometer.

A review of the current state-of-the-art in FT–Raman spectroscopy has appeared in a special issue of *Spectrochim. Acta,* **46A** (1990).

17.9 SAMPLING TECHNIQUES

Since 1980, most papers on FTIR technology have been devoted to sampling techniques. This activity has begun to taper off, but it still represents a major part of FTIR innovation. Much of the popularity of FTIR among chemists derives from its easier sampling techniques compared with dispersive spectrometers. The relatively high-quality FTIR signal allows inefficient sampling methods to be used. Most of these methods had been previously attempted with dispersive spectrometers, but had not found routine use owing to excessive measurement times.

17.9.1 Infrared microsampling

The area of small samples such as fibres is much smaller than the focus of the spectrometer, causing most of the radiation to travel directly to the detector. This leads to a severely washed-out spectrum diluted of its sample absorption. For this reason, it is necessary to match the illuminated area of the spectrometer beam to the sample.

Infrared microscopes have a long history. Barer *et al.* were among the first to use a microscope with a dispersive infrared spectrometer. Blout *et al.* (1949) described the design of such a microscope, which used Cassegrain optics to condense the infrared beam onto the sample, and an identical mirror arrangement to capture the transmitted light. Similar devices were used intermittently, throughout the 1950s and 1960s, attached to dispersive instruments, with limited success.

Today, two techniques are commonly used, which can be combined. First, the infrared beam can simply be reduced in diameter with a mask: the beam reaching the detector is then forced to travel through the sample. This method has the disadvantage of wasting all energy not travelling through the sample.

The second technique is to reduce the beam diameter by additional focusing optics. The simplest scheme is a beam condenser that accepts as input the slightly convergent spectrometer beam (having an f/number of about $f/4$ or $f/5$) and converting it with one or two mirrors to a more highly convergent beam of about $f/1$. This reduces the diameter of the focus proportionately, i.e. by a factor of about 4 or 5. In practice, it is awkward to reduce the beam diameter by more than a factor of about five by using off-axis mirrors: the mirrors get in the way of the very short focal length beam. It is then necessary to incorporate both a beam condenser and aperture mask to obtain a useful microsampling accessory.

A newer alternative (available since the early 1980s) is the infrared microscope. This is identical in concept to the beam condenser, but uses on-axis mirrors to permit much shorter focal lengths and less beam aberration. Besides their use for infrared optics, the mirrors can be corrected sufficiently to work at visible wavelengths, thereby allowing the user to view the sample region being measured by the spectrometer. The most sophisticated infrared microscopes include sample illuminators and adjustable aperture masks to define the region to be measured, and the ability to measure either transmittance or reflectance spectra.

17.9.2 Diffuse reflectance

For dense, opaque samples that cannot be measured by transmittance spectroscopy, reflectance techniques can be used. Unless the sample has a smooth, cleanly reflecting surface, it is easiest to measure its diffuse reflectance. The Diffuse Reflectance Infrared Fourier Transform (DRIFT) technique is frequently used for powdered samples.

In DRIFT, the modulated beam of the interferometer is focused onto a small area in which the sample is held. The radiation scattered by the rough sample surface is collected by one or more mirrors surrounding the sample. The sensitivity of a DRIFT accessory depends on the solid angle of radiation that it captures and channels to the infrared detector.

The "reference" spectrum in diffuse reflectance measurements is usually a transparent powder such as KBr or other suitable substance.

The Kubelka–Munk function (see Section 12.8.4) approximately relates the diffuse reflectance spectrum to sample concentration, transforming the reflectance spectrum into a format that resembles an absorbance spectrum. Although the Kubelka–Munk function is not exactly related to sample concentration, the diffuse reflectance technique has an unsurpassed dynamic range: samples ranging from nanogram to gram quantities can be measured.

The convenience of the method is counterbalanced by its severe attenuation. Light scattered from powders or rough surfaces is directed through a large solid angle, only part of which can be recaptured by mirrors or lenses and focused onto the detector.

Probably the first generally successful instrument for diffuse reflectance measurements was the Willey 318 spectrophotometer (Willey 1976). This slow-scanning FTIR instrument employed an integrating sphere to collect the light scattered by the sample. The integrating sphere, as its name suggests, is a hollow sphere with a highly reflecting inner surface. Small ports in the sphere allow light from the spectrometer to enter off-axis to strike the sample, so that the rays are multiply reflected from the inner surface. A detector, looking in through a port in the sphere, captures the light scattered in all directions from the sample.

In the Willey configuration, the input beam could be switched from a reference port to a sample port so that the beam struck either a reference or sample surface. The component of the radiation directly reflected from the sample was obstructed by removing a portion of the sphere wall in the path of the specularly reflected component. The infrared detector was mounted inside the sphere so that it received the multiply reflected light from all sides. This configuration ensured that most of the light scattered by the sample was received by the detector, neglecting losses at the surfaces of the integrating sphere.

The efficiency of the integrating sphere depends on the number of internal reflections that occur before the light reaches the detector. The number of reflections increases if the sphere diameter is increased or if the sample area is reduced. If the sphere is too small, the input and output apertures may become a significant fraction of the total surface area and lead to further losses. There is therefore a compromise between the signal intensity and the collection efficiency of a particular integrating sphere geometry.

Subsequent optical designs for diffuse reflectance spectroscopy have settled for collecting a smaller solid angle of light but sending it more directly to the detector. In general, this involves condensing modulated light from the spectrometer onto the sample surface, and then collecting the reflected energy by one or more mirrors near the sample surface. Unlike the Willey design, these optical arrangements collect not only some scattered light from the sample but also most of the specularly reflected portion. For theoretical studies, it can be necessary to measure these two components separately. Some commercially available diffuse reflectance accessories therefore include beam blockers or mirror arrangements that prevent most of the specular component from being collected. The optical arrangement of such accessories can be made compact enough to fit inside the ordinary sample compartment of most FTIR spectrometers.

17.9.3 Attenuated total reflectance

Some samples absorb too strongly to allow transmittance spectra to be obtained, and cannot easily be prepared in a form suitable for specular or diffuse reflectance. Examples include foods (with their high water content), rubber, and cured resins. For these samples the attenuated total reflectance (ATR) technique is most useful. The ATR method was invented by J. Fahrenfort in 1961.

Light or infrared radiation exiting to air from a transparent medium such as zinc selenide (ZnSe), KRS-5, germanium or silicon is partially reflected back into the medium; if the angle of incidence of the incident radiation is sufficiently large, it will be totally internally reflected. If, however, another less dense and partially transmitting substance is placed in contact with the ZnSe, the totally reflected radiation will be partially absorbed by the substance. This occurs because the radiation passes a short distance into the less dense substance as a so-called "evanescent wave". The depth of penetration is comparable to the wavelength of the light. Since the passage through the sample is so small, the absorption is much less than would be produced by a transmittance measurement through even a very thin sample.

In the ATR technique, a polished crystal of infrared transmitting material such as ZnSe is placed in the sample beam of the spectrometer so that the radiation enters and is totally internally reflected along its length. Ten or twenty reflections are commonly used. The radiation exiting at the opposite end is collected and directed to the infrared detector. The sample of interest is placed in contact with the one or more surfaces of the ATR crystal where the internal reflections occur. Mulls or gels may simply be smeared on one surface; elastic samples such as plastics can be held in close contact with a pressure pad. Even liquid samples can be measured by employing a liquid cell through which the ATR crystal passes. The "reference" in ATR measurements is the cell itself in the absence of a sample: in this condition, total internal reflectance should occur and any losses are caused by instrumental effects such as a misaligned beam or dirty crystal.

The ATR crystal is commonly trapezoidal in shape. The input and output beams should be perpendicular to the crystal surfaces so that reflection losses are minimized, but the internal surfaces must be situated at a shallow angle to promote total internal reflection.

17.9.4 Photo-acoustic spectroscopy

Samples in gaseous, liquid or solid state can be measured by using photo-acoustic spectroscopy (PAS). It is particularly applicable to highly absorbing samples such as rubber or coal, and so is complementary to techniques such as diffuse reflectance.

The method relies on the fact that when modulated infrared radiation is absorbed by a sample, the substance heats and cools in response to modulated infrared radiation impinging on it. This heating and cooling is converted into a pressure wave that can be communicated to a surrounding gas and so detected by an acoustic detector (essentially a sensitive microphone in the enclosed sample chamber). The acoustic detector replaces the infrared detector of the spectrometer. Carbon black is commonly used as a reference material.

The photo-acoustic effect was discovered by Alexander Graham Bell (Bell 1881). Bell employed what he called the "opto-acoustic effect" in his "photo-phone", an optical equivalent of the electrical telephone. Although investigated then by physicists such as Röntgen (the discoverer of X-rays) and Tyndall (known for research into light scattering), the photo-acoustic effect did not provoke much interest from researchers. It was not until the 1970s that the photo-acoustic effect was used with laser sources to measure the concentration of gases.

In 1978, G. Busse and B. Bullemer first used a photo-acoustic detector with a Fourier spectrometer. Their photo-acoustic cell (which they termed a "spectrophone") consisted of a gas cell with transparent windows at either end, and a sensitive microphone inside. Modulated light from the interferometer passed through the gas cell, where it was partially absorbed, and on to an infrared detector.

Both the microphone and infrared detector outputs were recorded; each yielded an interferogram. The microphone detector produced an interferogram of absorbed light, while the infrared detector produced the conventional transmission interferogram. Subsequent investigators modified the cell design for solid samples by using a smaller volume and filling the cell with a gas that does not absorb in the infrared.

An alternative to acoustic detection with a sensitive microphone is to measure the change in the refractive index of the gas surrounding the solid sample. As the sample is periodically heated by the absorbed infrared wave, some energy is transferred by convection to the gas immediately above it. The warmer gas is less dense, and so has a lower refractive index. The modulation of the refractive index of the gas can be detected by observing the deflection of a laser beam passed close to the sample. In the simplest version, the laser beam is directed onto a single detector, so that beam deflection is signalled by variations in overlap. More complex schemes have been used to compensate for alignment changes, mechanical vibration and acoustic noise. While beam deflection methods can give very good results, the microphonic detection technique is currently the more popular.

The spectrum resulting from the photo-acoustic interferogram is qualitatively different from either the transmittance or reflectance spectrum, because the technique detects nonradiative transitions in the sample. PAS is useful because the detected signal is often proportional to sample concentration, can be used with very black or highly absorbing samples, and probes mainly material on the surface or several microns below the surface of the sample.

There are a few drawbacks to PAS. First, the sample size is limited by the need for small photo-acoustic cells. Large samples lead to reduced sensitivity.

More fundamentally, rapid-scanning FTIR spectrometers produce a different type of photo-acoustic spectrum than do dispersive or slow-scan FTIRs. The photo-acoustic effect has two physical contributions: optical absorption, determined by the absorption coefficient of the sample, and thermal diffusion, a function of density, thermal conductivity and specific heat of the sample. Because of this, the observed PAS spectrum depends on sample thickness, transparency, and preparation. In particular, the depth of penetration of the thermal wave depends on the modulation frequency: a higher optical frequency leads to a shallower depth of the sample contributing to the photo-acoustic spectrum. The thermal penetration depth is typically tens of microns thick.

In a rapid-scanning interferometer, the modulation frequency depends on wavenumber, and on the scan speed of the interferometer. The PAS spectrum is a mixture of contributions from various sample depths. For dispersive or slow-scanning interferometers, the modulation frequency is simply the rate of the chopper that modulates the beam. This is constant for all wavenumbers, and so the resulting spectrum is a homogeneous record of the sample characteristics at a particular depth. The depth probed can be varied simply by changing the chopping frequency. With a rapid-scanning FTIR, on the other hand, changing the scan mirror speed will alter the depth probed, but this will be different for each wavenumber in the spectrum.

Despite these complications, PAS is a useful technique when purely optical methods are unusable because of excessive absorption or scattering.

17.9.5   Long-path gas cells

Samples that absorb weakly must be measured in a thick section to produce measurable absorbance. Gases are usually measured in long path cells that produce equivalent sample thicknesses of the order of a metre to tens of metres.

The simplest gas cell is simply a container with windows at both ends. This arrangement is adequate when the total gas path is of the order of 10 cm or less. For much longer paths, the converging beam from the interferometer is vignetted by the windows.

For paths longer than a few centimeters, a multiple pass cell is normally employed. These use focusing mirrors either in or immediately outside the cell to reflect the beam two or more times through the sample. The Pfund cell (Fig. 17.15) produces an optical thickness three times larger than the physical depth of gas in the cell. The optical beam enters through a small aperture at the centre of a focusing mirror, reflects from a second mirror at the opposite side of the cell which makes it parallel, and is then reflected out by the first mirror through an aperture in the second mirror.

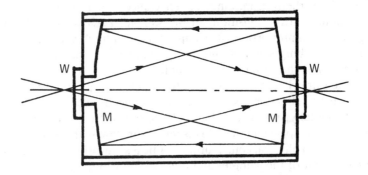

Fig. 17.15 — Pfund gas cell. Mirrors M collimate and then focus the beam to make three passes through the cell. W: entrance and exit windows.

A more versatile design, and one that is commonly used in commercial gas cells, is the cell developed by J. White of Standard Oil, New Jersey (White 1942). This more complex design allows an optical path to be produced that is a multiple of four times the cell length, as shown in Fig. 17.16. Light from the spectrometer is focused near the entrance window, and diverges toward a split mirror at the far end. One half of this "objective" mirror focuses the beam back onto a "field" mirror located near the entrance and exit windows. The beam is subsequently reflected back to the second half of the split objective mirror and back toward the field mirror. Depending on the relative orientation of the objective mirror halves, the refocused beam strikes either the field mirror to reverse its path again, or travels out through the exit window. The beams returned to the field mirror strike it at distinct places, and do not overlap. The relative size of the focused image (which is usually a refocused image of the light source of the spectrometer) and the diameter of the field mirror determine

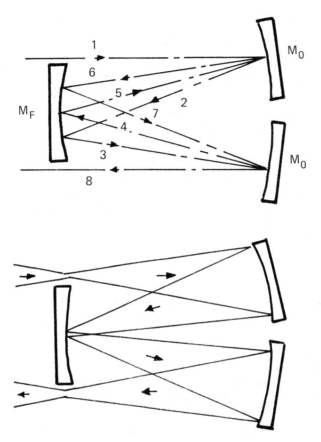

Fig. 17.16 — Optical configuration of White gas cell. M_O: objective mirrors; M_F: field mirror. These mirrors of equal curvature reflect beams a multiple of four times through the cell. Top: path of central ray for eight passes. Bottom: path of entire beam for four passes.

the maximum number of passes that a given White cell can achieve: if the image is too large, it will overlap others and lead to a mixed path length. Paths of twenty, forty or even 100 metres can be obtained in this way with relatively compact cells. The gas cells are sometimes constructed with inert walls to allow the study of corrosive gases or vapours. Alternatively, the cell can be constructed of silica so that the gas inside can be excited by ultraviolet lamps or lasers for particular studies.

Multiple-pass cells can significantly attenuate the spectrometer signal even when no sample is present. For example, the mirrors of a White cell seldom reflect more than 95% of the incident light. For the shortest optical length (four passes, and three reflections) the beam intensity is reduced to 86% by reflection losses; for 40 passes, the intensity is reduced to about 20%.

The cell windows, too, introduce losses by reflection at their surfaces and absorption. At least 15% is typically lost in this way.

A third major source of attenuation is mismatching of the spectrometer sample beam and the gas cell. If the spectrometer beam is too divergent, it will be too large to be entirely reflected by the split mirror of the cell. The remainder will be scattered from the walls. If, on the other hand, the beam is too parallel, the size of the focused image is likely to be too large: the light will be partially blocked at the entrance window of the gas cell, or will overlap on the field mirror, restricting the number of passes that can be used. Any gas cell is designed with an optimal f/number that should be matched by the spectrometer beam. The f/number of the cell is approximately given by its length divided by the shortest dimension of the split mirror at its far end. Commercial 20-m White cells are about $f/4$, while 40-m cells are usually about $f/6$ to $f/8$. Typical spectrometer sample beams are designed to have a convergence of about $f/3$ to $f/5$. If the f/number of the spectrometer is significantly different from that of the cell, it can be converted by a system of mirrors or lenses. This involves nothing more than receiving divergent light from the spectrometer sample beam and refocusing it with the appropriate angle of convergence into the gas cell. To ensure that the gas cell can be properly mounted, such transfer optics usually employ two or more flat "folding mirrors" to reflect the beam to a convenient orientation.

17.9.6 Fibre optics interfaces

Since the mid 1980s, a particularly convenient and practical remote sampling method has become available: infrared transmission along optical fibres.

The theory and application of optical fibres were first discussed in patent literature before 1930. The first fibres were made of glass or plastic and were at least a millimetre in diameter. The more recent growth in popularity of fibre optics is a result of their development for communications beginning in the 1960s. This has concentrated on developing optical materials that transmit at near-infrared wavelengths.

The availability of optical fibres that transmit between 1 and 15 μm allows the design of near- and mid-infrared spectrometers that can be situated in a secure location and yet used to monitor difficult samples and processes.

The infrared transmitting fibres in use today were developed because of telecommunications technology of the 1960s and 1970s. By the late 1970s, optical fibres made from glasses based on silica had reached practical limits of transparency. In a search for greater transparency (and therefore lower signal losses and fewer repeater amplifiers in communications systems) researchers turned to infrared materials. Three types of materials are presently used: chalcogenide glasses, polycrystalline glasses, and heavy-metal fluoride glasses (HMFG).

Chalcogenide fibres have a high refractive index, and are fabricated by mixing and melting metals such as antimony, germanium, and arsenic with the chalcogen elements, i.e. tellurium, selenium, and sulphur. The melt is made into a preform (a short, squat cylinder), drawn into a fibre, and finally coated with a plastic cladding. These fibres have a typical attenuation of between 2 and 6 dB/m between wavelengths of 4 and 11 μm, transmitting about 25–60% per m.

Polycrystalline fibres are extruded from a melt of mixtures of AgBr and AgCl. They are transparent over a wider range than chalcogenide fibres (3–15 μm) and are considerably more transparent (0.5–2 dB/m, or about 60–90% per m). The very slow die-extrusion process has limited the commercial availability of these fibres to date.

HMFG fibres are constructed from compositions such as ZrF_4–BaF_2–LaF_3–AlF_3–NaF. As with chalcogenide fibres, HMFG material is made into a preform and then drawn. The particular composition quoted, known as ZBLAN, has excellent near-infrared transmission: less than 0.1 dB/m in the 1–3.5 μm region, and usable between 0.5 and 4.5 μm.

Despite the improving transmittance of infrared-transmitting fibres, the losses are still considerable over lengths of more than a few metres or tens of metres. For example, a 10-m chalcogenide fibre transmits less than 1%. The maximum usable length of fibre depends on the signal quality of the spectrometer, and factors such as spectral range, resolution, and observation time.

A second problem is the interface between the fibre and the spectrometer. Optical fibres have a small aperture and a very large angular acceptance. Typical fibres have core diameters of less than 0.5 mm, considerably smaller than the focused image from a spectrometer light source. If fibres are packed together to yield a larger aperture, the cladding and circular cross sections limit the effective area to less than 50%. Although beam condensers can be used to produce small spot sizes, the resulting large angle of convergence can lead to excessive losses by reflection from the fibre surface; the efficiency of this interface seldom exceeds 20%. Because of the unavoidable mismatch of throughput for the fibre and an FTIR spectrometer, the Jacquinot advantage is not maintained. Even dispersive spectrometers can be well matched to optical fibres by packing the fibres at the spectrometer end into the form of a slit, and at the sample end into a compact circular form.

The Fellgett multiplex advantage is maintained for FTIR fibre optics; the simultaneous measurement of all wavelengths in the source is particularly beneficial in this energy-limited configuration. Signal-to-noise ratios exceeding 10 000 can be obtained with observation times of less than one minute, but acceptable results generally require cooled infrared detectors.

The first commercial instrument to employ infrared fibres was apparently a near-infrared dispersive spectrometer manufactured by Guided Wave Inc (El Dorado Hills, California, USA) beginning in the mid 1980s. Since then, several specialist companies have begun to offer fibre-optic sampling accessories for FTIR spectrometers.

Most applications at present are for industrial problems. In their simplest configuration, optical fibre cables are used simply to transport infrared radiation from a spectrometer to a remote sample and back. Typical samples include a moving multi-layer plastic web in a production line, fuel rods in the cooling pool of a fission reactor, and flowing high-pressure gas. Most industrial applications employ transmittance measurements, as these are easier to maintain in alignment than reflectance geometries. The input and output fibre on either side include lenses or mirrors to partially collimate the radiation through the sample.

The optical fibre itself can be used as a modulator or sensor. The refractive index, diameter and position of the fibre varies with temperature and mechanical stress. Numerous designs have been envisaged to measure temperature, pressure, vibration and other physical quantities by fibre optic techniques. These are likely to be combined in the near future with infrared spectroscopy.

REFERENCES

Ballantyne, J. M. (1967), Double Beam Operation of a Fourier Spectrometer, *Appl. Opt.*, **6**, 587.

Barer, R., Cole, R. H. and Thompson, H. W. (1949), Infra-red Spectroscopy With the Reflecting Microscope in Physics, Chemistry and Biology, *Nature*, **163**, 198.

Bar-Lev, H. (1967), A Dual-Beam Infrared Interferometer–Spectrometer, *Infr. Phys.*, **7**, 93.

Beer, R., Norton, R. H. and Seaman, C. H. (1971), Astronomical Infrared Spectroscopy with a Connes-Type Interferometer. I. Instrumental, *Rev. Sci. Instr.*, **42**, 1393.

Bell, A. G. (1881), Upon the Production of Sound by Radiant Energy, *Phil. Mag.*, **11**, 510.

Bell, E. E. (1966), Measurement of the Far Infrared Optical Properties of Solids with a Michelson Interferometer Used in the Asymmetric Mode: Part I, Mathematical Formulation, *Infr. Phys.*, **6**, 57.

Birch, J. R. (1972), A Far Infrared Reflection Interferometer, *Infr. Phys.*, **12**, 29.

Blout, E. R., Bird, G. R. and Grey, D. S. (1949), Infra-Red Microspectroscopy, *J. Opt. Soc. Am.*, **39**, 1052.

Brown, C. W., Obremski, R. J. and Anderson, P. (1986), Infrared Quantitative Analysis in the Fourier Domain: Processing Vector Representations, *Appl. Spectrosc.*, **40**, 734.

Busse, G. and Bullemer, B. (1978), Use of the Opto-Acoustic Effect for Rapid Scan Fourier Spectroscopy, *Infr. Phys.*, **18**, 631.

Chamberlain, J. (1965), On a Relation Between Absorption Strength and Refractive Index, *Infr. Phys.*, **5**, 175.

Chamberlain, J., Gibbs, J. E. and Gebbie, H. A. (1963), Refractometry in the Far Infrared Using a Two Beam Interferometer, *Nature*, **198**, 874.

Chamberlain, J., Gibbs, J. E. and Gebbie, H. A. (1969), The Determination of Refractive Index Spectra by Fourier Transform Spectroscopy, *Infr. Phys.*, **9**, 185.

Coffey, P. and Mattson, D. R. (1977), A Programmable Specific GC Detector — A GC-FTIR System Capable of On-The-Fly Functional Group Differentiation, *1977 International Conference on Fourier Transform Infrared Spectroscopy, Technical Digest*, 5.

Despain, A. M., Brown Jr., F. R., Steed, A. J. and Baker, D. J. (1970), A large-aperture field-widened interferometer–spectrometer for air-glow studies, *Aspen International Conference on Fourier Spectroscopy*, Bedford, Mass., AFCRL, 1971, p. 293.

Donini, J. C. and Michaelian, K. H. (1985), Near-, Mid- and Far-Infrared Photoacoustic Spectroscopy, *Proc. SPIE*, **553**, 344.

Fahrenfort, J. (1961), Attenuated total reflection: a new principle for the production of useful infra-red reflection spectra in organic compounds, *Spectrochim. Acta*, **17**, 698.

Filler, A. S. (1970), Feasibility of high resolution Fourier spectroscopy in the vacuum ultraviolet, *Aspen International Conference on Fourier Spectroscopy*, Bedford, Mass., AFCRL, 1971, p. 407.

Gault, W. A., Johnston, S. F. and Kendall, D. J. W. (1985), Optimization of a field-widened Michelson interferometer, *Appl. Opt.*, **24**, 1604.

Gast, J. and Genzel, L. (1973), An Amplitude Fourier Spectrometer for Infrared Solid State Spectroscopy, *Opt. Comm.*, **8**, 26.

Genzel, L. (1977), Double-Input, Double-Output Fourier Transform Spectroscopy, *1977 International Conference on Fourier Transform Infrared Spectroscopy, Technical Digest*, 15.

Griffiths, P. R. (1977), Optimized Sampling in the Gas Chromatograph in Infrared Spectroscopy, *Appl. Spectrosc.*, **31**, 284.

Griffiths, P. R. and deHaseth, J. A. (1986), *Fourier Transform Infrared Spectrometry*, Wiley, New York.

Guelachvili, G. (1986), Distortion-free inteferograms in Fourier transform spectroscopy with nonlinear detectors, *Appl. Opt.*, **25**, 4644.

Hall, R. T., Vrabec, D. and Dowling, J. M. (1966), A High Resolution, Far Infrared Double-Beam Lamellar Grating Interferometer, *Appl. Opt.*, **7**, 1147.

Hansen, G. (1955), The Visibility of the Fringes With a Twyman Interferometer, *Optik*, **12**, 5.

Haycock, R. H. and Baker, D. J. (1974), Infrared Prism Interferometer Spectrometer Using a Gas-Lubricated Drive Bearing, *Infr. Phys.*, **14**, 259.

Hicks, T. C., Reay, N. K. and Scaddan, R. J. (1974), A Servo Controlled Fabry–Perot Interferometer Using Capacitance Micrometers for Error Detection, *J. Phys. E*, **7**, 27.

Hilliard, R. L. and Shepherd, G. G. (1966), Wide-Angle Michelson Interferometer for Measuring Doppler Line Widths, *J. Opt. Soc. Am.*, **56**, 362.

Hirschfeld, T. (1978), New trends in the application of Fourier transform spectroscopy to analytical chemistry, *Appl. Opt.*, **17**, 1400.

Kahn, F. D. (1959), The Signal:Noise Ratio of a Suggested Spectral Analyzer, *Astrophys. J.*, **129**, 518.

Low, M. J. D. and Freeman, S. K. (1967), Measurement of Infrared Spectra of Gas-Liquid Chromatography Fractions Using Multiple-Scan Interference Spectrometry, *Anal. Chem.*, **39**, 194.

Luc, P. and Gerstenkorn, S. (1978), Fourier transform spectroscopy in the visible and ultraviolet range, *Appl. Opt.,* **17**, 1327.

Manel, M., Forman, M., Meilleur, T., Westcott, R. and Pritchard, J. (1969), Double-Beam Interferometer for the Middle Infrared, *Appl. Opt.,* **8**, 2059.

Margalit, E., Dodiuk, H., Kosower, E. M. and Katzir, A. (1989), Infrared Fiber Evanescent Wave Spectroscopy For *In-Situ* Monitoring of Chemical Processes, *Proc. SPIE,* **1048**, 145.

Martin, D. H. and Puplett, E. (1969), Polarised Interferometric Spectrometry for the Millimetre and Submillimetre Spectrum, *Infr. Phys.,* **10**,, 105.

Mertz, L. (1965), *Transformations in Optics,* Wiley, New York.

Richter, W. and Erb, W. (1987), Accurate Diffuse Reflection Measurements in the Infrared Spectral Range, *Appl. Opt.,* **26**, 4620.

Ridgway, S. T. and Capps, R. W. (1974), A Fourier transform spectrophotometer for astronomical applications, 700–10000 cm^{-1}, *Rev. Sci. Instr.,* **45**, 676.

Russell, E. E. and Bell, E. E. (1966), Measurement of the Far Infrared Optical Properties of Solids with a Michelson Interferometer Used in the Asymmetric Mode: Part II, the Vacuum Interferometer, *Infr. Phys.,* **6**, 75.

Schofield, J. W. and Ring, J. (1970), Field Compensated Michelson Spectrometers, in: Home-Dickson, J. (ed.) *Optical Instruments and Techniques,* Oriel Press.

Shepherd, G. G., Gault, W. A., Miller, D. W., Pasturczyk, Z., Johnston, S. F., Kosteniuk, P. R., Haslett, J. W., Kendall, D. J. W. and Wimperis, J. R. (1985), WAMDII: Wide Angle Michelson Doppler Imaging Interferometer for Spacelab, *Appl. Opt.,* **24**, 1571.

Shepherd, O., Reidy, W. and Vanasse, G. A. (1979), Background Suppression and spectral detection using double-beam interferometry: Instrumentation, *Proc. SPIE,* **191**, 64.

Sperline, R. P., Muralidharan, S. and Freiser, H. (1986), New Quantitative Technique for Attenuated Total Reflection (ATR) Spectrophotometry: Calibration of the 'Circle' ATR Device in the Infrared, *Appl. Spectrosc.,* **40**, 1019.

Steed, A. J. (1979), Field-Widened Interferometry at Utah State University (USU), *Proc. SPIE,* **191**, 2.

Thorne, A. P. (1987), High Resolution Visible/Ultra-Violet Fourier Transform Spectroscopy, in: Burgess, C. and Mielenz, K. D. (eds), *Advances in Standards and Methodology in Spectrophotometry,* Elsevier, Amsterdam.

Thorne, A. P. Harris, C. J., Wynne-Jones, I., Learner, R. C. M. and Cox, G. (1986), A Fourier transform spectrometer for the vacuum ultraviolet: design and performance, *J. Phys. E: Sci. Instrum.,* **20**, 54.

Thorpe, L. W., Milward, R. C., Hayward, G. C. and Yewen, J. D. (1970), Double-Beam Far-Infrared Interferometric Fourier Spectrometer System in Home-Dickson, J. (ed.), *Optical Instruments and Techniques,* Oriel Press, Newcastle upon Tyne.

Vanasse, G. and Sakai, H. (1977), Study of the Dual-Input Mode With the AFGL Two-Meter Path Difference Interferometer, Air Force Geophysical Laboratory Report, No. AFGL-TR-77-0213, Cambridge, MA.

Wall, D. and Mantz, A. W. (1977), Gas Chromatographic Analyses Incorporating Combined GC/IR Techniques, *1977 International Conference on Fourier Transform Infrared Spectroscopy, Technical Digest,* 5.

White, J. U. (1942), Long Optical Paths of Large Aperture, *J. Opt. Soc. Am.,* **32**, 285.

Willey, R. R. (1976), Fourier Transform Infrared Spectrophotometer for Transmittance and Diffuse Reflectance Measurements, *Appl. Spectrosc.,* **30**, 593.

Willis, J. N. (1976), Design and Performance of a New Double-Beam Fast Fourier Transform Interferometer, *Infr. Phys.,* **16**, 299.

Wimperis, J. R. and Johnston, S. F. (1984), Optical Cements for Interferometric Applications, *Appl. Opt.,* **23**, 1145.

Zehnpfennig, T. F., Shepherd, O., Rappaport, S, Reidy, W. P. and Vanasse, G. (1979), Background Suppression in Double-Beam Interferometry, *Appl. Opt.,* **18**, 1996.

Zwick, U., Irslinger, L. and Genzel, L. (1976), Automated Far-Infrared Fourier Interferometer for Amplitude-Phase Spectroscopy at Low Temperatures, *Infr. Phys.,* **16**, 263.

18

The shape of things to come

18.1 CHANGING MARKETS

The decade of the 1980s saw dispersive laboratory spectrometers being gradually replaced by FTIR alternatives. The transition is still not complete: in the early 1990s, several major companies continue to manufacture dispersive infrared spectrometers. FTIR spectrometers were able to make inroads into the routine chemistry laboratory for two reasons: they became simpler to use, and their price fell dramatically. The dispersives still being sold are all less expensive than FTIRs; price is the sole factor in their choice by purchasers. It can be expected that the last commercial dispersive spectrometer, at least in the form produced since the 1950s, will be sold within ten years.

In the 1990s, FTIR technology is beginning to influence significantly applications outside the physics and chemistry laboratory. With the advent of more inexpensive and robust interferometers in the mid-1980s, industrial and quality-control applications began to be considered. Some examples of the disparate applications are air-pollution monitoring, quality-control in milk production, and identification of laminated plastics composition and thickness in factories. The dedicated spectrometers designed by Nicolet, Analect, and Bomem are examples of the direction in which commercial instrument development will go.

Such applications will increase as manufacturers further adapt FTIR units to on-line monitoring, harsh environments and lower price.

The changing markets will likely see a redistribution of the companies manufacturing and selling FTIR instruments. The very first FTIR manufacturers were companies already producing instruments for far-infrared physicists. To these existing companies were added small new companies exploiting a clever design feature or a niche market. For example, Block, Bomem, Eocom, Idealab and Midac all started in commercial FTIR with contracts for custom-made instruments. The 1970s and early 1980s in particular, during the rapid expansion of commercial FTIR, saw both the birth and demise of several companies.

Today, there are over two dozen manufacturers of FTIR spectrometers or modules. Most of these specialize in the large analytical chemistry market, which currently purchases a few thousand instruments per year worldwide, most of which are low-priced. It can be expected that at least some FTIR manufacturers will leave the market in the foreseeable future. Those companies remaining will likely specialize in one of two markets: either analytical chemistry or industrial applications. This trend has already begun. Companies such as Perkin–Elmer have limited themselves to laboratory instruments, whereas smaller manufacturers such as Analect and Midac have adapted their instrument designs for quality assurance and industrial process control. Nicolet and Bomem have covered both ranges by marketing laboratory and factory-engineered equipment.

18.2   ADVANCES IN TECHNOLOGY

The principal achievements of the 1950s were the discovery of the advantages of Fourier spectroscopy, and tentative experimental demonstrations. In the 1960s, the fast Fourier transform, minicomputers and commercial products advanced the technique. The 1970s witnessed the commercial application of rapid-scanning FTIR, and its acceptance by research chemists. The achievements of the 1980s were less profound but wider reaching: less expensive commercial instruments coupled with practical sampling accessories. The lower prices and higher sales were the result of better interferometer designs and more advanced computers. Although the pace of fundamental development appears to have slackened, Fourier transform spectroscopy continues to benefit from incremental advances in technology.

18.3   DATA ANALYSIS

Despite the rapid advances in computer hardware and software, experimental methods continue to evolve that use them to full capacity.

One of the most serious problems with present-day FTIR is the treatment of large quantities of data. For example, GC/IR, TGA/IR and time-resolved spectroscopy generate spectra every few seconds (or even fractions of a second) during an experiment. The data must be transformed to spectra, displayed in a comprehensible format, stored for later use, and analysed in near real-time to extract useful information. Solutions to date have relied principally on brute-force techniques: storage of data on magnetic tape or high-capacity hard disks, and the use of specialized hardware processors for transformation, spectral search or other analyses.

While the ability to store large quantities of data will continue to improve as memory devices become cheaper, the solution to the data processing bottleneck probably lies in the direction of "intelligent" algorithms for information extraction. Instead of measuring and storing entire spectra, only the important characteristics will be identified and saved. Artificial intelligence will be increasingly applied to the problems of high-volume spectroscopy.

18.3.1   Neural nets

One form of analysis showing increasing promise is the neural network. A neural net is a simple model of a human brain, consisting of logical neurones that respond according to the distribution of several inputs applied to them. The neurones are interconnected in one or more stages or "layers" and culminate in a smaller number of observable outputs. In spectroscopic applications, for example, the inputs might consist of transmittance measurements for an unknown sample spectrum at twenty spectral points; the outputs could then consist of the concentration of a half-dozen components in the sample.

The neural net is not programmed with step-by-step algorithms to calculate concentrations. Instead, it is trained by presenting example data at its input, and feeding back the output until the response is correct. This can require many thousands of data sets, but is an automated, one-time process. Unlike a traditional computer program, a neural net will not provide grossly erroneous results if some inputs are incorrect or missing: it is tolerant of data error, and contains a high degree of redundancy.

In a spectroscopic system employing a neural network, the user might never see the infrared spectrum or interferogram; only the result would be provided. The knowledge "learned" by the network would be the basis of all output information.

18.3.2 Expert systems
A second type of artificial intelligence with increasing applications is the "expert system". This is a program that operates according to decision rules provided by a human expert. In principle, a complete set of heuristic rules can be collected for any field of expertise. The interpretation of unknown spectra is an example of an art that has been taught in "cookbook" form for several decades.

The performance of an expert system in spectral interpretation or any other task depends on the design rules and, ultimately, on the expertise that is codified.

18.3.3 Communication
The nature of computer use has evolved quickly. The first digital computers were isolated devices of ever-increasing capacity. A single application or "job" was run at any time, followed in sequence by other jobs.

By the late 1960s, time-sharing was common. Several individual users at separate terminals shared the computer's time in imperceptible "slices". These users remained isolated except for a limited amount of inter-terminal communication.

Minicomputers and microcomputers reversed the trend toward centralized computers, giving access to a single user at all times. In the early 1990s, microcomputers and minicomputers are coming full circle by being increasingly connected into networks. Such networks allow the interchange of data or the manipulation of data in a centrally available location, or the "collectivization" of several processors to work in parallel on a particularly large problem.

Computer networks are the first step towards an eventual merging of individual processors into a collective information network. Such a network will provide access to information such as centralized databases of spectroscopic data. It is likely that the identity of individual microprocessors or terminals will become increasingly indistinct as much of the memory and computing power is distributed through the network.

The advantages of this evolution for the laboratory spectroscopist will be varied. Data will be readily communicated between instruments, users and output devices. Remote operation and sequencing of multiple instruments will become straightforward.

Some starts have been made in this direction. A number of computer networking systems, electronic mail protocols and public databases exist. Perkin–Elmer's Laboratory Information Management System (LIMS) and Hewlett–Packard's HP-IB instrument communications bus protocol (a version of the IEEE 488 standard) enable instruments to communicate. The JCAMP-DX data exchange format for spectroscopic data files, originated in the mid 1980s, has been grudgingly accepted and implemented by most spectrometer manufacturers. It must be said, though, that it is still awkward and inconvenient to share spectroscopic data obtained on different instruments.

18.4 INTERFEROMETER DESIGN

For a device that is elegantly simple in concept, the interferometer has seen an unusually long period of evolution. This is partly a consequence of the difficulty of reconciling very high-precision mechanical movement with inexpensive, large-scale production.

As described in earlier chapters, the rate of evolution has been quite constant for four decades. The first lamellar and Michelson interferometers were adapted to various scan drives; the Michelson type was gradually made more robust and precise for near-infrared use; in the 1970s, self-compensating interferometers were increasingly tried. The 1980s produced a spate of rotating scan mechanisms.

This progress is likely to continue for some time. Interferometers must be as simple, robust and insensitive to external influences as possible. At present, details such as beamsplitter/compensator assemblies (which have changed little in thirty years) and mirror-mounting schemes appear most in need of improvement.

The fabrication of optical elements has also seen continued progress. The hand-lapped mirrors of the 1960s were replaced by replicated (moulded) optics in the 1970s and diamond-turned optics in the 1980s. Diamond-turning under numerical control has continued to be refined, now permitting the use of aspheric mirrors with quality good enough for use at visible wavelengths. The cost of aspherics will continue to fall, leading to simpler, more compact optical designs.

18.4.1 FTIR with no moving parts

The combination of interferometry and detector arrays can yield a Fourier spectrometer that does not require a precise scan mechanism or compensated optics. In this scheme, the optical path difference is arranged to be a function of position, and each detector element then measures a particular OPD at all times.

The idea of replacing a scanning interferometer with a fixed geometry has a long history. Fellgett, in his original thesis work on multiplex spectroscopy, used tilted glass plates to form an air wedge, in which the optical path difference varies with position. It was necessary to shift either the wedge or the detector(s) to measure the interferogram, though. Mertz (1965) described several schemes, including the use of a Wollaston prism to give an optical path difference.

Grechushnikov *et al.* (1963) developed a spectrometer in the late 1950s based on a quartz wedge between polarizers. Quartz has the property of birefringence, i.e. a refractive index that is different for two perpendicular polarizations of light. The first polarizing filter balances the intensities of the two polarizations entering the wedge; the wedge then introduces an optical path difference between them, because one travels faster through the quartz than the other. The second polarizing filter recombines the two components. As with a conventional Michelson interferometer, if the OPD is a multiple of one wavelength, the recombined beam will have maximum intensity, but other OPDs will cause intensity modulation. The changing thickness of the wedge, which varies from 2.5 mm to 1.0 mm, introduces an optical path difference that varies with position. As in the previous devices, the wedge was moved through the 20-mm diameter beam to change the optical path difference viewed by a single detector. The instrument can measure an interferogram to an OPD of about 1 mm with near-infrared light. The authors claimed a resolving power of only ten, limited mainly by their geometry for the wedge and by the crude method of Fourier transformation they used.

More recently, instruments incorporating a detector array have been designed by Aryamanya-Mugisha and Williams (1985) and Minami *et al.* (1985). These follow the same principle as the earlier configurations, but focus the light from the birefringent element onto a fixed array of detectors.

One commercial example of such an instrument is the Hitachi U-6000 Fourier-transform array spectrometer, introduced in 1990. This device, designed for measuring visible-range spectra through a microscope, consists of a Wollaston prism, photodiode array and collimating/focusing lenses. The Wollaston prism consists of three thin, birefringent quartz prisms sandwiched to form a flat plate. As described above, the combination has the property of introducing a phase shift on a transmitted beam that varies with angle of refraction. When the beam is focused onto a photodiode array, the varying path difference produces an intensity pattern, i.e. a spatially resolved interferogram. Each detector element of the array samples one point on the interferogram. When a Fourier transform is performed on the data from the detector array, the spectrum is obtained.

A limitation of this system is its restricted (and non-adjustable) number of interferogram points. There are 1024 elements in the Hitachi instrument. By choosing the appropriate focal length for the lenses, the interferogram pattern can be scaled on the detector array to trade the maximum optical path difference for sample interval. This effectively trades resolution for spectral range. In the Hitachi implementation, a 380–900 nm (26 300–11 000 cm^{-1}) spectral range is obtained with 150 cm^{-1} resolution. This is comparable to the specification of dispersive instruments. When the approximately tenfold increase in field brightness is compared to dispersives, however, the Fourier array spectrometer proves to give superior noise performance.

The more widespread use of FT-array spectrometers in near- and mid-infrared spectroscopy can be expected, owing to their low manufacturing tolerances and absence of moving parts.

18.4.2 FTIR within an optical fibre

Fibre optic sampling accessories have been discussed in Section 17.9.6. A new approach is to construct the interferometer itself from an optical fibre (e.g. Kersey *et al.* 1985, Takada *et al.* 1990).

Fibre optic interferometers have been developed through the 1980s for applications in metrology. Their use has been made possible by the development of single-mode optical fibres. These very narrow fibres allow only one "mode" or optical geometry to propagate through them, and so prevent different phases of light from overlapping and destroying the interference pattern produced by the interferometer.

The beamsplitter consists of a fibre coupler, which allows the light from two adjacent fibres to "leak through" one another. The moving mirror is quite conventional: a small flat mirror moved on a stage. Germanium and silicon photodiodes serve as detectors.

Because the fibre is so compact, it can be difficult to incorporate the laser reference channel—particularly if a quadrature detection scheme is needed. Takada *et al.* have used a piezoelectric transducer to stretch cyclically the fibre forming the fixed arm of the interferometer at a rate of 10 kHz. The stretching introduces polarization modulation of the output beam which is used to monitor optical path difference and direction of scanning.

The optical fibre interferometer is perturbed by motion of the fibres, but co-adding several dozen interferograms can yield good quality spectra of narrow-band sources such as light-emitting diodes.

With the growth of the field of "photonics" (photon-based technologies which are replacing the older electron-based technologies of electronics), fibre optics and associated devices are being developed at an increasing rate. It is likely that photonics will follow a course much like that of electronics: optical components will be miniaturized and integrated into modules that can then be interconnected for more complex functions. Fibre optic interferometers are one module of this burgeoning technology.

18.5 ADVANCES IN SAMPLING TECHNIQUES

The most apparent new sampling technique on the horizon is remote sampling. Measurement of a sample located far from the spectrometer is frequently a requirement in industrial situations, where the process being monitored or the factory environment are too harsh for the instrument. Remote sampling is also an advantage if several different locations must be monitored by a single instrument. This is usually determined by the relative cost of the instrument and sampling accessory.

Fibre optic accessories, discussed in Section 17.9.6, are the most likely candidates for new remote sampling techniques. Their development has been limited to date by the chicken and egg situation: industrial users will not consider purchasing a spectrometer unless it can sample remotely, but manufacturers cannot develop such an accessory without a demonstrated user need. A technical limitation is the transparency of infrared-transmitting optical glasses. These are already adequate, but much less efficient than visible-transmitting fibres and other types of infrared sampling accessory.

Specac (Orpington, UK) presently offers two types of "Fibreprobe" intended for sampling batches of chemicals without mounting in the spectrometer, for quality assurance and quality control. One probe allows transmittance measurements; the other permits attenuated total reflectance (ATR) measurements. Both probes consist of a short fibre-optic cable terminated at one end by the sampling unit and at the other by an interface that adapts the fibre bundle to the spectrometer optical system. The ATR probe typically uses a 2-m bifurcated zirconium fluoride optical fibre (0.5 mm core, with protective cladding), and a ZnS ATR crystal. This configuration can measure between 2200 and $10\,000\,cm^{-1}$. The transmittance probe normally uses a water-free quartz fibre (1-mm core diameter) with a variable pathlength transmission head, and is usable over the 5000–$30\,000\,cm^{-1}$ near infrared/ visible/ultraviolet range.

An alternative to fibre optics is the light pipe or hollow analogue of optical fibres. Axiom Analytical has introduced (1989) a "deep immersion probe" consisting of off-axis relay mirrors to direct a beam travelling through a light pipe terminated by an attenuated total reflectance (ATR) crystal. The beam is reflected through the crystal to the other side, where its direction is reversed by a cube-corner mirror to travel up a second metallic light guide to the infrared detector, minus the energy absorbed at the liquid interface. The entire probe is available in various sizes for use with small laboratory apparatus or large vats. The light pipes can be heated to avoid chemical condensation by pumping hot purge gas between their exteriors and the probe envelope. The probe interfaces with the "Optibus" beam direction accessory of Analect spectrometers.

18.6   THE EVENTUAL DEMISE OF FTIR

The tracing of the evolution of Fourier transform spectrometry has shown how it replaced early technologies and matured in a continually changing market. This process will of course continue, with newer technologies eventually replacing FTIR.

At present, there are at least two likely candidates as successors to FTIR. One may take over FTIR's current dominance in high resolution infrared spectroscopy; the second is likely to become a competitor for routine analytical spectroscopy.

18.6.1   Scanning laser spectroscopy

Since their invention in the early 1960s, lasers have been a tempting technology for spectroscopists. As a class of light sources, lasers are highly monochromatic and very intense. Secondary advantages of lasers include the ability to control the polarization, divergence and coherence of the laser beam.

Since the invention in 1961 of the first ruby laser, which emits a deep red light, other types have been developed covering the spectrum from far infrared to ultraviolet. The earliest experiments in absorption spectroscopy using a laser were carried out in the mid 1960s, using the 3.39 μm emission of the He–Ne laser. This wavelength is strongly absorbed by hydrocarbon molecules because of the excitation of the C–H stretching vibration.

Despite its many ideal characteristics, the typical laser has suffered from some practical problems:

(1) It is complex to operate, requiring periodic mirror adjustment, cooling mechanisms and systems to compensate for output power variations.
(2) The output wavelength is fixed, or adjustable to only a few discrete values.

The development of various forms of tunable laser has reduced these problems. Many techniques have been devised to use lasers for spectroscopy. For infrared measurements, two methods have so far been important: passive heterodyne detection, and absorption spectroscopy by tunable laser.

Passive heterodyne detection
The term "heterodyning" refers to the principle of detecting a signal by mixing it with another, reference, signal of similar frequency. The technique was invented for radio receivers in the 1930s. The receiver amplified a radio wave detected by its antenna. This radio signal is carried by a frequency much higher than the audio frequency. A "local oscillator", i.e. a frequency generator in the radio receiver, could be tuned to frequencies around the radio wave frequency. By electrically combining these two signals in a mixer, a modulated output signal is produced. The modulated portion is filtered, amplified and finally demodulated to yield an audio-frequency signal that is applied to a loudspeaker.

The same principle can be used at the much higher frequency of infrared light. Here, the local oscillator is a laser tuned to the frequency of interest; the mixer is the optical detector.

The sensitivity of the heterodyne technique depends on the laser, detection efficiency, and losses due to absorption and reflection of light. It has been shown (Wijntjes 1979) that heterodyne detection has a theoretical disadvantage compared with conventional spectrometers, unless very high spectral resolution is required. This conclusion does not consider the multiplex advantage of FTIR, which gives another gain of orders of magnitude.

Absorption spectroscopy by tunable laser
The principle of laser absorption spectroscopy is simple. The laser light source is tuned to a wavelength, directed through the sample, and its intensity is measured by the detector. Instead of rotating a mechanical assembly as in a prism or grating spectrometer, a laser spectrometer is successively tuned through wavelengths by electrical means. As in the heterodyne method, the spectrum is measured at each individual wavelength, and so does not benefit from the multiplex advantage.

Wijntjes has shown that laser absorption spectroscopy has a significant advantage over FTIR when measurements are made at resolutions narrower than about $0.02 \, cm^{-1}$. The advantage is primarily due to the very high output power available with tunable diode lasers; in FTIR, the broadband light source is limited in output power because it can emit no more than a heated blackbody of the same temperature. For practical source materials, the temperature is limited to less than 2000 K, resulting in relatively little power compared with a tunable laser source.

In practice, the sensitivity of laser absorption spectroscopy is often limited by low frequency instabilities in output power. Future technology is likely to improve output stability and spectral range of tunable lasers. They will then be somewhat simpler and more sensitive than the FTIR spectrometers that currently dominate high-resolution spectroscopy.

18.6.2   Infrared diode array spectrometers

Dispersive spectrometers for the ultraviolet and visible range were transformed in the early 1980s by diode-array technology. A diode array is a series of detector elements mounted on a single substrate, and electrically linked to allow rapid sequential "reading" of their signals. For diode arrays in UV/VIS spectrometers, each element views a portion of the spectrum dispersed by a prism or diffraction grating. The only moving part in the instrument is usually a rotating or alternating mirror to select periodically the sample or reference beam.

Because diode-array spectrometers use a monochromator and slit, they do not have the Jacquinot advantage: throughput falls dramatically with increasing resolution.

Still, when the detector outputs can be individually integrated before reading, the instrument benefits from the Fellgett advantage: each wavelength is observed for the entire duration of the scan, instead of sequentially as in a conventional dispersive spectrometer. Arrays of 1024 or 2048 elements are typically used, providing resolution of better than 1 nm over the 200–800 nm (0.2–0.8 µm) range.

The same principle can be applied to infrared instruments. To date, the factor limiting the application of diode arrays in infrared dispersive spectrometers has been the detector array. Cooled infrared detectors such as indium antimonide (InSb) or mercury cadmium telluride (MCT) cannot yet be manufactured in long arrays at reasonable cost. Current state-of-the-art is an array having a few hundred elements; this can be expected to improve over the next decade.

Besides the detector elements themselves, signal processing is required. Each detector signal must be amplified and digitized. If the elements are monitored sequentially, a single signal processing chain can be used, consisting of a device to switch between detector elements, a preamplifier and an ADC. Unless the signal from each detector element is monitored continuously, though, the multiplex advantage is lost. Such monitoring can be as straightforward as the integration of the detector signal by a simple capacitor circuit, which is subsequently "read out" channel by channel. Even this elementary scheme demands an identical circuit for each detector element.

Owing to variations in the fabrication of detectors and the components of analogue electronics, the responses of the channels will not be identical. The channels could be balanced individually, but a more practical strategy is to store correction data by which the measurements can be scaled.

18.7   THE WEAKNESSES OF FTIR

Forty years of concentrated development of Fourier technology have mapped its positive and negative attributes. Most of the difficulties that initially seemed

insurmountable — problems such as calculation complexity, high mechanical tolerances and sensitivity to misalignment — have been solved by advances in technology.
But, there are classes of problem where other techniques can be expected to fare
better.

The reliance of conventional FTIR spectrometers on a single moving part (the
moving mirror) makes it considerably simpler than old-fashioned dispersive scanning spectrometers. Still, that single movement must be extremely precise. Techniques that employ no moving parts have practical advantages in harsh
environments.

In visible and ultraviolet spectroscopy, conventional dispersive instruments can
achieve very high quality results. FTIR is of benefit in only a few restricted
circumstances.

18.8 THE STRENGTHS OF FTIR

Where, then, does FTIR excel? Is there a domain in which Fourier spectroscopy is
likely to remain unchallenged as a spectroscopic technique?

For broad-range, high-resolution spectroscopy, FTIR appears to have clear
advantages over laser methods. It can cover the entire infrared, visible and ultraviolet regions of the spectrum with as few as three or four beamsplitters and detectors.
The Connes advantage of precise wavenumber measurement is also important:
Fourier spectroscopy intrinsically provides high-quality wavenumber calibration
with every spectrum.

Again, for broad-band emission spectroscopy, Fourier methods remain the best.
Laser spectroscopy is limited to absorption methods. Dispersive spectrometers
cannot match the signal quality of FTIR instruments except in a few special cases of
visible and ultraviolet spectroscopy.

18.9 FTS OR FTIR?

The technology discussed in this book was called interferential spectroscopy by
Michelson, multiplex or Fourier spectroscopy by the physicists who developed it,
and interferometric spectrophotometry by those seeking to impress.

The acronym FTIR is almost universally used by chemists to refer to the
technique today. Will the term FTS (Fourier transform spectroscopy) eventually
take precedence? Despite its use by spectrometer manufacturers who sell instruments covering the range from far infrared to ultraviolet, "FTS" is little used, and
probably will remain so.

As discussed in Section 17.5, Fourier spectroscopy in the visible and ultraviolet is
marginally better than conventional techniques. The multiplex advantage, much
reduced or even cancelled by the different characteristics of noise sources that
dominate visible spectroscopy, is restricted to only a few special conditions. Such
niche benefits are not enough to make FT-VIS or FT-UV popular.

With the marginal advantages come much stricter operating conditions. The
transition from mid-infrared to ultraviolet Fourier spectroscopy demands an order-

of-magnitude improvement in optical quality, mirror drive regularity and data volume — even now, such specifications are relatively difficult and expensive to achieve.

The advantages of Fourier spectroscopy are indisputably overwhelming in the infrared, where the detectors are limited in sensitivity by the energy of the light and the light sources themselves are weak, and where the necessary operating tolerances can now be readily realized. Fourier spectroscopy began in the infrared, and will continue to be best there.

18.10   IN THE CRYSTAL BALL

Predictions of the future of technology are fraught with danger, or at least the threat of embarrassment. The direction of technological advances depends as much on fashion, user requirements and economic constraints as on theoretical advantages. Any forecast appears quaintly dated in retrospect, because the prognosticator is unable to foresee new discoveries.

Albert Michelson, who launched the past century of Fourier spectroscopy, had this to say in 1902:

> The more important fundamental laws and facts of physical science have all been discovered, and these are now so firmly established that the possibility of their ever being supplanted in consequence of new discoveries is exceedingly remote.

This pronouncement, from a leading American physicist, was made at a time when X-rays, radioactivity, wireless communication, electronics, and relativity were about to transform science and engineering.

On a smaller scale of error, consider the extrapolations made by planners: forecasts of traffic flow that cannot foresee the growth of new towns or the increasing popularity of automobiles; projections of power usage that cannot account for improved energy efficiency; and, predictions by marketing staff for the sales of scientific instruments that do not consider intangibles such as the user's opinion of the colour, familiarity and ease of use. Technology is inextricably linked with social questions.

With these uncertainties of prediction clearly in mind, a few broad forecasts can perhaps be made.

(1) Inexpensive FTIR spectrometers will be further adapted to niche applications. Instead of a greater selection of general-purpose laboratory instruments, we will see "black boxes" designed for particular types of analysis in quality control.

(2) FTIR technology will increasingly be simplified: interferometers will have fewer (or no) moving parts and reduced tolerances; electronic designs will be further integrated.

(3) Software will increasingly take responsibility for all aspects of an FTIR spectral measurement. The need to understand the principles of Fourier spectroscopy may diminish until only sample preparation will concern the user.

(3) Versatile, general purpose FTIR spectrometers will continue to be produced for research applications (Fig. 18.1). These will evolve toward multi-user, multi-experiment instruments to justify their high cost. When a better technique for obtaining broad-band, high-resolution spectra is found, these complex FTIR instruments will abruptly disappear.

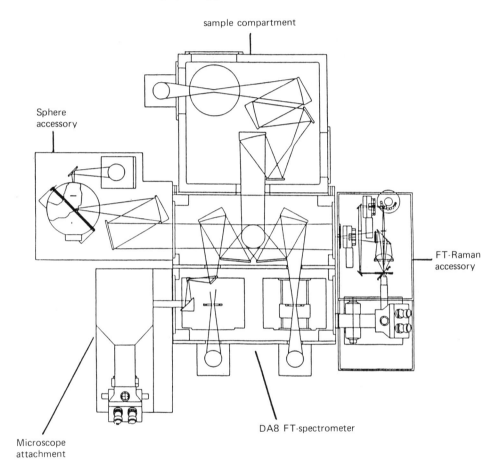

sample compartment

Sphere accessory

FT-Raman accessory

Microscope attachment

DA8 FT-spectrometer

Fig. 18.1 — Example of a multi-experiment spectrometer. The modulated output of the Bomem DA8 interferometer (not visible above the plane of the diagram) can be directed by mirrors to three parallel-beam outputs or two focused outputs. The microscope attachment at front left is accomodated by a manually adjusted pick-off mirror (reproduced with permission from Bomem Inc.).

(4) Competing technologies will have a resurgence. Dispersive spectroscopy will be revitalized by array detectors.

No matter which direction spectroscopy takes, it will continue to interest new generations of researchers and instrument designers. In the past two centuries, the study of light has given birth to new sciences; just the last tenth of that period has seen the flowering of FTIR. In time, Fourier spectroscopy will seem as dated and charming as Daguerrotype photography does today, but the underlying science that motivated it will remain. As Michelson wrote nearly a century ago, and as four or five generations of instrument designers have found since:

> This, to my mind, is one of the most fascinating, not only of the departments of science, but of human knowledge. If a poet could at the same time be a physicist, he might convey to others the pleasure, the satisfaction, almost the reverence, that the subject inspires....Especially is its fascination felt in the branch which deals with light, and I hope the day may be near when a Ruskin will be found equal to the description of the beauties of coloring, the exquisite gradations of light and shade, and the intricate wonders of symmetrical forms and combinations of forms which are encountered at every turn.

REFERENCES

Aryamanya-Mugisha, H. and Williams, R. R. (1985), A Fourier transform diode array spectrometer for the UV, visible, and near-IR, *Appl. Spectrosc.*, **39**, 693.

Gilpin, J. B., Roschen, J., Hampton, S. R. and Kniffin, M. J. (1978), A High-Performance 8 to 12 μm (Hg,Cd)Te 72-Element Detector Array, *Proc. SPIE*, **132**, 141.

Grechushnikov, B. N., Distler, G. I. and Petrov, I. P. (1963), Fourier Spectrometer for Working in the Near-Infrared Region of the Spectrum, *Sov. Phys. Crystallog.*, **8**, 369.

Hieftje, G. (1983), Low-cost tunable lasers: Prospects for Chemical Analysis, *Am. Lab.*, May.

Hirschfeld, T. (1977), New Trends in Fourier Transform Spectroscopy, *1977 International Conference on Fourier Transform Infrared Spectroscopy, Technical Digest*, 9.

Kersey, A. D., Dandridge, A., Tueten, A. B. and Gialorenzi, G. (1985), Single Mode Fiber Fourier Transform Spectrometer, *Electron. Lett.*, **21**, 463.

Michelson, A. A. (1902), *Light Waves and Their Uses*, The University of Chicago Press, Chicago.

Minami, S., Okamoto, T. and Kawata, S. (1985), Near IR Fourier transform spectrometer with an IR vidicon, *Proc. SPIE*, **553**, 346.

Takada, K., Kobayashi, M. and Nada, J. (1990), Fiber Optic Fourier Transform Spectrometer With A Coherent Interferogram Averaging Scheme, *Appl. Opt.*, **29**, 5170.

Wijntjes, G. (1979), Fourier transform spectroscopy (FTS) in the light of new developments such as passive heterodyne spectroscopy and diode laser absorption spectroscopy, *Proc. SPIE*, **191**, 33.

Appendix:
Practical evaluation of an FTIR spectrometer

It is important for the user or purchaser of an FTIR spectrometer to understand how design compromises and operational problems can affect the results obtained. This Appendix describes relatively simple tests that you can perform to evaluate your instrument. These tests have nothing to do with the "sales features" of the spectrometer, but are instead meant to show its fundamental limitations in performance.

A1.1 THE SINGLE-BEAM SPECTRUM: ALIGNMENT AND PURGING

1. Measure a "background" or "reference" spectrum using a few scans.
2. Display the spectrum on the computer screen or plot it on paper. Fig. A.1 shows an example of a single-beam spectrum.
3. Examine the relative intensity at the high frequency end and at the peak. Low intensity ($<5\%$) suggests that the interferometer is inadequately aligned: high frequencies are lost first as the interferometer loses alignment. If you can readjust the interferometer mirrors, it may be possible to improve the intensity at high frequencies. Less likely reasons for low intensity at high frequency include a reduced source temperature or distorted beamsplitter.
4. Examine the depth of the absorption lines due to water vapour and carbon dioxide. If they absorb more than 50% at their characteristic wavelengths, the spectrometer would benefit from the use of desiccant, purging with dry nitrogen, or (if possible) evacuation.

A1.2 THE 100% LINE: ALIGNMENT, STABILITY, SPEED VARIATION AND NOISE

1. Measure a "background" or "reference" spectrum using a few scans.
2. Measure a "sample" spectrum using the same number of scans and without a sample in the sample chamber. Calculate the ratio of the two spectra to obtain an open-beam spectrum. The result should be a reasonably straight 100% line.

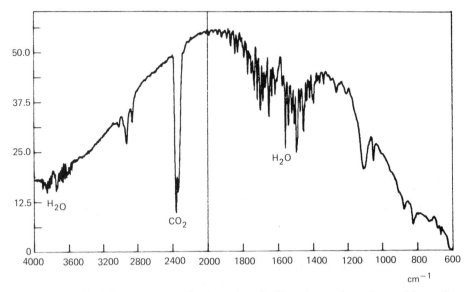

Fig. A.1 — Single-beam spectrum, showing carbon dioxide and water absorptions and drop-off
in efficiency at both high and low wavenumbers.

3. Display the spectrum on the screen or plot it on paper. If possible, show the region
   around 100%, e.g. 95–105%.
4. If the 100% line shows a distinct tilt, particularly towards higher frequencies, the
   spectrometer alignment has changed between the reference and sample scans.
   This is usually caused by temperature change or mechanical shock. If you have
   recently turned on the instrument, allow it to warm up before repeating this test.
   Some commercial spectrometers require several hours to warm up and stabilize
   adequately. If, after this period, the 100% line is still tilting for reference and
   sample scans more than a few minutes apart, the infrared source may be unstable.

   If successive tests show the 100% line tilting both upwards and downwards
   towards high frequencies, the alignment is unstable and not affected by temperature alone. The scan drive may be sloppy, or an interferometer mirror may be
   loose.
5. Examine the region around the carbon dioxide absorption ($2350 \, cm^{-1}$) and water
   bands.

   If the carbon dioxide peak shows up but the water bands are absent, the room
   is probably dry or the spectrometer is well desiccated. However, the presence of
   the carbon dioxide band means that the sample or optics compartments of the
   spectrometer are not well sealed. The variations in atmospheric CO_2 caused by
   breathing show up as fluctuations in the depth of the carbon dioxide absorption
   band.

If the water-vapour lines show up strongly, and you have taken care not to breathe near the spectrometer during the scans, the spectrometer scan speed is probably irregular. When the interferometer does not scan at a uniform rate, the resulting spectrum undergoes a slight distortion of its frequency scale. A subsequent spectrum ratioed against the first will not yield a flat 100% line; instead, any sharp features in the spectrum will overlap imperfectly, resulting in peaks. The 100% line has the characteristic appearance of the derivative of the single-beam spectrum: oscillations tend to show up both above and below the 100% line through the water band. If the speed variation is bad enough, even the broad carbon dioxide band will show up in this way.

Except in exceptionally humid environments, the presence of strong water features in a 100% line usually suggests interferometer speed variations. This is particularly true if the features have a derivative-like appearance rather than appearing solely above or below the 100% line.

6. Display or plot the region around 1900–2100 cm^{-1}. For a mid-infrared spectrometer, this is usually the spectral region at which the light source is brightest, and where the signal quality is best. Moreover, neither water vapour nor carbon dioxide absorb in this region, so the spectrum is not affected by fluctuations in atmospheric composition or by speed variations of the interferometer. Because of this, the region is commonly used for a "best-case" measurement of signal-to-noise ratio.

Examine the 100% line and note the maximum and minimum values in the spectral region. Ignore any general slope to the line, concentrating only on the fluctuations about the average value. The difference between the maximum and minimum values is the peak-to-peak noise level.

The measurement should not be significantly worse than the manufacturer's specification. If it is, the most likely problems are:

(1) excessive vibration;
(2) reduced signal level caused by source deterioration, misalignment, or dirty optics;
(3) electronic noise pick-up, probably near the detector or preamplifier.

Incidentally, you should beware of signal-to-noise specifications quoted as RMS (root-mean-square) values. RMS noise is a statistical measure of typical noise, and is four to five times lower than peak-to-peak noise. RMS specifications thus appear much better, but are difficult for the user to verify.

The noise level is affected by several factors. For a well-designed FTIR, it falls as the square root of the number of scans. For example, if a 100% line was measured by using one scan, it should be roughly four times "noisier" than a 100% line measured using 16 scans. If this is not the case, the spectrometer probably suffers from a source of non-random noise. An example of non-random noise is sensitivity to vibration.

The noise level is higher in other spectral regions. Near the extremes of the spectrum, the source will be weaker, the beamsplitter coating will be less efficient, the optical elements may begin to absorb light, and the detector preamplifier will be closer to the limits of its electrical passband.

A1.3 THE POLYSTYRENE TEST: AMPLIFIER LINEARITY AND FREQUENCY SCALE

1. Measure a "background" or "reference" spectrum using a few scans.
2. Measure a polystyrene sample spectrum using the same number of scans. Polystyrene samples are available from instrument manufacturers and accessory suppliers.
3. Display the ratioed spectrum on the computer screen or plot it on paper. An example is shown in Fig. A.2.

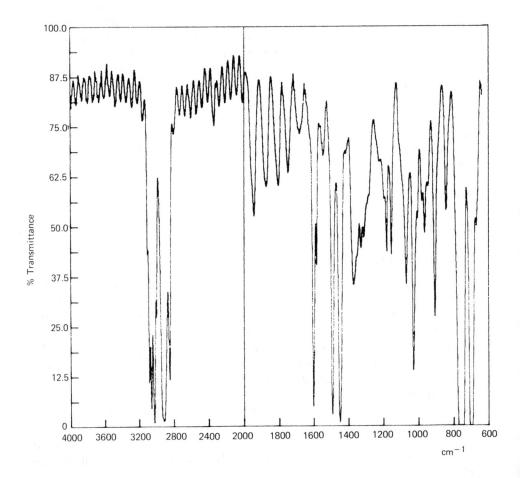

Fig. A.2 — Polystyrene spectrum.

Note whether the principal absorption bands of polystyrene reach 0% transmittance. If they transmit more than a few tenths of one percent, the signal chain of the FTIR spectrometer suffers from nonlinearity (alternatively, it is possible that the polystyrene contains a pinhole, or allows light to pass by it in its holder). This is usually caused by the detector/preamplifier combination. The problem may be improved by reducing the beam intensity: try repeating the reference and sample scans with a piece of metal gauze or other neutral absorber in the beam (note: metal gauze will diffract light more at longer wavenumbers, and may progressively distort the intensity scale there; the zeroes will not be affected, though). If the zeroes of polystyrene change with the attenuator in place, linearity is the problem.

Compare the positions of the absorption peaks with published figures. They should agree to within the manufacturer's stated wavenumber accuracy. If not, the interferometer may be optically misaligned: changes in the symmetry of the collimated beam entering the interferometer change the effective wavenumber scale. Similarly, the optical configuration of certain spectrometers can lead to a shift of focus when a thick sample is inserted at the sample position, again leading to wavenumber shift. A second cause of discrepancy between published and measured wavenumbers is software error. This is a less likely cause of error except in newly introduced instruments.

A1.4   ABSORBANCE RANGE AND LINEARITY

1   Measure a "reference" or "background" spectrum using a few scans.
2. Measure a "sample" spectrum using a piece of thin plastic sheet — for example, a 5×7 cm rectangle cut from a protective cover. Cut at least six identical pieces from the same sheet.
3. Display or plot the spectrum and locate an absorption band of low to moderate intensity: e.g. a spectral region transmitting about 80%. Measure the absorbance $(A = -\log T)$ at the peak.
4. Measure the "sample" spectrum from two pieces of the plastic. Measure the absorbance again.
5. Repeat this procedure using 3, 4, and more pieces of plastic in the sample position. Continue until the spectrum in the region of the absorption peak appears to have reduced to the noise level. Example spectra are shown in Fig. A.3.
6. Determine the linearity of the spectrometer: each successive sample should differ in absorbance by the same amount. That is, the absorbance should be proportional to the number of pieces of plastic measured. For some maximum number, this relationship will break down. Modern FTIR instruments can normally measure linearly up to at least 2.5 absorbance units, and sometimes up to 4. This amounts to photometric accuracy down to 0.3 or 0.01%. If the plastic surfaces reflect significantly, they may cause interference. Irregular, warped pieces will give better results than smooth flat pieces.

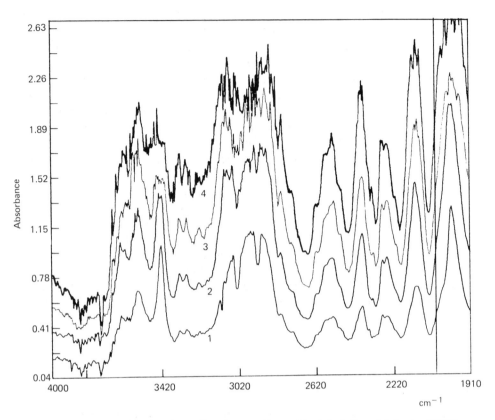

Fig. A.3 — Spectra for absorbance linearity test. Curves 1 to 4: 1, 2, 3, and 4 sheets of PVC plastic.

A1.5 SUBSTITUTION OF A FREQUENCY GENERATOR FOR DETECTOR AND PREAMPLIFIER

A more fundamental test of the FTIR system described by Saperstein (1987) can be performed by replacing the detector and preamplifier by a frequency generator. In this way, a near-perfect sine wave can be injected into the signal chain to produce a counterfeit monochromatic interferogram. The data processing system of the spectrometer will then digitize the signal and transform it into a spectrum, from which the measured full width at half maximum (FWHM) resolution can be compared with the manufacturer's specification. The result can then be compared with a real experimental spectrum, e.g. an absorption line of a low-pressure gas. Further comparison of the counterfeit and authentic sample can provide indications of the performance of the spectrometer. It should be noted that only the infrared signal, and not the laser or white light reference channel, is replaced by a sine wave. This means that the sampling time is still determined by the scanning of the interferometer. Any jitter in the scan will therefore cause sampling jitter in the artificial interferogram signal.

1. Select a frequency generator capable of producing sine waves in the proper frequency range for the FTIR spectrometer. An interferometer having an optical path velocity of v will produce an electrical frequency

$$f = v\sigma \tag{A1.1}$$

   where σ is the wavenumber of the monochromatic source. So, for example, if the optical velocity is 1 mm/sec (0.1 cm/sec) and the counterfeit peak in the spectrum is desired at about $2000\,cm^{-1}$, the oscillator frequency should be set to 200 Hz.

2. Set the frequency generator output voltage to the value normally provided by the detector/preamp combination. This can be checked by observing the preamp output on an oscilloscope while the spectrometer scans. Voltages in the 1–5 V range are common.

3. Attach the generator to the digital input of the spectrometer at the point where the detector preamplifier cable is normally connected.

4. Perform a scan with this arrangement. The resulting interferogram should very closely approximate the input sine wave. If the spectrometer applies apodization, the sine wave amplitude will decrease to zero at the end of the interferogram.

5. Observe the transformed spectrum. If it resembles a symmetrical peak, the software has correctly transformed the interferogram. If, on the other hand, the peak has both a negative and positive component, the phase of the spectrum has been incorrectly calculated. The most likely cause for this is that the fast Fourier transform has calculated a one-sided (cosine) spectrum rather than a magnitude $(sine^2 + cosine^2)$ spectrum. This saves calculation time if the instrument can unambiguously identify the zero-path position. Here, however, the artificial interferogram has no principal peak, and so may cause the instrument confusion.

6. If the peak is symmetrical, measure its width at half intensity. The value should correspond closely to the manufacturer's claim. If various apodization functions can be selected, try another to observe how resolution depends on apodization.

Results of the gas and generator spectra can be summarized as follows:

(a) Broad, asymmetric gas lines but narrow, symmetric frequency generator line: the interferometer optics and/or aperture are probably misaligned.

(b) Broad, symmetric gas lines but narrow, symmetric frequency generator line: the spectral resolution is limited by optical effects, for example an aperture (Jacquinot stop) too large for the desired resolution.

(c) Narrow, asymmetric gas lines and narrow, asymmetric frequency generator line: the interferogram sampling shows jitter. The most likely source is the scan-mirror drive. A second possibility is the sampling electronics: if the laser channel signal is too noisy (for example, if the laser itself is misaligned) the sampling points may be irregularly chosen.

(d) Broad, asymmetric frequency generator line: several aspects of spectrometer operation are suspect. The signal levels into the analogue-to-digital converter may be incorrect (either too high, causing saturation and distortion, or too low, making the signal less distinguishable from noise). There may be pickup between the frequency generator and ADC, or elsewhere in the electronics, causing ripple on the interferogram and spurious peaks in the spectrum. Finally, the software may be digitizing the sine wave incorrectly: check the appearance of the recorded interferogram, if possible.

A1.6   INTERFEROGRAM EXAMINATION: MODULATION EFFICIENCY AND LONG-TERM STABILITY

The interferogram is the basic data measured by an FTIR spectrometer and provides information about the interferometer itself.

1. Record an interferogram and display or plot it for examination.
2. If the interferogram shows an upward (positive) peak, measure the intensity I_{max} at the zero path difference peak and the intensity I_{av} at a point far from ZPD (Fig. A.4, Top). If, on the other hand, the interferogram has a downward-facing

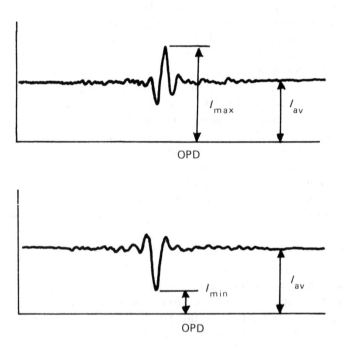

Fig. A.4 — Interferogram measurement for calculating modulation efficiency. Top: positive ZPD peak; Bottom: negative ZPD peak.

(negative) peak, measure the intensity I_{min} of this minimum and the intensity I_{av} at a point far from ZPD (Fig. A.4, Bottom). Caution: the analogue electronics may apply a voltage offset to the signal, or the software of the spectrometer may automatically scale the interferogram to have the peak fill the display area. Ensure that the vertical scale is correctly indicated. This may be possible by blocking the sample beam during a portion of the scan to obtain zero signal.

3. Calculate the modulation efficiency: for the case of a positive peak,

$$\text{modulation efficiency} = (I_{max} - I_{av})/I_{av} \tag{A1.2}$$

and for the case of a negative peak,

$$\text{modulation efficiency} = (I_{av} - I_{min})/I_{av} . \tag{A1.3}$$

For an ideal interferometer, the modulation efficiency is exactly 1. A practical FTIR spectrometer may have a modulation efficiency above 0.9 or as low as 0 (for a completely misaligned interferometer). Intermediate values can be attributed to imperfect beamsplitter or interferometer mirror flatness or poor alignment.

4. Keep a record of modulation efficiency and the values of I_{av} and I_{max} (or I_{min}). I_{av} is an indication of detector alignment, source intensity and optical throughput of the spectrometer. I_{max} (or I_{min}) is also related to interferometer alignment. Variation in these values with instrument temperature or usage will point out stability problems and show when realignment is necessary.

REFERENCE

Saperstein, D. D. (1987), The Sine Wave Test for Fourier Transform Infrared Spectrometers, *Spectroscopy*, **2**, 45.

Index